BIOLOGY
The Dynamics of Life

Chapter Assessment

Glencoe
McGraw-Hill

New York, New York   Columbus, Ohio   Woodland Hills, California   Peoria, Illinois

A GLENCOE PROGRAM
BIOLOGY: THE DYNAMICS OF LIFE

Student Edition
Teacher Wraparound Edition
Laboratory Manual, SE and TE
Reinforcement and Study Guide, SE and TE
Content Mastery, SE and TE
Section Focus Transparencies and Masters
Reteaching Skills Transparencies and Masters
Basic Concepts Transparencies and Masters
BioLab and MiniLab Worksheets
Concept Mapping
Chapter Assessment
Critical Thinking/Problem Solving
Spanish Resources
Tech Prep Applications
Biology Projects

Computer Test Bank Software and Manual
  WINDOWS/MACINTOSH
Lesson Plans
Block Scheduling
Inside Story Poster Package
English/Spanish Audiocassettes
MindJogger Videoquizzes
Interactive CD-ROM
Videodisc Program
Glencoe Science Professional Series:
  Exploring Environmental Issues
  Performance Assessment in the Biology Classroom
  Alternate Assessment in the Science Classroom
  Cooperative Learning in the Science Classroom
  Using the Internet in the Science Classroom

Send all inquiries to:
Glencoe/McGraw-Hill
8787 Orion Place
Columbus, OH 43240

ISBN 0-02-828254-X
Printed in the United States of America.
   4 5 6 7 8 9 10   047   08 07 06 05 04 03 02 01

Contents

To the Teacher iv

1 Biology: The Study of Life 1

2 Principles of Ecology 7

3 Communities and Biomes 13

4 Population Biology 19

5 Biological Diversity and Conservation . . 25

6 The Chemistry of Life 31

7 A View of the Cell 37

8 Cellular Transport and the Cell Cycle . . 43

9 Energy in a Cell 49

10 Mendel and Meiosis 55

11 DNA and Genes 61

12 Patterns of Heredity and
Human Genetics 67

13 Genetic Technology 73

14 The History of Life 79

15 The Theory of Evolution 85

16 Primate Evolution 91

17 Organizing Life's Diversity 97

18 Viruses and Bacteria 103

19 Protists 109

20 Fungi 115

21 What Is a Plant? 121

22 The Diversity of Plants 127

23 Plant Structure and Function 133

24 Reproduction in Plants 139

25 What Is an Animal? 145

26 Sponges, Cnidarians, Flatworms, and
Roundworms 151

27 Mollusks and Segmented Worms 157

28 Arthropods 163

29 Echinoderms and Invertebrate
Chordates 169

30 Fishes and Amphibians 175

31 Reptiles and Birds 181

32 Mammals 187

33 Animal Behavior 193

34 Protection, Support, and
Locomotion 199

35 The Digestive and Endocrine
Systems 205

36 The Nervous System 211

37 Respiration, Circulation, and
Excretion 217

38 Reproduction and Development 223

39 Immunity from Disease 229

ANSWER PAGES T235

This *Chapter Assessment* book provides materials to assess your students' learning of concepts from each of the thirty-nine chapters of **Biology: The Dynamics of Life**. Each chapter test includes several sections that assess students' understandings at different levels.

The *Reviewing Vocabulary* section tests students' knowledge of the chapter's vocabulary. A variety of formats is used, including matching, multiple choice, completion, and comparison of terms.

The *Understanding Main Ideas* section consists of two parts: Part A tests recall and basic understanding of facts presented in the chapter. Part B is designed to be more challenging and requires deeper comprehension of concepts than does Part A. Students may be asked to explain biological processes and relationships or to make comparisons and generalizations.

The *Thinking Critically* section requires students to use several different higher-order learning skills. For some questions, students will need to interpret data and discover relationships presented in graphs and tables. Other questions may require them to apply their understanding of concepts to solve problems, to compare and contrast situations, and to make inferences or predictions.

In the final section, *Applying Scientific Methods*, students are put into the role of researcher. They may be asked to read about an experiment, simulation, or model and then apply their understanding of chapter concepts and scientific methods to analyze and explain the procedure and results. Many of the questions in this section are open-ended, giving students the opportunity to demonstrate both reasoning and creative skills. This section, as well as the other sections of each test, begins on a separate page, so that if you wish to omit it from a particular test, you can easily do so.

Answers or possible responses to all questions are provided on the reduced pages at the back of the book.

Chapter 1

Biology: The Study of Life

Reviewing Vocabulary

Match the definition in Column A with the term in Column B.

Column A	Column B
_____ **1.** The process whereby an organism produces more of its own kind	**a.** adaptation
_____ **2.** The part of an experiment in which all conditions are kept the same	**b.** control
_____ **3.** An organism's tendency to maintain a stable internal environment	**c.** evolution
_____ **4.** Any structure, behavior, or internal process that enables an organism to better survive in an environment	**d.** homeostasis
_____ **5.** A testable explanation for a question or problem	**e.** hypothesis
_____ **6.** The gradual change in the characteristics of a species over time	**f.** reproduction

Compare and contrast each pair of related terms.

7. stimulus, response

_____

_____

_____

8. independent variable, dependent variable

_____

_____

_____

9. organism, species

_____

_____

_____

Chapter 1 Biology: The Study of Life, *continued*

Understanding Concepts (Part A)

Match the definition in Column A with the term in Column B.

Column A	Column B

_____ **1.** Scientists commonly use these steps in gathering information to test hypotheses and solve problems.

a. energy

_____ **2.** Over time, gradual changes in structures, behaviors, and internal processes of organisms result in diversity of species.

b. evolution

c. homeostasis

_____ **3.** Scientists use this system of measurement because of its ease of understanding.

d. scientific methods

_____ **4.** A variety of structural and behavioral adaptations help organisms regulate their internal environment.

e. SI (metric)

_____ **5.** Its flow through ecosystems determines how organisms interact and powers all life processes.

In the space at the left, write <u>true</u> if the statement is true; if the statement is false, change the italicized word or phrase to make it true.

_____ **6.** Biologists discover problems by *observing the world around them*.

_____ **7.** A *natural law* is based on the analysis of data collected in a controlled experiment.

_____ **8.** In an experiment, the *control* group is used to test the effect of the independent variable.

_____ **9.** Counts or measurements are examples of data produced by *descriptive* research.

_____ **10.** Whether applications of science to everyday life are considered good, bad, right, or wrong comes under the category of *technology*.

_____ **11.** The *liter* is a metric unit of volume.

Chapter
1 Biology: The Study of Life, *continued*

Understanding Concepts (Part B)

Identify the characteristic of life illustrated in each picture

1.

_____

2.

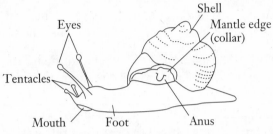

_____

3.

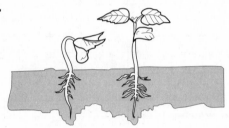

_____

4.

_____

Identify the independent variable and the dependent variable that would be used in testing each hypothesis below.

5. An electromagnet can be made by wrapping insulated wire around an iron nail and connecting the ends of the wire to a 6-volt battery. HYPOTHESIS: Increasing the number of coils of wire wrapped around the nail increases the strength of the electromagnet, as measured by the number of paper clips the magnet can pick up.

_____

_____

6. Sugar dissolves in, or mixes completely with, water. The solubility of a substance in water is determined by measuring the maximum amount of the substance that dissolves in a given amount of water at a given temperature. HYPOTHESIS: The solubility of sugar in water increases as the temperature of the water decreases.

_____

_____

Chapter 1

Biology: The Study of Life, *continued*

Thinking Critically

One hundred pregnant women and their developing fetuses were monitored over the course of pregnancy in a study designed to compare the average weight gain of a woman during pregnancy with the average weight gain of the developing fetus. (Note that the weight gain of the developing fetus is its actual weight.) The averages for the group are recorded in the table below.

1. Graph the data for the mother and the fetus on the same grid. Decide on a method to distinguish the sets of data. Be sure to label each graph.

Week of pregnancy	Weight gain of mother (kg)	Weight gain of fetus (kg)
8	1.5	not measureable
12	1.8	0.25
16	3.0	0.25
20	4.0	0.50
24	5.5	0.75
28	8.0	1.25
32	10.0	2.00
36	13.0	2.25
40	15.0	3.00

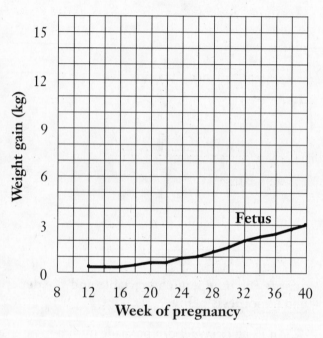

2. How would you describe the weight gain of the developing fetus?

_____

_____

3. During the last 16 weeks of pregnancy, how does the mother's total weight gain compare with the total weight gain of the developing fetus?

_____

_____

4. Overall, how does the mother's rate of weight gain compare with the rate of weight gain of the developing fetus? How can you determine this by looking at the graphs?

_____

_____

Chapter 1 **Biology: The Study of Life,** *continued*

Applying Scientific Methods

Paramecia are single-celled, microscopic organisms that live in fresh water. Like other living things, paramecia respond to changes in their environment. For example, if a paramecium encounters an obstacle in its path, it will avoid it by swimming away from or around the obstacle.

A paramecium may respond positively or negatively to a stimulus, or it may not respond at all. A positive response is indicated by movement toward the stimulus; a negative response is indicated by movement away from the stimulus.

A student prepared several covered slides of paramecia in fresh water. The student added different stimuli and observed the behavior of the organisms under the microscope. The diagrams below show what the student viewed.

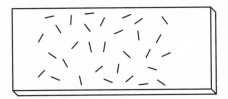

In fresh water

Reaction to drop of dilute salt water (0.5% solution)

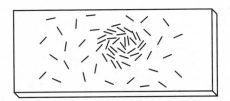

Reaction to drop of vinegar

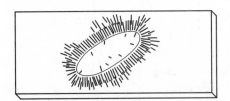

Reaction to piece of food

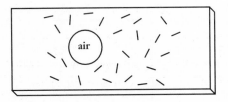

Reaction to air bubble

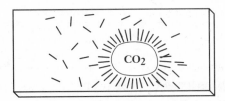

Reaction to carbon dioxide bubble

Applying Scientific Methods   continued

Compare the data chart. Use + for a positive response; − for a negative response, and 0 for no response.

Stimulus	Response (+, −, 0)
1.	0
2. 0.5% salt solution	
3.	
4.	
5.	
6.	

7. Which stimulus represents the natural environment of paramecia?

_____

8. What purpose does observing the response to this stimulus serve?

_____

_____

9. To which substance(s) did the paramecia have the strongest positive response? Explain your reasoning.

_____

_____

_____

10. Predict how a population of paramecia would respond to the addition of a drop of 10% salt solution. Give reasons for your prediction.

_____

_____

_____

_____

Chapter 2 Principles of Ecology

Reviewing Vocabulary

Match the definition in Column A with the term in Column B.

Column A	Column B
_____ 1. Tiny organisms that break down and absorb nutrients from dead organisms	**a.** autotroph
_____ 2. Obtains energy by feeding on other organisms	**b.** commensalism
_____ 3. Step in the passage of energy and matter through an ecosystem	**c.** decomposer
_____ 4. Place where an organism lives out its life	**d.** food chain
_____ 5. Relationship between species in which one species benefits at the expense of another	**e.** food web
_____ 6. Manufactures nutrients using energy from the sun or from chemical compounds	**f.** heterotroph
_____ 7. Collection of interacting populations	**g.** parasitism
_____ 8. Simple model for showing how matter and energy move through an ecosystem	**h.** scavenger
_____ 9. Eats dead organisms	**i.** trophic level
_____ 10. Portion of Earth that supports life	**j.** habitat
_____ 11. Relationship between species in which one species benefits and the other is neither harmed nor benefited	**k.** community
_____ 12. Network of interconnected food chains	**l.** biosphere
_____ 13. Relationship between species in which both species benefit	**m.** ecology
_____ 14. Study of interactions among organisms and their environments	**n.** mutualism

Chapter Assessment

Understanding Main Ideas (Part A)

In the space at the left, write the word or phrase in parentheses that correctly completes the statement.

_____ **1.** Wind, humidity, and (mosses, rocks) would be considered abiotic factors in a terrestrial ecosystem.

_____ **2.** The size of a population does not directly depend on the availability of (food, decomposers).

_____ **3.** To show how the weight of living material at each trophic level of a food chain changes, you could use a pyramid of (numbers, biomass).

_____ **4.** In the nitrogen cycle, bacteria and (lightning, decomposers) convert atmospheric nitrogen into nitrogen compounds usable by plants.

_____ **5.** Some energy that passes through a food chain is lost to the environment as (heat, matter).

_____ **6.** Carbon and nitrogen are released back into the atmosphere during (symbiosis, decomposition).

_____ **7.** Both the alga and the fungus of a lichen benefit from their relationship. This relationship is one of (mutualism, commensalism).

In the space at the left, write the word or phrase that includes all the rest.

_____ **8.** trophic level, food web, food chain

_____ **9.** parasitism, commensalism, mutualism, symbiosis

_____ **10.** organism, ecosystem, population, community

_____ **11.** ecosystems, biotic factors, biosphere, abiotic factors

_____ **12.** omnivores, consumers, carnivores, herbivores, scavengers, decomposers

_____ **13.** evaporation, precipitation, water cycle, condensation, urination

Understanding Main Ideas (Part B)

Questions 1–5 refer to the food chain pictured below. In the space at the left, write the letter of the word or phrase that best completes the statement or answers the question.

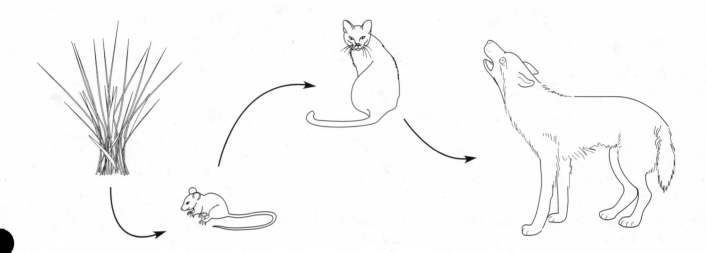

_____ 1. Energy flows from
    a. coyotes to grasses.
    b. cats to mice.
    c. mice to cats.
    d. coyotes to cats.

_____ 2. The coyotes are
    a. herbivores.
    b. third-order heterotrophs.
    c. second-order heterotrophs.
    d. decomposers.

_____ 3. How many trophic levels does the food chain include?
    a. four
    b. one
    c. three
    d. two

_____ 4. As matter and energy move from grasses to coyotes, the amount of available energy
    a. always decreases and population size always increases.
    b. always increases and population size always decreases.
    c. always decreases but population size may increase or decrease.
    d. increases or decreases but population size remains the same.

_____ 5. Suppose 10 000 units of energy are available at the level of the grasses. What is the total number of energy units lost by the time energy reaches the coyote?
    a. 90 units
    b. 990 units
    c. 9900 units
    d. 9990 units

Thinking Critically

Use the diagram to complete the table below. Classify each member of the food web as *autotroph* or *heterotroph* and identify each heterotroph as *herbivore*, *carnivore*, or *omnivore*. Then answer the questions that follow.

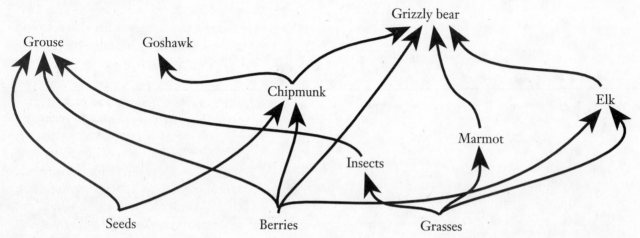

Autotrophs	Heterotrophs		Type of Heterotroph
1.	**4.**		**11.**
2.	**5.**		**12.**
3.	**6.**		**13.**
	7.		**14.**
	8.		**15.**
	9.		**16.**
	10.		**17.**

18. How would you describe the marmot's habitat and its position in the food chain?

_____

_____

19. When a grouse eats berries, the berry seeds are eliminated as waste and may be dropped in another part of the forest where they may sprout and eventually grow into new berry plants. How would you classify the relationship between the berry plant and the grouse? Explain your reasoning.

_____

_____

Chapter 2 **Principles of Ecology,** *continued*

Applying Scientific Methods

Milkweed is a plant commonly found throughout fields and pastures and along roadsides in eastern and central North America. It gets its name from the milky white sap that oozes when the plant is broken or cut. Milkweed plants bloom in June and July. When fertilized, the flowers form large seedpods that open in the fall. The following observations were taken from a scientist's field study of milkweed plants from spring through fall.

In the summer, the sugary nectar secreted by the milkweed's flowers attracts many bees, butterflies, moths, and a variety of smaller insects that carry away pollen when they depart. Milkweed nectar seems to be the major source of nutrition for several species of small moths, flies, mosquitoes, and ants. Monarch butterflies, which visit in large numbers, lay their eggs on milkweed plants, and the hatching caterpillars feed on the leaves. As fall approaches, milkweed bugs begin to attack the developing seeds, and milkweed beetles eat the foliage.

Aphids, which suck milkweed sap, are found throughout the year. Crab spiders do not feed on the plant itself but on most of the insects that visit the plant. In the two to three weeks while the milkweed are in bloom, successful adult female crab spiders may increase ten times in mass before laying their eggs on the inner surface of leaves. Some species of flies and wasps, which feed on crab spider eggs, visit the plants periodically. Harvestmen, also known as daddy longlegs, eat the remains left by predators.

1. Did the scientist conduct quantitative or descriptive research?

_____

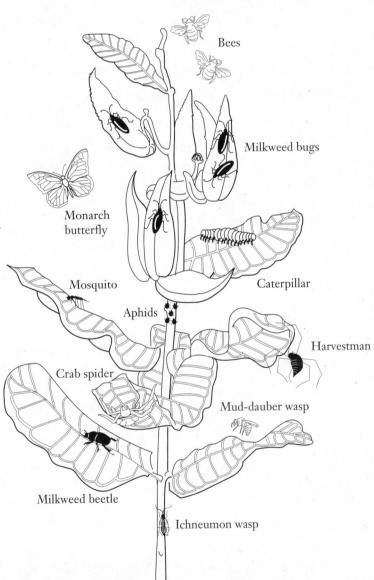

Bees

Milkweed bugs

Monarch butterfly

Mosquito

Aphids

Caterpillar

Harvestman

Crab spider

Mud-dauber wasp

Milkweed beetle

Ichneumon wasp

Applying Scientific Methods   continued

2. What level of organization in an ecosystem is represented by the milkweed and the organisms that visit or live on the plant?

_____

3. Based on the scientist's observations, what is one food chain that begins with a milkweed plant?

_____

4. What is the niche of the harvestmen?

_____

5. How would you describe the symbiotic relationship between the milkweed plant and bees?

_____

6. Based on the scientist's observations, formulate two possible hypotheses about the effects of crab spiders on the survival of the milkweed plant.

_____

_____

_____

Chapter
3 **Communities and Biomes**

Reviewing Vocabulary

In the space at the left, write <u>true</u> if the statement is true; if the statement is false, change the italicized word or phrase to make it true.

_____ **1.** The *taiga* is an arid region characterized by little or no plant life.

_____ **2.** Small organisms that live in the sunlit regions of the ocean are *pioneer species*.

_____ **3.** *Humus* is a layer of soil that remains permanently frozen.

_____ **4.** A body of water near the coast that is partly surrounded by land and contains both freshwater and salt water is known as an *intertidal zone*.

_____ **5.** *Succession* is the replacement of species in a community as environmental conditions change.

_____ **6.** The portion of the marine biome shallow enough for sunlight to penetrate is the *photic zone*.

_____ **7.** The portion of the shoreline that lies between high and low tide lines is the *aphotic zone*.

_____ **8.** Conditions that restrict the existence, number, reproduction, or distribution of organisms are called *ranges of tolerance*.

_____ **9.** A *climax* community is a stable, mature community that undergoes little or no change in species.

_____ **10.** The colonization of new sites by communities of organisms is *secondary* succession.

_____ **11.** A large group of ecosystems characterized by the same type of climax community is called a *taiga*.

_____ **12.** The *temperate forest* is a region dominated by broad-leaved hardwood trees.

_____ **13.** *Primary* succession is the sequence of changes that takes place after a community is disrupted.

Understanding Main Ideas (Part A)

Write the word or phrase that best completes the statement. Use these choices:

abiotic	optimum	soil	tundra
climax communities	pioneer species	taiga	
photic zone	salinity	tolerance	
grassland	secondary succession	tropical rain forest	

1. _____ is the ability of an organism to withstand changes in abiotic and biotic factors in an ecosystem.

2. The first species to live in an area are known as _____ .

3. Shallow marine environments along coastlines are part of the _____ .

4. The _____ is the most species-rich biome.

5. The _____ biome occupies more area than any other terrestrial biome.

6. Natural disasters and human actions are possible causes of _____ .

7. Tropical rain forest and _____ biomes are both characterized by a thin layer of nutrient-poor topsoil that can support only shallow-rooted plants.

8. _____ are characterized by many different species of organisms and little or no succession.

9. Water temperature and light are two _____ factors that affect organisms in a deep lake.

10. The tides affect the _____ of water in an estuary.

11. The presence of coniferous trees as the dominant climax plants characterizes the _____ .

12. During primary succession, the decay of pioneer species results in the formation of _____ .

13. The greatest number of organisms is found within the _____ range of environmental conditions for a particular population.

Chapter
3 **Communities and Biomes,** *continued*

Understanding Main Ideas (Part B)

Identify the biomes on the map and then answer the questions that follow.

1. _____

3. _____

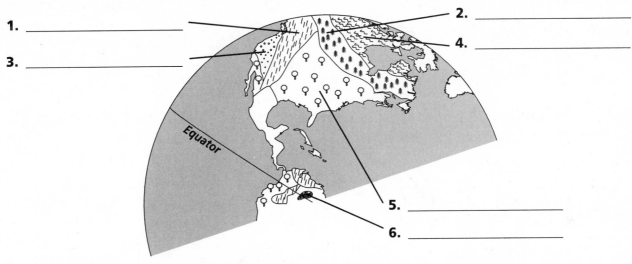

2. _____

4. _____

5. _____

6. _____

7. Which biome has the warmest temperatures and the most rainfall? _____

8. Which biome has the coldest temperatures? _____

9. Which biome is the driest? _____

Study the diagram and then answer the questions.

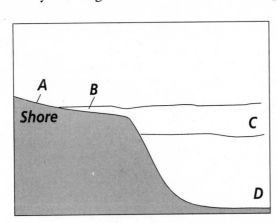

10. Identify the regions of the marine biome shown in the diagram. Use these choices: aphotic zone, photic zone, intertidal zone, shallow-water region.

A. _____

B. _____

C. _____

D. _____

11. Why are few producers found in region A?

_____

12. In which regions are plankton found?

_____

Thinking Critically

The illustrations below show succession in a pond within a forest community. Use the illustrations to answer questions 1–5.

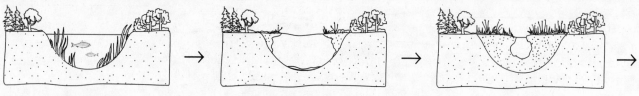

Figure 1   **Figure 2**   **Figure 3**

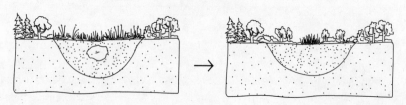

Figure 4   **Figure 5**

1. How is the pond in Figure 2 different from the pond in Figure 1?

_____

_____

_____

2. What might account for these differences?

_____

_____

_____

_____

3. What changes are illustrated in Figure 4?

_____

_____

_____

4. What type of succession is illustrated? Explain.

_____

_____

_____

Applying Scientific Methods

Epiphytes are plants that grow on other plants. In the tropical rain forest, epiphytes sprout from seeds or spores carried by the wind or animals and take root on the trunks and branches of the canopy trees. Epiphytes are not parasitic; they gain nothing from the trees except support and access to sunlight. Under favorable conditions, however, they may form dense, water-logged, tangled mats of roots and stems, weighing up to several thousand kilograms. This weight is often enough to break the limbs of the more fragile trees. Some tree species have developed adaptations to protect against the growth of epiphytes. Two known mechanisms are (1) the frequent shedding of bark layers that periodically removes young epiphytes and (2) the manufacturing of chemicals that inhibit the growth of other plants.

In his explorations of the Costa Rican tropical rain forest, Donald Perry developed an apparatus consisting of a platform base built on one tree and connected to two other trees by means of ropes. From this base, a system of ropes and pulleys attached to a harness allowed an investigator to access previously unexplored areas of the canopy and to move within the canopy with minimal contact or interference with organisms.

During his studies, Perry noticed that some trees were completely free of epiphytes, although the tree species were known not to shed bark or to manufacture plant-inhibiting chemicals. Other scientists speculated that *Azteca* ants, which live on certain species of tropical rain-forest trees, were responsible for the absence of epiphytes on those trees. These aggressive ants were known to swarm and attack other insects and mammals that might damage their trees. To test the effect of the ants on epiphytes, Perry tied some moss and other small epiphytes to the limbs of a tree inhabited by the ants. Perry found that the ants destroyed the epiphytes.

1. What problem did Perry try to solve regarding certain epiphyte-free trees that he observed in the tropical rain forest?

_____

_____

_____

2. What was Perry's hypothesis regarding those trees?

_____

_____

_____

3. On what did Perry base his hypothesis?

_____

_____

_____

4. Why might the ants want to destroy the epiphytes?

_____

_____

Chapter 3 **Communities and Biomes,** *continued*

Applying Scientific Methods   continued

5. What kind of symbiotic relationship do the ants and trees have? Explain.

_____

_____

_____

_____

_____

6. How was Perry's rope-and-pulley apparatus helpful in the testing of his hypothesis?

_____

_____

_____

_____

_____

7. In what other ways might Perry's apparatus be useful?

_____

_____

_____

_____

_____

Chapter 4 **Population Biology**

Reviewing Vocabulary

In the space at the left, write the letter of the word or phrase that best completes the statement.

_____ **1.** Limiting factors whose effects increase as the size of the population increases are
  a. abiotic factors.
  b. density-dependent factors.
  c. exponential in nature.
  d. density-independent factors.

_____ **2.** The movement of individuals from a population is
  a. immigration.   **b.** a reproductive pattern.
  c. a life-history pattern.   **d.** emigration.

_____ **3.** The proportions of a population that are at different age levels make up the population's
  a. fertility rate.   **b.** growth rate.
  c. age structure.   **d.** carrying capacity.

_____ **4.** Unrestricted populations of organisms experience
  a. exponential growth.   **b.** linear growth.
  c. infertility.   **d.** biotic growth.

_____ **5.** For a particular species, the carrying capacity is the maximum number of individual organisms that
  a. the species could reach in a given time period if all the offspring survive and reproduce.
  b. can be supported by a given environment.
  c. are in their post-reproductive years.
  d. can be supported if there are no limiting factors.

_____ **6.** Density-independent factors are limiting factors whose effects are
  a. confined to the habitat of a population.
  b. determined by the degree of competition for resources.
  c. not influenced by population densities.
  d. determined by the difference between birthrate and death rate.

Understanding Main Ideas (Part A)

In the space at the left, write the term in parentheses that correctly completes each statement.

_____ **1.** A (J, S)-shaped curve describes the tendency of a population to grow without limit to its size.

_____ **2.** If a population's death rate is (less, greater) than its birthrate, the population will grow.

_____ **3.** (Food availability, Earthquake damage) would be a density-dependent limiting factor on the growth of a population.

_____ **4.** The number of offspring produced by a female during her reproductive years defines the (fertility, birth) rate.

_____ **5.** The production of many offspring in a short period of time is characteristic of a (slow, rapid) life-history pattern.

_____ **6.** Instead of growing explosively, population growth tends to level off because the population reaches the (competitive limit, carrying capacity) of a particular environment.

_____ **7.** (Immigration, Emigration) can greatly increase the size of the population and create stresses within the population.

Label the graph below, which depicts the population growth for a sample of paramecium. Use these terms: beginning growth stage, exponential growth stage, leveling-off stage, carrying capacity.

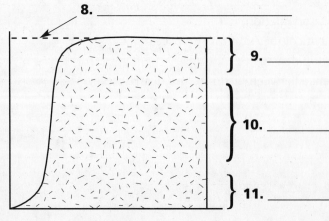

8. _____

9. _____

10. _____

11. _____

Number of paramecia

Time (days)

Chapter 4 Population Biology, *continued*

Understanding Main Ideas (Part B)

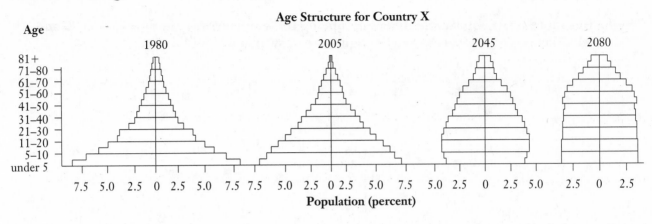

The first age structure graph for country X shows the percent of the population in each age group for 1980. The remaining three graphs are projections of how the age structure of country X will change. Use the graphs to answer questions 1–5.

1. In 1980, does country X exhibit an age structure more typical of a developing nation or an industrialized nation? Explain.

_____

_____

_____

2. How is the age structure expected to change by 2005?

_____

_____

_____

3. What can you conclude about the stage of population growth for country X from 1980 to 2005?

_____

4. Describe the overall trend in population growth predicted.

_____

_____

5. What might account for the age structure predicted for 2080?

_____

_____

_____

Chapter 4 **Population Biology,** *continued*

Thinking Critically

The figures represent a population of bees occupying the same territory in the years 1990 and 1992. Each ■ represents 100 bees. Use the figures to answers questions 1–6.

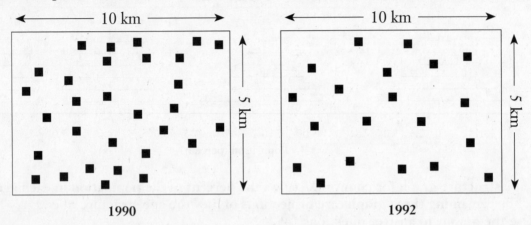

1990   1992

1. What is the area of the territory occupied by the bees?

_____

2. What was the size of the bee population in 1990?

_____

3. What was the density per square kilometer of the bee population in 1990?

_____

4. How did the size and density of the bee population change by 1992? Describe the changes in numbers.

_____

_____

5. What environmental factors might explain this change?

_____

_____

_____

6. Suppose in a population of 1000 wild horses, there are 400 births and 220 deaths. Also, 180 new horses join the population from an area that was destroyed by fire, and 380 horses are captured by park rangers. Describe the overall change in this horse population. What is the percentage of increase or decrease?

_____

_____

_____

Chapter 4 **Population Biology,** *continued*

Chapter Assessment

Applying Scientific Methods

A student grew a yeast culture on sterilized nutrient medium in a closed dish for 5 days. Each day, she took the same size sample from the dish and placed it on a special slide used for counting microorganisms. She examined the samples under a microscope and drew the following illustrations of her observations over the course of the investigation. Each dot represents 10 yeast cells.

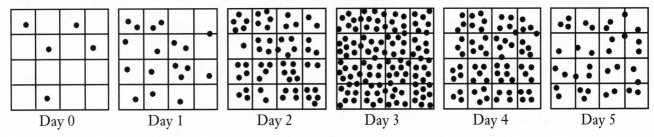

Day 0   Day 1   Day 2   Day 3   Day 4   Day 5

1. Why did the student use sterilized medium and keep the dish closed?

_____

_____

2. What problem was this student investigating?

_____

_____

3. During which two-day period was population growth most rapid?

_____

_____

4. At what point did the population reach the carrying capacity of the culture dish?

_____

_____

5. What factors limited the growth of the yeast population?

_____

_____

6. How could the student change the investigation so that the carrying capacity of the yeast's environment is increased?

_____

_____

_____

Applying Scientific Methods continued

7. What steps could the student take to ensure the accuracy of her results?

_____

_____

_____

_____

8. Which graph best illustrates the growth of the student's yeast population?

_____

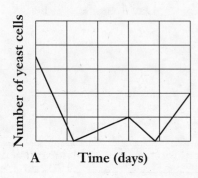
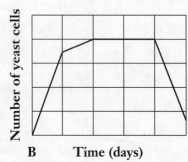
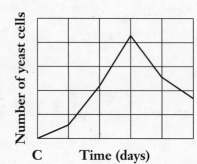

Chapter 5

Biological Diversity and Conservation

Chapter Assessment

Reviewing Vocabulary

In the space at the left, write <u>true</u> if the statement is true; if the statement is false, change the italicized term to make it true.

_____ **1.** Acid precipitation is rain, snow, sleet, or fog with a *high* pH value.

_____ **2.** Zoo animals are in *captivity*.

_____ **3.** The different conditions along the boundaries of an ecosystem, caused by habitat fragmentation, are called *a boundary effect*.

_____ **4.** *Conservation biology* studies methods and implements plans to protect biodiversity.

_____ **5.** When an *exotic species* is introduced into an area, it can grow at an exponential rate due to a lack of competitors.

_____ **6.** *Conservation* is the disappearance of a species when the last of its members dies.

_____ **7.** Air, water, and land pollution cause habitat *fragmentation*.

_____ **8.** The harvesting of food in a protected area is an example of *sustainable use*.

_____ **9.** The ozone layer protects organisms from *CFCs*.

_____ **10.** Because the number of African elephants is declining rapidly, the African elephant is *an endangered species*.

_____ **11.** The greater the number of species in a certain area, the greater is the area's *biodiversity*.

_____ **12.** *Habitat corridors* allow organisms to migrate from one protected area to another.

_____ **13.** *Reintroduction* programs release organisms into areas where their species once lived.

Understanding Main Ideas (Part A)

In the space at the left, write the letter of the word or phrase that best completes the statement or answers the question.

_____ **1.** Habitat degradation can be limited by
      a. decreasing the edge effect.   **b.** reducing pollution.
      c. establishing habitat corridors.   **d.** increasing biodiversity.

_____ **2.** Which of the following sequences is the most likely to occur?
      a. endangered species → threatened species → extinct species
      b. extinct species → threatened species → endangered species
      c. threatened species → endangered species → extinct species
      d. threatened species → extinct species → endangered species

_____ **3.** Which of the following is not caused by air pollution?
      a. algal blooms   **b.** acid precipitation
      c. increased UV radiation   **d.** loss of the ozone layer

_____ **4.** Which of the following animals would be least affected by habitat fragmentation?
      a. wolves   **b.** hawks   **c.** zebras   **d.** lions

_____ **5.** Reintroduction programs involve the
      a. establishment of protected areas.   **b.** reduction of pollution.
      c. capture of endangered species.   **d.** introduction of exotic species.

_____ **6.** The removal of coral reefs by people is an example of habitat
      a. fragmentation.   **b.** degradation.   **c.** loss.   **d.** preservation.

_____ **7.** National parks help prevent the extinction of many species by
      a. preserving the species' habitats.   **b.** reducing pollution.
      c. introducing exotic species.   **d.** allowing the sustainable use of resources.

_____ **8.** Problems associated with habitat fragmentation can be lessened by
      a. reducing pollution.   **b.** establishing habitat corridors.
      c. introducing exotic species.   **d.** establishing national parks.

_____ **9.** DDT had been passed to large birds, such as the bald eagle, through
      a. water.   **b.** food chains.   **c.** air.   **d.** soil.

_____ **10.** Acid precipitation is caused by
      a. pesticides.   **b.** CFCs.   **c.** the release of acid fumes.   **d.** burning fossil fuels.

Chapter 5 | **Biological Diversity and Conservation,** *continued*

Understanding Main Ideas (Part B)

Use the map to answer questions 1–3. Explain your answers.

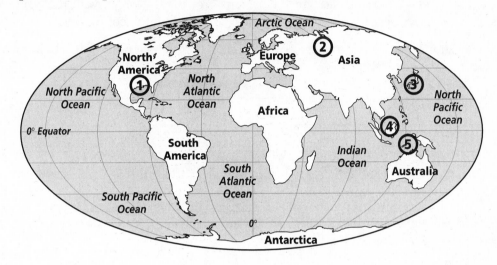

1. In which numbered location on the map would you expect to find the least biodiversity?

_____

_____

2. Would you expect to find more biodiversity on island 4 or 5?

_____

_____

3. Would you expect to find more biodiversity on island 3 or island 5?

_____

_____

Answer the following questions.

4. How does acid precipitation affect land and water organisms?

_____

_____

_____

_____

5. What are some problems associated with the introduction of an exotic species into an ecosystem?

_____

_____

Chapter 5 Biological Diversity and Conservation, *continued*

Thinking Critically

Suppose that fertilizers are being used by a farmer to add nutrients to depleted soil. At present, a nearby lake is a healthy ecosystem with floating algae and lake plants growing in balance with the fish and other lake inhabitants. Aerobic (oxygen-using) bacteria in the lake are the major decomposers.

1. Under what conditions could the fertilizer become a pollutant? Which part of the environment would be affected?

_____

_____

_____

_____

2. How might fertilizer pollution affect the organisms in the lake?

_____

_____

_____

_____

When a dam is built across a river, the dam creates an artificial lake or reservoir upstream. Dams are useful because they hold river water and collect and store runoff. Dams can also cause problems, however.

3. How could the building of a dam just downstream of a shorebird habitat cause a species of shorebirds to become threatened?

_____

_____

_____

_____

4. How could the building of the dam affect farmland located downstream from the dam?

_____

_____

_____

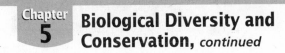

Chapter 5 **Biological Diversity and Conservation,** *continued*

Applying Scientific Methods

You are an environmental scientist who has been hired by the management of a nuclear power plant to help decide how and where to store the plant's radioactive waste materials. The power plant is located along the ocean coast, close to several large cities and towns. Although some of the radioactive waste is stored on site at the plant, most of it has been sealed in steel storage tanks that have been buried just a few feet under the soil surface of a nearby open field. Some people have suggested that the tanks be taken out to deep sea and lowered to the bottom of the ocean. Another group has suggested building a permanent storage area deep under the soil surface.

1. Why is the disposal of radioactive wastes a problem?

_____

_____

_____

2. What are some of the limitations of the present method of shallow burial of radioactive wastes?

_____

_____

_____

_____

3. What environmental problems could deep-sea burial present?

_____

_____

_____

_____

_____

4. What abiotic factors would need to be considered in choosing a deep-burial site on land?

_____

_____

_____

_____

Applying Scientific Methods   continued

5. What biotic factors would need to be considered?

_____

_____

_____

_____

6. In order to determine the possible effects of building a deep-burial land site in a particular area, what preliminary steps would you recommend?

_____

_____

_____

_____

7. After deciding on deep-sea or underground burial for storing the radioactive wastes, how might scientists monitor the effectiveness of the chosen storage method?

_____

_____

_____

_____

Chapter 6 The Chemistry of Life

Reviewing Vocabulary

Match the definition in Column A with the term in Column B.

Column A	Column B
_____ **1.** Center of an atom	**a.** diffusion
_____ **2.** Mixture in which one or more substances are distributed evenly in another substance	**b.** enzyme
_____ **3.** All of the chemical reactions that occur within an organism	**c.** metabolism
_____ **4.** Bond formed between amino acids	**d.** nucleus
_____ **5.** Protein that changes the rate of a chemical reaction	**e.** peptide bond
_____ **6.** Molecule with unequal distribution of charge	**f.** polar molecule
_____ **7.** Large molecule formed when many smaller molecules bond together	**g.** polymer
_____ **8.** Net movement of particles from an area of higher concentration to an area of lower concentration	**h.** solution

In the space at the left, write the term in parentheses that makes each statement correct.

_____ **9.** Atoms of the same element with different numbers of neutrons are (*isotopes, isomers*).

_____ **10.** Atoms of two or more elements chemically combined are (*mixtures, compounds*).

_____ **11.** Two atoms that share electrons are held together by (*ionic, covalent*) bonds.

_____ **12.** Any substance that forms hydrogen ions in water is a(n) (*acid, base*).

_____ **13.** The smaller subunits that make up nucleic acids are (*amino acids, nucleotides*).

_____ **14.** Some substances move into cells by (*hydrogen bonding, diffusion*).

Understanding Main Ideas (Part A)

In the space at the left, write the letter of the word or phrase that best completes the statement.

_____ **1.** Unlike carbohydrates and lipids, proteins contain

    a. nitrogen.   **b.** carbon.   **c.** hydrogen.   **d.** oxygen.

_____ **2.** A(n) _____ is formed when two atoms share electrons, such as with hydrogen and oxygen in water.

    a. solution   **b.** covalent bond

    c. ionic bond   **d.** isotope

_____ **3.** An atom of fluorine has 9 electrons. Its second energy level has

    a. 2 electrons.   **b.** 8 electrons.   **c.** 7 electrons.   **d.** 9 electrons.

_____ **4.** The total number of atoms in a molecule of sucrose, $C_{12}H_{22}O_{11}$, is

    a. 11.   **b.** 12.   **c.** 22.   **d.** 45.

_____ **5.** Carbon-12, carbon-13, and carbon-14 are

    a. isotopes.   **b.** polymers.   **c.** radio-isotopes.   **d.** macromolecules.

_____ **6.** A very strong base might have a pH of

    a. 3.   **b.** 5.   **c.** 9.   **d.** 13.

_____ **7.** Glucose and fructose, both with the formula $C_6H_{12}O_6$, differ in

    a. numbers of atoms.   **b.** arrangement of atoms.

    c. kinds of atoms.   **d.** arrangement of electrons.

_____ **8.** The various enzymes in our bodies are

    a. lipids.   **b.** carbohydrates.   **c.** nucleotides.   **d.** proteins.

_____ **9.** A chlorine atom becomes a chloride ion when it

    a. gains an electron.   **b.** loses an electron.

    c. gains a neutron.   **d.** loses a proton.

_____ **10.** When molecules of glucose and fructose combine to form sucrose, they do so by

    a. hydrolysis.   **b.** electron clouds.   **c.** condensation.   **d.** radiation.

_____ **11.** Water dissolves many ionic and molecular compounds because of its

    a. ionic bonding.   **b.** polarity.

    c. capillary action.   **d.** size.

_____ **12.** When is there no difference in the concentration of a substance from one area to another,

    a. diffusion occurs.   **b.** dynamic equilibrium has been reached.

    c. the atoms stop moving.   **d.** there is a concentration gradient.

Understanding Main Ideas (Part B)

Study the diagram, which shows the formation of magnesium chloride and hydrogen fluoride. Then answer the questions.

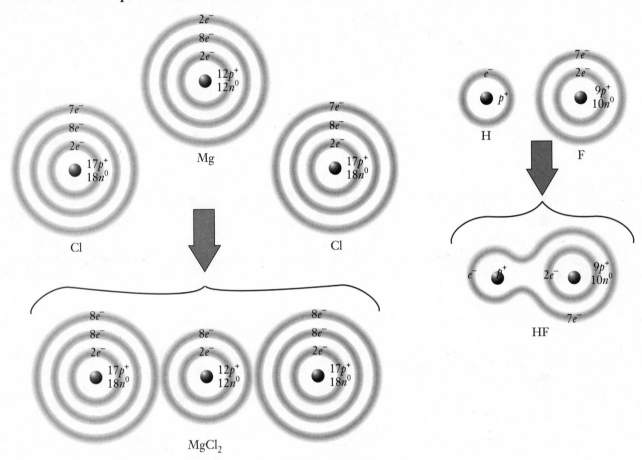

1. Which compound is formed by ionic bonding? Explain.

_____

_____

_____

2. Which compound is formed by covalent bonding? Explain.

_____

_____

3. How many electrons are in the third energy level of a magnesium atom? _____

4. Which atom forms an ion by the loss of electrons? _____

Chapter
6 The Chemistry of Life, *continued*

Chapter Assessment

Thinking Critically

To answer questions 1 and 2, use the table of acid–base indicators below.

Indicator	Color at lower pH values	pH range of color transition	Color at higher pH values
Methyl red	Red	4.4–6.0	Yellow
Litmus	Red	5.5–8.0	Blue
Bromothymol blue	Yellow	6.0–7.6	Blue
Phenol red	Yellow	6.8–8.4	Red
Phenolphthalein	Colorless	8.3–10.0	Red

1. A small volume of dilute hydrochloric acid is placed in a beaker and two drops of phenolphthalein are added. The solution remains colorless. A dilute solution of sodium hydroxide is then added drop by drop until a color change occurs. In what pH range does the color change occur? Describe the color change that occurs.

_____

2. If you exhale carbon dioxide (CO_2) into a solution of bromothymol blue, the solution turns from blue to yellow. Does CO_2 dissolve in water to form an acid or a base?

_____

Refer to the figure at the right for questions 3–5.

3. What type of biological compounds are A and B?

_____

4. Classify A and B as either saturated or unsaturated. Explain.

_____

_____

5. In most lipids, compounds like A and B are attached

to a 3-carbon molecule of _____ .

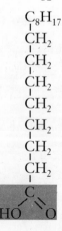

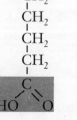

Chapter 6 **The Chemistry of Life,** *continued*

Chapter Assessment

Applying Scientific Methods

Two students carry out an investigation to determine the action of the enzyme pepsin on protein digestion in the human stomach. They know that gastric juice in the stomach contains water, pepsin, and hydrochloric acid. They decide to use small, equal-sized pieces of cooked egg white as the protein to be digested.

They set up four test tubes and place equal small amounts of egg white in each test tube. Then they fill each test tube with a different liquid to a height of 3 centimeters. To test tube 1, they add water; to test tube 2, they add hydrochloric acid (HCl diluted in water); to test tube 3, they add pepsin dissolved in water; and to test tube 4, they add pepsin solution and dilute hydrochloric acid. They place the four test tubes in an incubator set at 37°C (body temperature).

After one day, they observe the results. Then they return the test tubes to the incubator and observe them again the next day. The following table is the record of the results.

Test tube	1 day	2 days
1. egg + water	no change	no change
2. egg + hydrochloric acid	no change	no change
3. egg + pepsin solution	liquid slightly cloudy, egg pieces unchanged	liquid cloudy, egg pieces smaller
4. egg + pepsin solution + hydrochloric acid	liquid cloudy, egg pieces smaller	liquid very cloudy, almost no egg remains

1. Which test tube is the control? Explain its purpose.

_____

_____

_____

_____

2. What is the independent variable in the experiment? The dependent variable?

_____

_____

_____

_____

Applying Scientific Methods continued

3. What is the hypothesis on which this experiment is based?

_____

_____

_____

4. Was the hypothesis correct? Explain?

_____

_____

_____

5. What kind of results would have shown that the hypothesis is not correct?

_____

_____

_____

_____

6. What did the results from test tube 2 tell about protein digestion in the stomach?

_____

_____

_____

_____

7. Write a conclusion to the experiment. Base your conclusion on the experimental results.

_____

_____

_____

_____

Chapter

7   A View of the Cell

Reviewing Vocabulary

Write the word or phrase that best completes the statement.

1. A structure outside the plasma membrane in some cells is the _____ .

2. The functions of a eukaryotic cell are managed by the _____ .

3. In a cell, the tangles of long strands of DNA form the _____ .

4. The folded system of membranes that forms a network of interconnected compartments inside the cell is called the _____ .

5. The pigment that gives plants their green color is _____ .

6. The network of tiny rods and filaments that forms a framework for the cell is called the

_____ .

7. In plants, the structures that transform light energy into chemical energy are called

_____ .

In the space at the left, write the term in parentheses that makes each statement correct.

_____   **8.** (*Phospholipids, Transport proteins*) make up the selectively permeable membrane that controls which molecules enter and leave the cell.

_____   **9.** Short, hairlike projections used for locomotion are (*cilia, flagella*).

_____   **10.** In a cell, the breakdown of molecules in order to release energy occurs in the (*mitochondria, Golgi apparatus*).

_____   **11.** An organism with a cell that lacks a true nucleus is a(n) (*prokaryote, eukaryote*).

_____   **12.** The movement of materials into and out of the cells is controlled by the (*cytoplasm, plasma membrane*).

_____   **13.** The small, membrane-bound structures inside a cell are (*chromatin, organelles*).

_____   **14.** In a cell, the sites of protein synthesis are the (*ribosomes, nucleolus*).

_____   **15.** Cell structures that contain digestive enzymes are (*plastids, lysosomes*).

Chapter
7 **A View of the Cell,** *continued*

Chapter Assessment

Understanding Concepts (Part A)

In the space at the left, write the letter of the word or phrase that best completes the statement.

_____ **1.** Cell walls of multicellular plants are composed mainly of
    a. cellulose.   **b.** chitin.   **c.** pectin.   **d.** vacuoles.

_____ **2.** The term *least* closely related to the others is
    a. cytoskeleton.   **b.** microfilament.
    c. microtubule.   **d.** cell juncture.

_____ **3.** In a chloroplast, the stacks of membranous sacs are called
    a. stroma.   **b.** grana.
    c. plastids.   **d.** thylakoid membrane.

_____ **4.** The structure most responsible for maintaining cell homeostasis is the
    a. cytoplasm.   **b.** mitochondrion.   **c.** cell wall.   **d.** plasma membrane.

_____ **5.** If a cell contains a nucleus, it must be a(n)
    a. plant cell.   **b.** eukaryotic cell.
    c. animal cell.   **d.** prokaryotic cell.

_____ **6.** One advantage of electron microscopes over light microscopes is their
    a. size.   **b.** higher magnification.
    c. two-dimensional image.   **d.** use of live specimens.

_____ **7.** When a cell is ready to reproduce, its DNA is packed into
    a. chromosomes.   **b.** chromatin.   **c.** nucleoli.   **d.** nucleoids.

_____ **8.** The scientist who first described living cells as seen through a simple microscope was
    a. van Leeuwenhoek.   **b.** Schleiden.
    c. Hooke.   **d.** Schwann.

_____ **9.** Each of the following is a main idea of the cell theory *except*
    a. all organisms are composed of cells.
    b. the cell is the basic unit of organization of organisms.
    c. all cells are similar in structure and function.
    d. all cells come from preexisting cells.

_____ **10.** A plasma membrane is made up of a(n)
    a. cholesterol layer.   **b.** enzyme bilayer.
    c. phospholipid bilayer.   **d.** protein layer.

Chapter
7 **A View of the Cell,** *continued*

Chapter Assessment

Understanding Concepts (Part B)

The diagram below of a bacterium shows a light area with no surrounding membrane in the center of the cell. This area contains a single large DNA molecule. Use the diagram to answer questions 1 and 2.

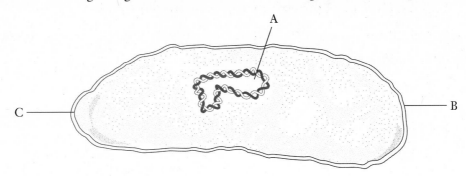

1. Identify the structures labeled A, B, and C.

_____

2. Based on the diagram, would scientists classify this cell as a prokaryote or a eukaryote? Explain.

_____

_____

_____

_____

Answer the following questions.

3. In plants, cells that transport water against the force of gravity are found to contain many more mitochondria than do some other plant cells. What is the reason for this?

_____

_____

_____

_____

4. Why did it take almost 200 years after Hooke discovered cells for the cell theory to be developed?

_____

_____

_____

Chapter 7 A View of the Cell, *continued*

Chapter Assessment

Thinking Critically

Answer the following questions.

1. Many types of animal cells have a thin, flexible cell covering outside the plasma membrane. This cell covering, called a glycocalyx, consists of complex carbohydrates bonded to the proteins and lipids in the plasma membrane. How is the glycocalyx similar to the cell wall of a green plant? How is it different?

_____

_____

_____

_____

_____

2. The stomach lining contains mucus, which helps prevent the digestion of the stomach lining. If this mechanism fails, digestive enzymes in the stomach cause the stomach to digest itself, producing an ulcer. Compare this process with the way lysosomes prevent destruction of the cell's proteins.

_____

_____

_____

_____

3. Between which cell types is the difference greater—plant and animal cells or prokaryotic and eukaryotic cells? Give reasons for your answer.

_____

_____

_____

_____

_____

_____

_____

Chapter
7 **A View of the Cell,** *continued*

Chapter Assessment

Applying Scientific Methods

For many years, scientists thought of the nucleus as "a bag of chromatin floating in a sea of cytoplasm." Using electron microscopes, scientists saw that the nucleus was much more complex. The nuclear envelope was two-layered and covered with pores.

Scientists began further research. Scientist S punched small holes in the nuclear envelope, allowing the contents to pour out. He observed that the nucleus retained its spherical shape. From this, scientist S hypothesized that the nucleus had some other structural framework, beyond the membrane itself. The next experiment performed by scientist S revealed that the nucleus indeed had a fibrous protein framework, now called the nuclear matrix.

Three other scientists repeated this experiment, but each changed one part of it. Scientist X used detergents and salt to remove the nuclear contents. Scientist Y used chemicals, and scientist Z used enzymes. All three observed that a nuclear matrix remained.

Further electron microscopy revealed that the chromatin strands are anchored to a fibrous layer that lines the inner layer of the nuclear envelope.

1. What was the hypothesis of scientist S in his first experiment?

_____

2. What observation from scientist S's second experiment supported the original hypothesis?

_____

_____

3. Why did scientists X, Y, and Z carry out their experiments?

_____

_____

4. What was the variable in the experiments by scientists X, Y, and Z?

_____

_____

_____

5. Why did scientists X, Y, and Z use different substances to remove the nuclear contents?

_____

_____

_____

6. Describe a procedure to determine whether the attachment of the chromatin to the nuclear envelope is necessary for the chromatin to become chromosomes.

_____

_____

Applying Scientific Methods continued

In the 1890s, E. Overton performed experiments to determine the structure of the plasma membrane. After many years and various procedures, he determined that large, uncharged molecules enter a cell at a rate proportional to their solubility in lipids. This observation was the first indication that the plasma membrane is probably made up of lipids. Many scientists began to pursue the question of how the lipids were arranged.

In 1925, two Dutch scientists determined that the area covered by the lipids from a single red blood cell is twice the area of the surface of the cell. From this, they reasoned that the cell is covered by a double layer of lipid molecules. Based on this work, various scientists hypothesized that the membrane was like a "fat sandwich" with two outer layers of protein on the surface of the lipid layer.

None of the ideas seemed a satisfactory explanation until microscopic studies of membranes prepared by a new technique of "freeze-fracture" revealed that the proteins are actually embedded in the lipid layer. In 1972, on the basis of these results and other evidence, two American scientists proposed the fluid-mosaic model.

7. What was the problem that Overton was trying to solve with his experiments?

_____

8. Is his hypothesis stated in the discussion above? If so, what was it?

_____

9. The result of one experiment often leads to further experiments. How do Overton's experiments illustrate this fact?

_____

_____

10. What conclusion did the Dutch scientists reach?

_____

11. What inference did the Dutch scientists make to reach their conclusion?

_____

_____

12. What model of the plasma membrane was based on their results?

_____

13. Why was it almost 50 years between the Dutch scientists' research and the proposal of a fluid mosaic model?

_____

_____

_____

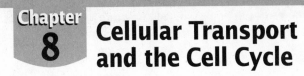

Chapter 8 Cellular Transport and the Cell Cycle

Reviewing Vocabulary

Write the word or phrase that best completes each statement.

1. The transport of materials against a concentration gradient is called _____ .

2. The phase of mitosis in which the sister chromatids separate from each other is

_____ .

3. A solution in which the concentration of dissolved substances is lower than the concentration inside

a cell is _____ .

4. The sequence of growth and division of a cell make up the _____ .

5. The period during which chromosomes duplicate is _____ .

6. The segment of DNA that controls the production of a protein is a _____ .

7. The phase of mitosis in which chromosomes line up on the equator of the spindle is

_____ .

8. The two halves of a doubled chromosome structure are called _____ .

9. The uncontrolled division of cells may result in _____ .

10. Passive transport with the aid of transport proteins is _____ .

11. The process by which nuclear material is divided equally between two new cells is

_____ .

12. Some cells surround and take in materials by the process of _____ .

13. The structures that hold together sister chromatids are _____ .

Write a sentence that uses each pair of terms.

14. (spindle, centrioles)

_____

_____

15. (tissues, organs)

_____

_____

Chapter 8 **Cellular Transport and the Cell Cycle,** *continued*

Understanding Main Ideas (Part A)

In the space at the left, write the letter of the word or phrase that best completes the statement or answers the question.

_____ **1.** When placed in a hypotonic solution, a cell will

    a. diffuse.   **b.** shrink.   **c.** swell.   **d.** stay the same.

_____ **2.** As the size of a cell increases,

    a. volume increases faster than surface area.

    b. volume increases and surface area decreases.

    c. volume and surface area increase at the same rate.

    d. surface area increases faster than volume.

_____ **3.** The longest phase of the cell cycle is

    a. prophase.   **b.** interphase.   **c.** metaphase.   **d.** mitosis.

_____ **4.** Which of the following does *not* control the cell cycle?

    a. DNA   **b.** mitosis   **c.** enzymes   **d.** genes

_____ **5.** Tangled strands of DNA wrapped around protein molecules make up the

    a. spindle.   **b.** microtubules.   **c.** nuclear envelope.   **d.** chromatin.

_____ **6.** By the end of prophase, each of the following has occurred *except*

    a. chromatin coiling into visible chromosomes.

    b. breaking down of the nuclear envelope.

    c. forming of the spindle.

    d. lining up of chromosomes in the cell.

_____ **7.** Each of the following is an example of passive transport *except*

    a. diffusion.   **b.** osmosis.

    c. exocytosis.   **d.** facilitated diffusion.

_____ **8.** The cells that make up a tissue

    a. are different.   **b.** are the result of interphase.

    c. have the same function.   **d.** no longer undergo mitosis.

_____ **9.** Each of the following is a cause of some cancers *except*

    a. damaged genes.   **b.** bacteria.

    c. ultraviolet radiation.   **d.** viruses.

_____ **10.** Among the following, the term that includes all of the others is

    a. interphase.   **b.** nuclear division.   **c.** mitosis.   **d.** cell cycle.

Chapter 8 — Cellular Transport and the Cell Cycle, *continued*

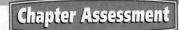
Understanding Main Ideas (Part B)

The diagrams below show six cells in various phases of the cell cycle, labeled A through F. Use the diagrams to answer questions 1–7.

Phases of the Cell Cycle

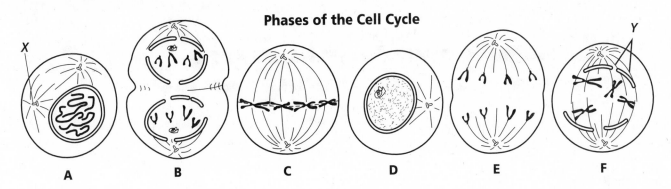

A   B   C   D   E   F

1. Which cell is in metaphase? _____

2. Cells A and F show an early and a late stage of the same phase of mitosis. What phase is it?

_____

3. In cell A, what structure is labeled X?

_____

4. In cell F, what structure is labeled Y?

_____

5. Which cell is not in a phase of mitosis?

_____

6. What two main changes are taking place in cell B?

_____

7. Sequence the six diagrams in order from first to last.

_____

Answer the following question.

8. What are the main differences between cytokinesis in plant cells and in animal cells?

_____

_____

_____

_____

Thinking Critically

The graph shows typical concentrations of several ions inside and outside an animal cell. Concentrations of ions inside the cell are shown in gray, outside in black. Use the graph to answer questions 1–5.

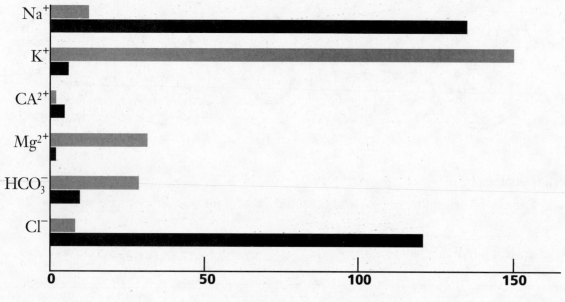

Concentration (mM)

1. Compared to its surroundings, does an animal cell contain a higher or lower concentration of

   potassium (K^+) ions? _____

2. Which ions are in the greatest concentration outside the animal cell? _____

3. Which ions are in the lowest concentration inside the animal cell? _____

4. What is the approximate concentration, in mM, of Mg^{2+} ions inside the cell? _____

5. If all available Na^+ and Cl^- ions combine to form NaCl, do any excess Na^+ or Cl^- ions remain?

   If so, which? _____

Answer the following question.

6. Describe the process by which a cell maintains differences in concentrations of certain ions on either side of the plasma membrane.

   _____

   _____

   _____

Chapter 8 Cellular Transport and the Cell Cycle, *continued*

Chapter Assessment

Applying Scientific Methods

The large size of many fruits and flowers is the result of polyploidy, a condition in which the nuclei of an organism's cells contain extra sets of chromosomes. Polyploidy often occurs naturally, but it can also be artificially induced by plant breeders. How have breeders been able to mimic a naturally occurring phenomenon?

Researchers have determined that the chemical colchicine suppresses cell division by preventing the formation of spindle fibers. Without these fibers, the sister chromatids cannot become properly oriented for separation into individual nuclei. In effect, mitosis is stopped after prophase. However, the cell may continue to make copies of its chromosomes. As a result, the nucleus of the cell contains multiple sets of chromosomes.

Suppose a researcher wished to investigate how extra sets of chromosomes are produced. First, she treated two onion roots with a colchicine solution and left two roots untreated. After a period of several days, she placed thin slices from each root tip on separate microscope slides, stained the specimens, and examined the slides under a microscope at high power.

1. What is the hypothesis the researcher investigated?

_____

_____

2. Which root tips were the control group? Which root tips were the experimental group?

_____

_____

3. What was the independent variable in the investigation?

_____

_____

4. What was the dependent variable?

_____

_____

5. How do you predict the slides of treated and untreated root tips will differ?

_____

_____

_____

6. If the researcher finds only cells in interphase and prophase on the slides of treated root tips but not on the slides of untreated root tips, what might be her interpretation?

_____

_____

Applying Scientific Methods   continued

7. What results might lead the researcher to conclude that the colchicine had no effect on the onion cells?

_____

_____

_____

8. "How does treating cells with colchicine prevent the formation of spindle fibers?" Is this question the statement of the problem or the conclusion of a further investigation? Explain.

_____

_____

9. How might the researcher proceed to find out how treating cells with colchicine prevents the formation of spindle fibers?

_____

_____

_____

10. Why does polyploidy result in larger fruits and flowers?

_____

_____

_____

_____

Chapter 9 Energy in a Cell

Reviewing Vocabulary

Complete each statement.

1. The reactions in photosynthesis in which light energy from the sun is converted to chemical energy are called _____ .

2. The process by which plants trap the sun's energy to build carbohydrates is called _____ .

3. The transfer of electrons along a series of proteins, releasing energy as they pass, is known as an _____ .

4. _____ is a plant pigment that absorbs most wavelengths of light except green.

5. The splitting of water during photosynthesis is _____ .

6. The anaerobic process of breaking down glucose to form pyruvic acid is called _____ .

7. In photosynthesis, the cycle of reactions that uses carbon dioxide to synthesize glucose is known as the _____ .

8. A cycle of reactions in aerobic respiration that begins and ends with the same 4-carbon compound is the _____ .

Compare and contrast each pair of related terms.

9. aerobic process : anaerobic process

_____

_____

10. photosynthesis : cellular respiration

_____

_____

_____

_____

_____

_____

Understanding Main Ideas (Part A)

In the space at the left, write the letter of the word or phrase that best completes the statement or answers the question.

_____ **1.** Which of the following is *not* a part of adenosine diphosphate?
    a. glucose   **b.** adenine
    c. ribose   **d.** two phosphate groups

_____ **2.** The light-independent reactions of photosynthesis take place in the
    a. thylakoids.   **b.** stroma.   **c.** mitochondria.   **d.** cytoplasm.

_____ **3.** The energy in glucose *cannot* be released by
    a. glycolysis.   **b.** the citric acid cycle.
    c. cellular respiration.   **d.** photosynthesis.

_____ **4.** Cells store energy when
    a. the third phosphate group breaks off from an ATP molecule.
    b. they break down sucrose to glucose and fructose.
    c. a third phosphate group is bonded to an ADP molecule.
    d. ions are released into the bloodstream.

_____ **5.** Leaves appear green because the green portion of the light that strikes them is
    a. changed to heat.   **b.** absorbed.   **c.** destroyed.   **d.** reflected.

_____ **6.** Which of the following equations best represents photosynthesis?
    a. $C + O_2 + H_2O \rightarrow CO_2 + HOH$ **b.** $6CO_2 + 6H_2O \rightarrow C_6H_{12}O_6 + 6O_2$
    c. $6C + 6H_2O \rightarrow C_6H_{12}O_6$ **d.** $C_6H_{12}O_6 \rightarrow 6CO_2 + 6H_2O$

_____ **7.** Kidneys use energy to move molecules and ions in order to keep the blood chemically balanced. This process is an example of cells using energy to
    a. carry on chemosynthesis.   **b.** control body temperature.
    c. transmit impulses.   **d.** maintain homeostasis.

_____ **8.** In respiration, the final electron acceptor in the electron transport chain is
    a. oxygen.   **b.** ATP.   **c.** hydrogen ions.   **d.** water.

_____ **9.** In glycolysis, ____ molecules of ATP are used in the first step and ____ molecules of ATP are produced in the second step.
    a. four, two   **b.** two, four   **c.** two, two   **d.** four, four

_____ **10.** In the process of photosynthesis, the
    a. Calvin cycle yields CO_2.   **b.** light-dependent reactions release oxygen.
    c. Calvin cycle breaks down H_2O.   **d.** light-dependent reactions produce $NADP^+$.

Understanding Main Ideas (Part B)

Answer the following questions.

1. Synthesis of molecules, transmission of nerve impulses, movement of cilia, and bioluminescence are various activities of organisms.
   a. What requirement do these activities have in common?

   _____

   b. Why is ATP important in each activity?

   _____

   _____

2. Both the wine industry and the bread industry use the process of alcoholic fermentation.
   a. In what way is the use of alcoholic fermentation by these industries similar?

   _____

   _____

   b. In what way does their use of alcoholic fermentation differ?

   _____

   _____

3. In cellular respiration, the steps following glycolysis depend on whether oxygen is present. Explain.

   _____

   _____

   _____

4. Explain what is meant by carbon fixation. During which stage of photosynthesis does this process take place?

   _____

   _____

5. If you run as fast as you can, your muscles may begin to feel weak and have a burning sensation. Explain what is occurring in your muscle cells that accounts for this muscle fatigue.

   _____

   _____

   _____

   _____

Thinking Critically

Answer the following questions.

The table below shows the average yield of ATP molecules from the oxidation of glucose in eukaryotic cells.

Reaction	ATP Produced	ATP Used
Glycolysis	2	4
Citric acid cycle	2	
Electron transport chain	32	

1. What is the net production of ATP molecules by *each* of the four reactions?

_____

_____

2. What is the total net gain of ATP molecules per glucose molecule?

_____

_____

3. The combination of glycolysis and fermentation yields a net gain of 2 ATP molecules. How many molecules of ATP does fermentation yield? Explain.

_____

_____

_____

In an experiment conducted to determine whether green plants take in CO_2, a biologist filled a large beaker with aquarium water to which she added bromothymol blue. She exhaled CO_2 into the solution of bromothymol blue, which made the solution turn yellow. Then she placed a sprig of *Elodea* into two test tubes. She left a third test tube without *Elodea* to serve as a control. She added the yellow bromothymol solution to all three test tubes and placed a stopper in each. Next, she placed all the test tubes in sunlight. After several hours in sunlight, the bromothymol solution in the test tubes with the *Elodea* turned blue. The bromothymol solution in the control remained yellow.

4. What conclusion can be drawn from the experiment? Explain.

_____

_____

_____

Applying Scientific Methods

In 1803, Thomas Engelmann of Germany used a combination of aerobic bacteria and a filamentous alga to study the effect of various colors of the visible light spectrum on the rate of photosynthesis. He passed white light through a prism in order to separate the light into the different colors of the spectrum; then he exposed different segments of the alga to the various colors. He observed in which areas of the spectrum the greatest number of bacteria appeared. Refer to the diagram below to answer the questions that follow.

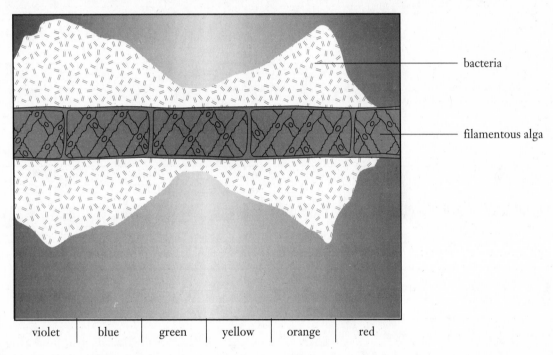

| violet | blue | green | yellow | orange | red |

1. Using his setup, Engelmann was able to determine in which areas of the visible light spectrum the alga was releasing the most oxygen. Explain his reasoning.

   _____

   _____

2. Was determining where there was more oxygen the purpose of his experiment? If not, state the purpose.

   _____

   _____

   _____

3. How was the observation of the amount of oxygen present related to Engelmann's purpose?

   _____

   _____

Applying Scientific Methods continued

4. Why did Engelmann select aerobic rather than anaerobic bacteria?

_____

_____

_____

5. Based on the diagram, what would Engelmann's conclusion be?

_____

_____

_____

6. What was the independent variable in this experiment?

_____

_____

_____

7. Describe one control Engelmann might have used. Explain.

_____

_____

_____

8. Did Engelmann's observations verify his hypothesis? Explain.

_____

_____

_____

_____

Chapter 10 Mendel and Meiosis

Reviewing Vocabulary

Match the definition in Column A with the term in Column B.

Column A	Column B
_____ 1. The different forms of a gene	**a.** crossing over
_____ 2. The alleles present for a trait are the same.	**b.** homozygous
_____ 3. A cell that contains one member of each chromosome pair	**c.** fertilization
_____ 4. The type of cell division that produces gametes	**d.** meiosis
_____ 5. The cell produced when a male gamete fuses with a female gamete	**e.** nondisjunction
_____ 6. The uniting of the male and female gametes	**f.** zygote
_____ 7. The exchange of genetic material between homologous chromosomes	**g.** haploid
_____ 8. The failure of homologous chromosomes to separate properly during meiosis	**h.** alleles

In the space at the left, write the letter of the word or phrase that best completes the statement.

_____ 9. Pollination can best be described as
    a. the fusing of the egg nucleus with the pollen nucleus.
    b. the transfer of a male pollen grain to the pistil of a flower.
    c. the formation of male and female sex cells.
    d. the type of cell division that produces diploid gametes.

_____ 10. The gamete that contains genes contributed by the mother is
    a. a sperm.   **b.** an egg.   **c.** a zygote.   **d.** dominant.

_____ 11. Cells containing two alleles for each trait are described as
    a. haploid.   **b.** gametes.   **c.** diploid.   **d.** homozygous.

_____ 12. The statement: "In meiosis, the way in which a chromosome pair separates does not affect the way other pairs separate," is another way of expressing Mendel's law of
    a. dominance.   **b.** heredity.   **c.** independent assortment.   **d.** segregation.

Understanding Main Ideas (Part A)

In the space at the left, write the letter of the word or phrase that best completes the statement or answers the question.

_____ **1.** A white mouse whose parents are both white produces only brown offspring when mated with a brown mouse. The white mouse is most probably

    a. homozygous recessive.   **b.** heterozygous.

    c. homozygous dominant.   **d.** haploid.

_____ **2.** Polyploid organisms result from

    a. crossing over.   **b.** nondisjunction.   **c.** mitosis.   **d.** random assortment.

_____ **3.** The numbers in the diagram below represent the number of chromosomes found in each of the dog cells shown.

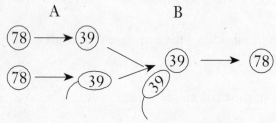

    The processes that are occurring at A and B are

    a. mitosis and fertilization.   **b.** meiosis and fertilization.

    c. mitosis and pollination.   **d.** meiosis and pollination.

_____ **4.** If a female guinea pig homozygous dominant for black fur color is mated with a male that is homozygous recessive for white fur color, in a litter of eight offspring, you would expect

    a. 8 black guinea pigs.

    b. 4 black and 4 white guinea pigs.

    c. 2 black, 4 gray, and 2 white guinea pigs.

    d. 8 white guinea pigs.

_____ **5.** A dog's phenotype can be determined by

    a. looking at the dog's parents.

    b. examining the dog's chromosomes.

    c. mating the dog and examining its offspring.

    d. looking at the dog.

_____ **6.** A couple has two children, both of whom are boys. What is the chance that the parents' next child will be a boy?

    a. 0%   **b.** 50%   **c.** 25%   **d.** 75%

Chapter
10 **Mendel and Meiosis,** *continued*

Chapter Assessment

Understanding Main Ideas (Part B)

In the space at the left, write the letter of the word or phrase that best completes the statement or answers the question.

_____ **1.** The diagram below shows a diploid cell with two homologous pairs of chromosomes.

Due to independent assortment, the possible allelic combinations that could be found in gametes produced by the meiotic division of this cell are
a. *Bb, Dd, BB,* and *DD*.   **b.** *BD, bD, Bd,* and *bd*.
c. *BbDd* and *BDbd*.   **d.** *Bd* and *bD* only.

_____ **2.** When Mendel allowed tall heterozygous plants to self-pollinate, some of their off-spring were short because the alleles of the tall plants
a. were dominant.   **b.** segregated during meiosis.
c. were homozygous.   **d.** crossed over during meiosis.

_____ **3.** Which process would result in the formation of chromosome **C** from homologous chromosomes **A** and **B**?

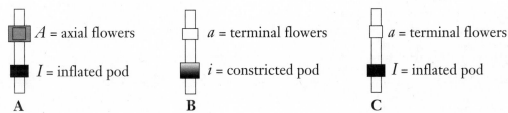

a. asexual reproduction   **b.** independent assortment
c. crossing over   **d.** segregation

_____ **4.** In chickens, rose comb (*R*) is dominant to single comb (*r*). A homozygous rose-combed rooster is mated with a single-combed hen. All of the chicks in the F_1 generation were kept together as a group for several years. They were only allowed to mate within their own group. What is the expected phenotype of the F_2 chicks?
a. 100% rose comb   **b.** 75% rose comb and 25% single comb
c. 100% single comb   **d.** 50% rose comb and 50% single comb

Thinking Critically

1. Approximately one out of every 20 Caucasian Americans has a recessive allele for a hereditary disorder known as cystic fibrosis (CF), but only one out of every 2000 Caucasian babies born in the United States is afflicted with the disorder. These individuals have two alleles for CF. They produce large amounts of mucus that accumulate in the lungs, liver, and pancreas. The mucus clogs important ducts in these organs and causes extensive damage. Why is there such a difference between the number of individuals who have the allele for CF and the number actually born with the disorder?

_____

_____

_____

_____

_____

_____

_____

2. How can genetic recombination through segregation and crossing over during meiosis lead to variation in the offspring?

_____

_____

_____

_____

3. In guinea pigs, the allele for rough coat (*R*) is dominant to the allele for smooth coat (*r*), and the allele for black fur (*B*) is dominant to the allele for white fur (*b*). If two guinea pigs that are heterozygous for rough, black fur (*RrBb*) are mated, what are the possible phenotypes and what is the frequency of each? Use a Punnett square to find the answers.

_____

_____

_____

_____

_____

Applying Scientific Methods

Some biology students wanted to determine whether a pair of brown mice purchased at a pet store was homozygous dominant or heterozygous for fur color. They let the mice mate and examined the offspring. Six mice were born. All six had brown fur.

Some of the students felt that this was enough evidence to prove that the parent mice were homozygous for brown fur color. Other students did not, so another experiment was planned.

1. Do you think the experiment described above was adequate to prove that the parent mice were homozygous brown? Explain your answer, using the principles of genetics you have studied.

_____

_____

_____

_____

_____

_____

_____

_____

_____

_____

2. Describe the next experiment the students could conduct to determine whether the parent mice are homozygous brown or heterozygous brown.

_____

_____

_____

_____

_____

_____

_____

_____

_____

_____

_____

Applying Scientific Methods   continued

_____

_____

_____

_____

_____

_____

_____

3. What could you conclude if three of the offspring had white fur?

_____

_____

4. What could you conclude if all six of the offspring had white fur?

_____

_____

_____

_____

Chapter 11 DNA and Genes

Reviewing Vocabulary

From the words provided in the list, write the one that best completes each of the following statements. Use these choices:

mRNA	point mutation	codon	replication
nitrogen bases	tRNA	double helix	nondisjunction
frameshift mutation	translation	chromosomal mutation	cancer

1. During the process of transcription, DNA serves as the template for making

_____ , which leaves the nucleus and travels to the ribosomes.

2. A _____ involves the addition or deletion of a single base in a DNA molecule.

3. Watson and Crick developed the _____ model of DNA.

4. Thymine, adenine, guanine, and cytosine are _____ .

5. The process by which DNA makes a copy of itself is called _____ .

6. Each set of three nitrogen bases representing an amino acid is referred to as a

_____ .

7. _____ brings amino acids to the ribosomes for the assembly of proteins.

8. A change in a single base pair of the DNA molecule is called a _____ .

9. _____ is the failure of a pair of homologous chromosomes to separate

properly during meiosis.

10. The process of converting RNA code into an amino acid sequence is called

_____ .

11. When parts of chromosomes are broken off and lost or reattached incorrectly during mitosis or

meiosis, the result is a _____ .

12. Mutations in DNA can result in cells reproducing rapidly, producing the disease called

_____ .

Chapter 11 **DNA and Genes,** continued

Understanding Main Ideas (Part A)

In the diagram, label the strand of DNA represented.

1. Use the letter **P** to label all of the phosphate groups.

2. Use an **S** to label all the sugar molecules.

3. For labeling the nitrogen bases, use a **T** for thymine and a **C** for cytosine. Guanine and adenine have been filled in for you.

4. Circle and label a codon.

5. Circle and label a nucleotide.

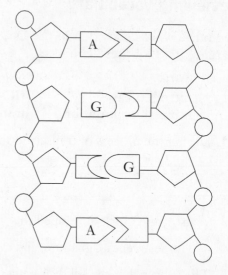

In the space at the left, write the letter of the word or phrase that best completes the statement or answers the question.

_____ **6.** X rays, ultraviolet light, and radioactive substances that can change the chemical nature of DNA are classified as

    a. growth regulators.   **b.** metamorphic molecules.

    c. hydrolytic enzymes.   **d.** mutagens.

_____ **7.** An RNA molecule is a polymer composed of subunits known as

    a. polysaccharides.   **b.** ribose molecules.

    c. nucleotides.   **d.** uracil molecules.

_____ **8.** The hereditary information for a particular trait is generally

    a. controlled by alleles located on chromosomes.

    b. controlled by chromosomes located on an allele.

    c. carried from the nucleus by tRNA to the gamete.

    d. coded for by a ribosome located on the reticulum.

_____ **9.** Which series is arranged in order from largest to smallest in size?

    a. chromosome, nucleus, cell, DNA, nucleotide

    b. cell, nucleus, chromosome, DNA, nucleotide

    c. nucleotide, chromosome, cell, DNA, nucleus

    d. cell, nucleotide, nucleus, DNA, chromosome

_____ **10.** A DNA nucleotide may be made up of a phosphate group, along with

    a. deoxyribose sugar and uracil.   **b.** ribose sugar and adenine.

    c. deoxyribose sugar and thymine.   **d.** ribose sugar and cytosine.

CHAPTER ASSESSMENT

Understanding Main Ideas (Part B)

In the space at the left, write the letter of the word or phrase that best completes the statement or answers the question.

_____ **1.** The diagram labeled **Insect A** represents the chromosomes taken from the body cell of a normal female insect. The diagram labeled **Insect B** represents those taken from the body cell of a female of the same species but with an abnormal phenotype.

Insect A   **Insect B**

The chromosomal alteration seen in Insect B could have resulted from

a. nondisjunction   **b.** crossing over.

c. a frameshift mutation.   **d.** a point mutation.

Refer to the diagram below to answer questions 2–5.

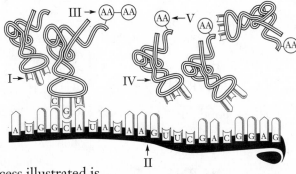

_____ **2.** The process illustrated is

a. translation.   **b.** replication.   **c.** monoploidy.   **d.** transcription.

_____ **3.** Structure III represents a(n)

a. gene.   **b.** amino acid.   **c.** codon.   **d.** DNA molecule.

_____ **4.** Which of the above structures are composed of RNA?

a. II and IV   **b.** III and IV   **c.** I and V   **d.** III and V

_____ **5.** Where in the cell does this process occur?

a. in the nucleus   **b.** in food vacuoles

c. at the ribosomes   **d.** within the plasma membrane

Thinking Critically

For each set of terms in questions 1–3, complete the analogy by writing the appropriate term in the space provided. Then explain why you chose the term.

1. adenine: thymine :: guanine: _____

_____

_____

_____

2. DNA: RNA :: double-stranded: _____

_____

_____

_____

3. translation: protein :: transcription: _____

_____

_____

_____

In the blank at the left, write the letter of the term that best completes the statement.

_____ **4.** Applicants for the first job, "Positions Available," could qualify if they were

    a. DNA.   **b.** mRNA.
    c. tRNA.   **d.** rRNA.

_____ **5.** Applicants for the second job, "Accuracy and Speed," could qualify if they were

    a. DNA.   **b.** mRNA.
    c. tRNA.   **d.** rRNA.

_____ **6.** Applications for the third job, "Executive Position," could qualify if they were

    a. DNA.   **b.** mRNA.
    c. tRNA.   **d.** rRNA.

_____ **7.** Applicants for the fourth job, "Supervisor," could qualify if they were

    a. DNA.   **b.** mRNA.
    c. tRNA.   **d.** rRNA.

Help Wanted

Positions Available in the genetics industry. Hundreds of entry-level openings for tireless workers. No previous experience necessary. Must be able to transcribe code in a nuclear environment. The ability to work in close association with ribosomes is a must.

Accuracy and Speed vital for this job in the field of translation. Applicants must demonstrate skills in transporting and positioning amino acids. Salary commensurate with experience.

Executive Position available. Must be able to maintain genetic continuity through replication and control cellular activity by regulation of enzyme production. Limited number of openings. All benefits.

Supervisor of production of proteins—all shifts. Must be able to follow exact directions from double-stranded template. Travel from nucleus to the cytoplasm is additional job benefit.

Chapter 11 **DNA and Genes,** *continued*

Applying Scientific Methods

Watson and Crick explained the structure of DNA in 1953. How DNA actually replicated was still a mystery. Matthew Meselson and Frank Stahl set out in 1957 to determine exactly how it was accomplished. There were three different ways of thinking about replication. (See Figure 1.) Some scientists believed that the two strands of the double helix separated during replication but that each strand remained intact. Each strand then served as the template for the assembly of a new DNA strand that it would bond with. This method is called *semiconservative replication*.

According to a second hypothesis, referred to as *conservative replication*, the original double-stranded DNA remains intact while an entirely new double-stranded DNA is formed alongside it. Hence, all of the new molecules lack any of the original DNA.

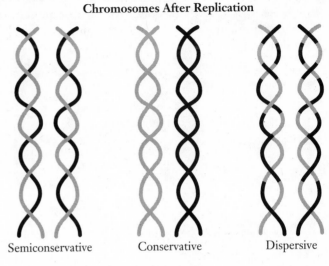

Chromosomes After Replication

Semiconservative   Conservative   Dispersive

Figure 1

According to a third hypothesis, the DNA molecule is dismantled piece by piece and replication occurs along the pieces. The new DNA contains some of the original molecule and some new material. This hypothesis is referred to as *dispersive replication*.

Meselson and Stahl used the ultracentrifuge and isotope-labeled biomolecules to answer the replication question. Special techniques were used to isolate DNA from bacteria. The DNA was then centrifuged in a way that allows each type of molecule to settle in distinct bands based on density. Under normal conditions, bacteria are exposed to nutrients that contain the common isotope of nitrogen, N-14. The researchers grew and then isolated DNA from normal bacteria, centrifuged this DNA, and established a reference line for where DNA containing N-14 would settle and form a band when centrifuged. (See Figure 2.) A second reference line was also established by growing many generations of bacteria on a nutrient source that contained nucleotides labeled with N-15. The DNA extracted from these bacteria contained only molecules with the heavier N-15. It formed a band lower in the centrifuge tube than that of the DNA containing N-14. Once these two reference points were established, the experiment to determine how DNA replicates could begin.

First, bacteria were grown for many generations on a food source that contained N-15. This was done to insure that most of the bacteria in these cultures would have N-15 present in their chromosomes. The bacteria from this culture were removed, washed, and re-suspended in a culture that contained food with only N-14 nucleotides. Only one round of replication was permitted. Cells from this culture were removed, and the DNA was extracted and centrifuged.

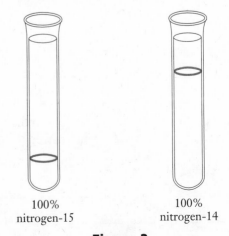

100%
nitrogen-15

100%
nitrogen-14

Figure 2

Chapter 11 **DNA and Genes,** *continued*

Chapter Assessment

Applying Scientific Methods   continued

1. Prediction: In each of the appropriate tubes in Figure 3 below, draw a band or bands where the DNA would settle if replication is (a) semiconservative, (b) conservative, and (c) dispersive. (Hint: Determine how much of each resulting molecules is made with heavy nitrogen bases and how much with lighter ones.)

Figure 3

(a)
Semiconservative
replication

(b)
Conservative
replication

(c)
Dispersive
replication

2. Explain why you drew each of the bands where you did.

_____

_____

_____

_____

_____

_____

_____

_____

_____

3. Is one round of testing enough to distinguish among all three possible types of replication? Explain the reasoning behind your answer.

_____

_____

_____

Chapter 12 — Patterns of Heredity and Human Genetics

Reviewing Vocabulary

In the space at the left, write the term that best fits the definition. Use these choices:

incomplete dominance   carrier   codominant alleles
completely dominant alleles   simple recessive heredity   polygenic inheritance
pedigree   autosomes   sex-linked traits

_____ **1.** Phenotypes of both homozygotes are produced in the heterozygote.

_____ **2.** Phenotypes of both heterozygous and homozygous dominant individuals have the same phenotype.

_____ **3.** The phenotype of the heterozygote is intermediate between those phenotypes expressed by the homozygotes.

_____ **4.** Another name for a heterozygous individual

_____ **5.** Inheritance pattern of phenylketonuria and Tay-Sachs disease

_____ **6.** Inheritance pattern of a trait controlled by two or more genes

_____ **7.** A graphic representation of an individual's family tree

_____ **8.** Humans have 22 pairs of these types of chromosomes.

_____ **9.** Traits controlled by genes located on the X or Y chromosome

In the space at the left, write the letter of the word or phrase that best completes the statement.

_____ **10.** The 23rd pair of chromosomes that differ in males and females are called
   a. autosomes.   **b.** sex chromosomes.
   c. multiple alleles.   **d.** polygenes.

_____ **11.** A trait controlled by four alleles is said to have
   a. homologous alleles. **b.** autosomes.
   c. hybridization.   **d.** multiple alleles.

Chapter Assessment

Understanding Main Ideas (Part A)

In the space at the left, write the letter of the word or phrase that best completes the statement or answers the question.

_____ **1.** When roan cattle are mated, 25% of the offspring are red, 50% are roan, and 25% are white. Upon examination, it can be seen that the coat of a roan cow consists of both red and white hairs. This trait is one controlled by

    a. multiple alleles.   **b.** codominant alleles.

    c. sex-linked genes.   **d.** polygenic inheritance.

_____ **2.** If a female fruit fly heterozygous for red eyes ($X^R X^r$) crossed with a white-eyed male ($X^r Y$), what percent of their offspring will have white eyes?

    a. 0%   **b.** 25%   **c.** 50%   **d.** 75%

Base your answers to questions 3–6 on the pedigree shown at the right, which shows the incidence of hemophilia over three generations of a family.

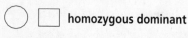 homozygous dominant

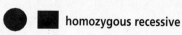 homozygous recessive

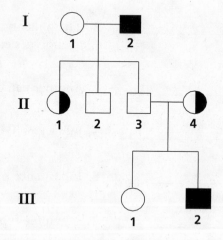

_____ **3.** What is the relationship between individual I-1 and individual III-2?

    a. grandfather–granddaughter   **b.** grandmother–grandson

    c. great aunt–nephew   **d.** mother–son

_____ **4.** For the trait being followed in the pedigree, individuals II-1 and II-4 can be classified as

    a. homozygous dominant.   **b.** mutants.

    c. homozygous recessive.   **d.** carriers.

_____ **5.** What type of inheritance pattern does the trait represented by the shaded symbols illustrate?

    a. incomplete dominance   **b.** multiple alleles

    c. codominance   **d.** sex-linked

_____ **6.** If individual III-2 marries a person with the same genotype as individual I-1, what is the chance that one of their children will be afflicted with hemophilia?

    a. 0%   **b.** 25%   **c.** 50%   **d.** 75%

Chapter 12 **Patterns of Heredity and Human Genetics,** *continued*

Understanding Main Ideas (Part B)

In the space at the left, write the letter of the word or phrase that best completes each statement.

_____ **1.** Which of the bar graphs represents what the phenotypic frequencies might be for polygenic inheritance?

a.
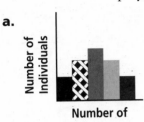

b.
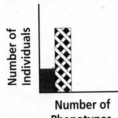

c.
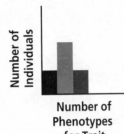

d.
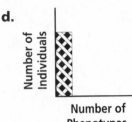

_____ **2.** Because the gene for red-green colorblindness is located on the X chromosome, it is normally *not* possible for a

　a. carrier mother to pass the gene on to her daughter.

　b. carrier mother to pass the gene on to her son.

　c. colorblind father to pass the gene on to his daughter.

　d. colorblind father to pass the gene on to his son.

_____ **3.** A cross between a white rooster and a black hen results in 100% blue Andalusian offspring. When two of these blue offspring are mated, the probable phenotypic ratio seen in their offspring would be

　a. 100% blue.　　　　　　　　**b.** 75% black, 25% white.

　c. 75% blue, 25% white.　　　　**d.** 25% black, 50% blue, 25% white.

_____ **4.** A human genetic disorder caused by a dominant gene is

　a. Tay-Sachs disease.　**b.** cystic fibrosis.　**c.** PKU.　**d.** Huntington's disease.

Answer the following questions.

5. How does polygenic inheritance differ from Mendelian inheritance?

_____

_____

_____

6. How does incomplete dominance differ from multiple alleles?

_____

_____

_____

Chapter 12 Patterns of Heredity and Human Genetics, *continued*

Thinking Critically

In the space at the left, write the term that does *not* belong in the list. Then explain your choice.

_____ **1.** heterozygous, carrier, homozygous

Explanation: _____

_____

_____

_____ **2.** genotype, phenotype, heterozygous, homozygous

Explanation: _____

_____

_____

_____ **3.** autosomes, X and Y chromosomes, sex-linked traits, sex chromosomes

Explanation: _____

_____

_____

Answer the following questions.

4. Explain how some traits are expressed differently in males and females. Give an example of such a trait.

_____

_____

_____

5. The gene for nearsightedness in humans is found on the X chromosome. A boy has a nearsighted father. Will the boy be nearsighted? Explain.

_____

_____

6. A male is said to be *hemizygous* for genes on the X chromosome. Explain why you think this term was chosen.

_____

_____

_____

Chapter 12 **Patterns of Heredity and Human Genetics,** *continued*

Chapter Assessment

Applying Scientific Methods

Geneticists are constantly on the lookout for organisms with mutations. Such individual organisms provide information about the heredity and development of the entire species. When a mutation is discovered, phenotypic differences are examined. Then unique details of the mutation's genotype and inheritance pattern are carefully analyzed. This was true in the time of Thomas Morgan and is still true today. Historically, much work in the field of genetics has been done with fruit flies, because huge numbers of them can be cultured in a relatively small space, and because large populations of offspring can be obtained in short periods of time.

Forearmed with this knowledge and seeking scientific fame, you search your garden for fruit flies. You trap one male with miniature wings and several normal females. You carefully place the flies in a culture vial and allow them to mate. When you see tiny larvae feeding on the culture medium, you place the adults in another culture vial. All that is left in the original culture vial is the F_1 generation of flies. When these mature, you note that none of the flies has miniature wings.

1. How might the disappearance of the trait of miniature wings be explained?

_____

_____

_____

_____

You next place males and females from the F_1 generation in a number of fresh culture vials and allow them to mate. Eventually, you end up with close to 4000 F_2 offspring. Of these, 740 have miniature wings. The remainder of the flies have normal wings.

2. What does this tell you about the trait for miniature wings?

_____

_____

Next, you examine all of the flies with miniature wings. If you are to become famous for your work in genetics, you need to keep very precise records, so you carefully record information about each of the flies in your cultures. When you are finished, you notice something truly unusual. All of the flies with miniature wings are males.

3. How can this odd result be explained? Use Punnett squares illustrating the first (F_1) and second (F_2) generation to confirm your answer.

_____

_____

_____

_____

_____

Applying Scientific Methods   continued

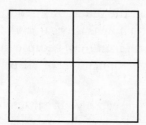 

_____

_____

_____

4. Just to be safe, you want to be sure that this isn't a situation where it is lethal for female flies to inherit two alleles for miniature wings. Design an experiment that should result in some female flies with miniature wings. Illustrate the cross with a Punnett square.

_____

_____

_____

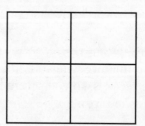

Chapter
13 Genetic Technology

Reviewing Vocabulary

Write the word or phrase that best completes the statement. Use these choices:

human genome	transgenic organisms	linkage map	gene therapy	
vectors	restriction enzymes	plasmid	inbreeding	testcross

1. _____ are used to cut DNA into fragments.

2. _____ is based on the insertion of normal genes into cells with defective genes in an attempt to correct genetic disorders.

3. The entire collection of genes within human cells is referred to as the _____ .

4. A(n) _____ is a small, circular piece of DNA found in bacterial cells.

5. A(n) _____ shows the location of genes on a chromosome.

6. _____ are produced when DNA from another species is inserted into the genome of an organism, which then begins to use the foreign DNA as its own.

7. A(n) _____ is a cross of an individual of unknown genotype with an individual of known genotype.

8. A gene gun and a virus may both be classified as _____ because they are mechanisms by which foreign DNA may be transferred into a host cell.

9. _____ is mating between closely related individuals.

Explain the following terms. Use complete sentences.

10. genetic engineering

_____

_____

11. gene splicing

_____

_____

12. recombinant DNA

_____

_____

Chapter 13 Genetic Technology, *continued*

Chapter Assessment

Understanding Main Ideas (Part A)

In the space at the left, write the letter of the word or phase that best completes the statement or answers the question.

_____ **1.** A small amount of DNA obtained from a mummy or from a human long frozen in glacial ice may be cloned through

    a. polymerase chain reaction techniques.   **b.** gel electrophoresis.

    c. DNA fingerprinting.   **d.** gene splicing.

_____ **2.** Examine the piece of DNA represented in the figure at the right. The nucleotide sequences on both strands, but running in opposite directions, are in an arrangement called a

    a. vector

    b. chromosome mutation.

    c. palindrome.

    d. transgenic codon.

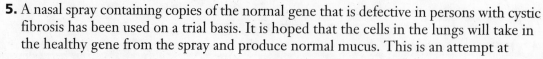

_____ **3.** Transgenic bacteria are currently used to produce

    a. human growth hormone, insulin, and phenylalanine.

    b. human growth hormone, PKU, and interferon.

    c. hexosaminidase *A*, phenylalanine, and insulin.

    d. PKU, insulin, and interferon.

_____ **4.** Gel electrophoresis is a technique used to

    a. clone chromosomes of various species.

    b. cut DNA into fragments of various sizes.

    c. separate DNA fragments by charge and length.

    d. inject foreign DNA into animal and plant cells.

_____ **5.** A nasal spray containing copies of the normal gene that is defective in persons with cystic fibrosis has been used on a trial basis. It is hoped that the cells in the lungs will take in the healthy gene from the spray and produce normal mucus. This is an attempt at

    a. palindrome formation.   **b.** gene therapy.

    c. DNA fingerprinting.   **d.** linkage mapping.

_____ **6.** How might a breeder determine if a certain golden retriever is a carrier of an undesirable trait?

    a. prepare a linkage map

    b. perform a testcross

    c. clone the dog

    d. splice the undesirable allele into the dog's genome

Chapter 13 Genetic Technology, *continued*

Understanding Main Ideas (Part B)

In the space at the left, write the letter of the word or phase that best completes the statement or answers the question.

_____ 1. A linkage map such as the one illustrated in the figure at the right, for human chromosome number 4, can be produced as a result of

 a. a study of antigen-antibody reactions and PCR.

 b. a determination of the frequency with which the genes occur together.

 c. a process called karyotyping.

 d. both karyotyping and palindrome formation.

— Huntington's disease

— Atypical PKU

— Serum album

— Red hair color

_____ 2. Below follows a list of procedures involved in the production of a transgenic organism. From the choices provided, what is the sequence that represents the proper order of events?

 A. Recombinant DNA is transferred into a suitable host.

 B. A desirable gene is identified in a DNA sequence.

 C. The DNA fragment to be inserted is joined with a vehicle to transport it.

 D. The DNA fragment to be inserted is isolated.

 a. A, B, C, D **b.** B, C, A, D **c.** B, D, C, A **d.** D, A, B, C

In 1973, Stanley Cohen and Herbert Boyer inserted a gene from an African clawed frog into a bacterium. The bacterium produced the protein coded for by the inserted frog gene.

_____ 3. In their experiment, Cohen and Boyer produced a DNA molecule composed of both frog DNA and bacterial DNA. Because the new genetic material consisted of DNA from two different organisms, it can be referred to as

 a. recombinant DNA.   **b.** a linkage map.

 c. a vector.   **d.** gene therapy.

_____ 4. This insertion of a small fragment of frog DNA into the DNA of another species can most accurately be called

 a. cloning. **b.** genetic engineering.

 c. electrophoresis. **d.** gene therapy.

_____ 5. At the conclusion of the experiment, a bacterium containing functional frog DNA would be classified as a

 a. clone. **b.** DNA fingerprint.

 c. plasmid. **d.** transgenic organism.

Thinking Critically

Read the paragraph below. Then answer the questions that follow.

Agrobacterium tumefaciens is a bacterium that causes crown gall disease, a tumorous growth on the growing tip of certain plants. The bacterium is able to enter a plant through small cuts in the outer cell layer. When *Agrobacterium* enters a plant cell, a DNA sequence from the bacterium integrates into the plant's DNA. This new section of DNA causes the plant's cell to reproduce quickly to form a tumor and to synthesize a food molecule needed by the bacterium. A critical bit of information that scientists have learned about the process is that the tumor-causing information is carried on a large plasmid that is separate from the bacterium's main chromosome. During the infection process, the DNA on the plasmid that codes for food production and rapid reproduction leaves the plasmid, moves into the plant cell nucleus, and integrates with one of the plant cell's chromosomes. Thus, when the plant cell reproduces, it passes along the bacterium's genetic information, which has been incorporated into the plant genome.

1. Why is the above information about how *Agrobacterium* causes crown gall disease important to scientists hoping to produce transgenic plants?

_____

_____

_____

2. What could be used to cut open an *Agrobacterium* plasmid and insert a gene that would increase the rate of conversion of atmospheric nitrogen into nitrates?

_____

_____

3. Illustrate and label what the plasmid might look like with the desired gene inserted.

4. What benefits to agriculture could stem from scientists being able to engineer plants genetically?

_____

_____

_____

Chapter
13 **Genetic Technology,** *continued*

Applying Scientific Methods

At the DNA level, humans are very similar, and the genes that code for their proteins follow fairly standard patterns. However, the segments of noncoding DNA found between the genes—referred to as "junk" DNA—follow patterns that vary from one individual to another. For example, in Individual A the "junk" DNA base sequence represented by CAT (cytosine, adenine, and thymine) could be repeated 3 times (CATCATCAT) in one place in that individual's genome and 6 times in another place. In Individual B, the same noncoding DNA sequence could form a different pattern, with 10 repetitions of CAT in one place and 30 repetitions in another. In a given population, there may be a large number of segments of DNA that differ on the basis of the noncoding DNA pattern. Therefore, if Individuals A and B have a child, the child is likely to be heterozygous for the segments of DNA involving noncoding sequences.

The patterns of noncoding DNA sequences give all individuals (except identical twins) a distinctive "fingerprint." The fingerprint is constructed by isolating DNA from a few cells, cutting it into fragments using restriction enzymes, and sorting the fragments by size using gel electrophoresis. The shorter the DNA fragment, the farther it will migrate through the gel. The result is a visual representation of an individual's DNA, or a DNA fingerprint.

A DNA fingerprint can be used to identify a child's biological father. The basis for such an identification is that a repetitive, noncoding sequence present in the child but not found in the mother must have been inherited from the father. Examine the bands in the diagram of the DNA fingerprints shown below. Each band represents a fragment of DNA. The first vertical lane of bands represents standard markers of known size, which are used as a reference. To the right of the standard markers is the lane of bands representing the child's DNA fingerprint. The next lane is the mother's DNA, followed by the DNA fragments from two men who might be the child's father. Study the pattern of each lane of DNA bands. Then answer the questions.

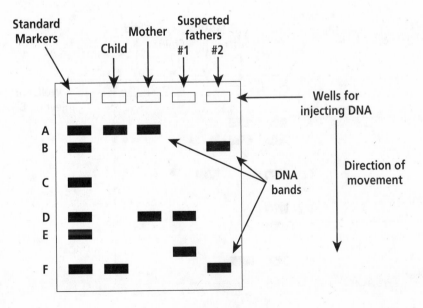

Chapter
13 **Genetic Technology,** *continued*

Applying Scientific Methods   continued

1. Which location represents the longest DNA fragment? Which location represents the shortest fragment? Explain.

   _____

   _____

   _____

2. Which of the men, Father #1 or Father #2, is probably the biological father of the baby? Explain.

   _____

   _____

3. What would be indicated if you saw only one band in a lane?

   _____

   _____

   _____

4. Below is a drawing of a hypothetical gel. Included on the gel is the banding pattern of the mother and father of two children. Draw what the pattern of bands for each of the children might look like. Indicate the possible parental source using ♂ for the male (father) and ♀ for the female (mother).

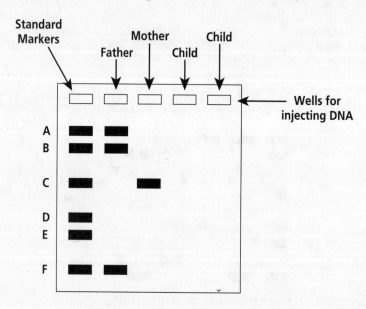

Chapter 14 — The History of Life

Reviewing Vocabulary

Complete the paragraph by writing the correct term on the appropriate line. Use these choices:

archaebacteria   fossils   protocells

biogenesis   plate tectonics   spontaneous generation

From ancient times until recently, it was believed that living organisms could arise from nonliving materials. This belief is referred to as **(1)** _____ . According to the three-century-old writings of Jean Van Helmont, if a dirty shirt and grains of wheat are placed in a container and left for 21 days, mice will form from the fermenting wheat. With the invention of the microscope and careful experimentation, it has been reasonably proven that life arises only from life. This idea is referred to as **(2)** _____ . The oldest organisms of which scientists have any record are approximately 3.5 billion years old. **(3)** _____ provide evidence of such organisms. The question of how the first unicellular organisms were produced from inorganic materials is a problem scientists are still studying. One possible answer is that conditions on the ancient Earth led to the formation of organized structures that carried out some life activities. These structures, called **(4)** _____ , were capable of growth and division. After much time, they evolved into heterotrophic prokaryotes. Over more time, organisms evolved that could synthesize food from inorganic raw materials. These organisms were probably similar to today's prokaryotes that survive in harsh conditions without oxygen. These organisms are known as **(5)** _____ .

The geological activity of Earth has influenced the development of organisms. For example, at the beginning of the Mesozoic era, the modern continents were merged into one large landmass. The landmass broke into individual continents that moved apart. The geological explanation of how the continents moved is called **(6)** _____ . As the continents moved apart, descendants of organisms living on the continents may have experienced different climates because of the new locations of the continents.

Understanding Main Ideas

In the space at the left, write the letter of the word or phrase that best completes the statement or answers the question.

_____ 1. A clear fish imprint in a rock indicates that the rock is probably
   a. volcanic. **b.** sedimentary. **c.** metamorphic. **d.** igneous.

_____ 2. Which fact is the basis for using the fossil record as evidence for the order of evolution?
   a. In undisturbed layers of rock strata, the older fossils are found in the deeper layers.
   b. There are fossils of all life forms to be found in rock layers.
   c. All fossils were formed at the same time.
   d. Fossils have been shown to provide a complete record of human evolution.

_____ 3. A theory concerning the origin of life states that Earth's ancient atmosphere contained
   a. water vapor, methane, and ammonia.
   b. water vapor, oxygen, and hydrogen.
   c. methane, ammonia, and oxygen.
   d. methane, carbon dioxide, and oxygen.

_____ 4. Which group of organisms is believed to have been the earliest to evolve?
   a. land plants **b.** cyanobacteria **c.** aquatic dinosaurs **d.** mammals

_____ 5. According to one theory, the first prokaryotes probably obtained their food
   a. through the synthesis of organic molecules from inorganic molecules.
   b. through a combination of photosynthesis and aerobic respiration.
   c. by eating carbohydrates formed by autotrophs.
   d. by consuming organic molecules available in their environment.

_____ 6. Entire organisms, with even their most delicate parts intact, have been found preserved in
   a. igneous rock formations and ice.
   b. mineral deposits and metamorphic rock.
   c. amber and ice.
   d. amber and mineral deposits.

_____ 7. While looking for fossils on an eroded hillside, you discover fossil coral and fish in one layer. In a layer just above, you find the fossil imprint of a fern frond and some fossil moss. Assuming the rock has not been disturbed, which of the following is the most probable conclusion?
   a. The area had been a sea until recent times.
   b. A forest had once grown there but had become submerged by water.
   c. A sea had been replaced by land in ancient times.
   d. A saltwater sea had changed to a freshwater lake in ancient times.

Understanding Main Ideas (Part B)

In the space at the left, write the letter of the word or phrase that best completes the statement or answers the question.

_____ **1.** Which event contributed most directly to the evolution of aerobic organisms?

    a. an increase in the concentration of methane in the ancient atmosphere

    b. a decrease in the sun's light intensity

    c. the presence of organisms able to carry on photosynthesis

    d. an increase in the number of organisms carrying on fermentation

_____ **2.** Urey and Miller subjected water, ammonia, methane, and hydrogen to heating and cooling cycles and jolts of electricity in an attempt to

    a. determine how the dinosaurs became extinct.

    b. find out whether the conditions of ancient Earth could have formed complex organic compounds.

    c. determine the age of microfossils.

    d. find out how ozone forms in the atmosphere.

Answer the following questions.

3. Explain the role of plate tectonics in the theory of continental drift.

_____

_____

_____

_____

4. Explain the relationship between early photosynthetic autotrophs and the eventual rise of aerobic life forms.

_____

_____

_____

_____

Chapter
14 **The History of Life,** continued

Thinking Critically

Read the paragraph below. Then answer the questions that follow.

Radioactive isotopes, atoms with unstable nuclei, decay over time, giving off radiation as they break down. The decay rate of every radioactive element is known; moreover, radioactive decay continues at a steady rate. Scientists compare the amount of the original radioactive element to the amount of the new element present, which has formed as a result of the decay. Suppose that you start with 100 grams of a certain radioisotope that decays to half its original amount in 50 000 years.

1. Complete the following table so that the amount of parent material (original radioisotope) and the amount of daughter material (nonradioactive end product) are correct for the number of years that have passed.

Amount of Parent Material	Amount of Daughter Material	Years That Have Passed
100 grams	0 grams	0
		50 000
		100 000
		150 000
		200 000
3.125 grams	96.875 grams	250 000

2. On the following grid, graph the data in your table in order to show the relationship between the passage of time and the amount of original radioisotope. (Consider the time 0 as that point at which the decay of the full amount of the isotope begins. The 250 000-year point is the present time.)

Years Passed vs. Amount of Radioisotope

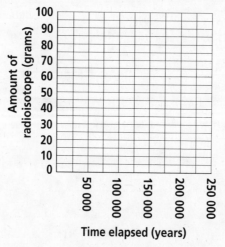

Time elapsed (years)

CHAPTER ASSESSMENT

Applying Scientific Methods

Examine the illustration of rock strata and fossil remains recorded by a paleobiologist who was studying rock layers located at the base of a mountain. Then answer the questions that follow.

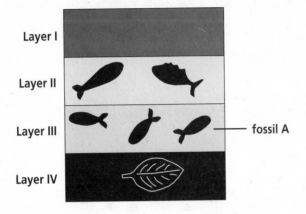

1. Assuming that the oldest of the strata is layer IV and that the youngest is layer I, name and describe two techniques that could be used to determine the age of fossil A.

_____

_____

_____

_____

_____

_____

_____

_____

2. Based on the fossil record, explain what has happened to the type of habitat found in the area as time passed.

_____

_____

_____

_____

_____

_____

_____

Applying Scientific Methods   *continued*

Through a chemical analysis of the rock layers represented in the illustration on the previous page and of other, deeper layers, scientists were able to construct a graph of the amount of oxygen present in the atmosphere when the rocks were formed. Examine the graph.

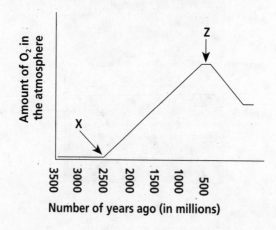

3. Describe what major event occurred in the evolution of life on Earth at point X that is directly related to the change in the graph above.

_____

_____

4. How did this event affect the level of oxygen in the atmosphere?

_____

_____

5. What major evolutionary event occurred at the point on the graph indicated by Z?

_____

6. How did this event affect the oxygen level?

_____

7. What could paleontologists look for to confirm your answers to questions 3 and 6?

_____

_____

Chapter
15 The Theory of Evolution

Reviewing Vocabulary

Write the word or phrase that best completes the statement. Use these choices:

adaptive radiation	vestigial structure	punctuated equilibrium
mimicry	natural selection	gene pool
polyploid	stabilizing selection	camouflage
genetic drift	artificial selection	allelic frequency

1. _____ is a technique in which the breeder selects particular traits.

2. A structural adaptation enabling an organism to blend in with its environment is

   _____ .

3. Another structural adaptation called _____ protects an organism by copying

   the appearance of another species.

4. The total number of genes present in a population is the _____ .

5. The _____ is the percentage of a particular allele in a population.

6. The alteration of allelic frequencies by chance events is known as _____ .

7. _____ is the type of selection that favors average individuals in a population.

8. Any species with a multiple set of chromosomes is known as a(n) _____ .

9. _____ is a mechanism for change in a population in which organisms with

   favorable variations live, reproduce, and pass on their favorable traits.

10. The concept that evolution occurs over long periods of stability that are interrupted by geologically

    brief periods of change is known as _____ .

11. Any structure that is reduced in function in a living organism but may have been used in an ancestor

    is known as a(n) _____ .

12. The evolution of an ancestral species into an array of species that occupy different niches is called

    _____ .

Understanding Main Ideas (Part A)

In the space at the left, write the letter of the word or phrase that best completes the statement.

_____ **1.** Natural selection can best be defined as the

    a. survival of the biggest and strongest organisms in a population.

    b. elimination of the smallest organisms by the biggest organisms.

    c. survival and reproduction of the organisms that occupy the largest area.

    d. survival and reproduction of the organisms that are genetically best adapted to the environment.

_____ **2.** Structures that have a similar embryological origin and structure but are adapted for different purposes, such as a bat wing and a human arm, are called

    a. embryological structures.   **b.** analogous structures.

    c. homologous structures.   **d.** homozygous structures.

_____ **3.** Mutations such as polyploidy and crossing over provide the genetic basis for

    a. evolution.   **b.** spontaneous generation.

    c. biogenesis.   **d.** sexual reproduction.

_____ **4.** Within a decade of the introduction of a new insecticide, nearly all of the descendants of the target pests were immune to the usual-sized dose. The most likely explanation for this immunity to the insecticide is that

    a. eating the insecticide caused the bugs to become resistant to it.

    b. eating the insecticide caused the bugs to become less resistant to it.

    c. it destroyed organisms that cause disease in the insects, thus allowing them to live longer.

    d. it selected random mutations that were present in the insect population and that provided immunity to the insecticide.

_____ **5.** The flying squirrel of North America very closely resembles the flying phalanger of Australia. They are similar in size, have long, bushy tails, and skin folds that allow them to glide through the air. The squirrel is a placental mammal, while the phalanger is a marsupial. These close resemblances, even though genetically and geographically separated by great distances, can best be explained by

    a. convergent evolution.   **b.** divergent evolution.

    c. spontaneous generation.   **d.** vestigial structures.

_____ **6.** Hawaiian honeycreepers are a group of birds with similar body shape and size. However, they vary greatly in color and beak shape. Each species occupies its own niche and is adapted to the foods available in its niche. The evolution from a common ancestor to a variety of species is an example of

    a. divergent evolution.   **b.** cross-pollination.

    c. vegetative propagation.   **d.** convergent evolution.

Chapter 15 The Theory of Evolution, *continued*

Chapter Assessment

Understanding Main Ideas (Part B)

In the space at the left, write the letter of the word or phrase that best completes the statement or answers the question.

_____ **1.** Which of the following is *not* a factor that causes changes in the frequency of homozygous and heterozygous individuals in a population?

    a. mutations   **b.** migration   **c.** random mating   **d.** genetic drift

_____ **2.** When checking shell color for a species of snail found only in a remote area seldom visited by humans, scientists discovered the distribution of individuals that is shown in the graph.

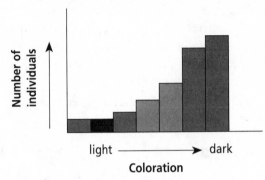

Based on the information shown in the graph, the snail population is undergoing

    a. stabilizing selection.   **b.** disruptive selection.

    c. artificial selection.   **d.** directional selection.

_____ **3.** The theory of continental drift hypothesizes that Africa and South America slowly drifted apart after once being a single landmass. The monkeys on the two continents, although very similar, show numerous genetic differences. Which factor is probably the most important in maintaining these differences?

    a. comparative anatomy   **b.** comparative embryology

    c. geographic isolation   **d.** fossil records

_____ **4.** Which combination of characteristics in a population would provide the *greatest* potential for evolutionary change?

    a. small population, few mutations   **b.** small population, many mutations

    c. large population, few mutations   **d.** large population, many mutations

_____ **5.** Upon close examination of the skeleton of an adult python, a pelvic girdle and leg bones can be observed. These features are an example of

    a. artificial selection.   **b.** homologous structures.

    c. vestigial structures.   **d.** comparative embryology.

_____ **6.** Mutations occur because of

    a. the introduction of new variations from elsewhere.

    b. the introduction of new variations through mistakes in DNA replication.

    c. the chance survival and reproduction of new variations.

    d. change in allele or genotype frequencies.

Chapter
15 **The Theory of Evolution,** *continued*

Thinking Critically

Read the information that follows and then answer the questions.

A study of the squirrel population in a large northern city revealed that many of the squirrels inhabited large park areas that were also populated by numerous squirrel predators. The graph at the right reflects the data collected in regard to color and number of squirrels.

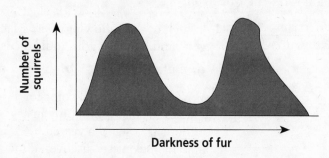

1. Explain why the light- and dark-colored squirrels might be selected for and the medium-colored squirrels selected against.

_____

_____

_____

_____

_____

_____

2. Explain how this type of disruptive selection can lead to the separation of this population into two distinct species.

_____

_____

_____

_____

_____

_____

_____

_____

_____

Chapter 15 **The Theory of Evolution,** *continued*

Applying Scientific Methods

A biologist studying a variety of fly in the rain forest noticed that the types of foods the fly preferred were located either high in the trees or in the foliage on the ground. There didn't seem to be any of the preferred foods anywhere in between. An experiment was designed that would select for a genetically determined behavior known as *geotaxis*. If a fly shows positive geotaxis, it flies downward. If the fly shows negative geotaxis, it flies upward.

1. In terms of evolution and natural selection, why would the researcher suspect that the flies being studied would show geotaxis?

   _____

   _____

   _____

To conduct the experiment, the flies being studied were marked and placed in a maze (illustrated below). Each fly was placed in the "start" chamber. To exit from this area, the fly had to make a decision about which of the three exits to enter. One exit faced upward, indicating negative geotaxis, and another exit aimed downward, indicating positive geotaxis. A third exit permitted the fly to remain on middle ground. Each fly was placed in the maze 15 times and its choice of direction recorded. Some flies consistently went upward and entered the food vial at the end of the exit tube. Others consistently went downward and entered the food vial at the lower end. Some flies chose the upward and downward exits equal numbers of times; others went for the middle exit.

Fly Maze

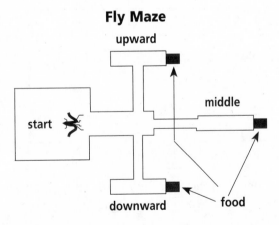

2. If the selection of direction is a genetic trait, what should happen when flies consistently selecting the upward exit are mated, those selecting the downward exit are mated, and the "no preference" and middle choice flies discarded?

   _____

   _____

   _____

Applying Scientific Methods   continued

3. What type of selection pressure is operating in this experiment? Explain your answer.

_____

_____

_____

_____

4. Describe what would be happening to the frequency of the allele for negative geotaxis in the above experiment.

_____

_____

5. What might be acting in the flies' environment to select for flies that do not exhibit a distinct preference for flying upward at every trial or downward at every trial?

_____

_____

_____

_____

_____

_____

_____

6. What might eventually happen if in the wild the flies developed into two populations, with one showing positive geotaxis and the other showing negative geotaxis?

_____

_____

_____

Chapter 16 Primate Evolution

Reviewing Vocabulary

Complete the paragraphs by writing the correct term on the appropriate line. Use these choices:

anthropoids	bipedal	australopithecines	Neanderthals	primates
hominids	prehensile tail	opposable thumb	Cro-Magnon	

A distinctive characteristic of humans is **(1)** _____ locomotion, the ability to

walk on two legs in an upright position. Another characteristic that humans share with most

(2) _____ is the ability to touch the thumb to the forefinger. Called the

(3) _____ , it permits objects to be tightly grasped.

Anthropologists are also concerned with the origin of humans. Primates are classified in two groups,

the prosimians and the **(4)** _____ . The prosimians are small-bodied and include

the lemurs and tarsiers. The other group can be divided into Old World monkeys, New World monkeys,

and hominoids. Hominoids include the humanlike, bipedal primates such as the apes, chimpanzees, and

gorillas. New World monkeys are entirely arboreal. Their success in the tree tops can be partially attrib-

uted to their **(5)** _____ , which functions almost like an extra hand, enabling

them to tightly grasp branches.

Modern humans and humanlike fossils are classified as **(6)** _____ . Based on

fossil evidence and biochemical evidence, it is believed that apes and humans began to evolve about

30 million years ago, developing along different paths but arising from the same common ancestor. In

1924, Raymond Dart discovered a skull with both apelike and human characteristics. The skull derived

from the first of several African primates, now collectively referred to as **(7)** _____ ,

which show both humanlike and apelike qualities. *Homo sapiens* may have first appeared between 100 000

and 400 000 years ago. The first of the species to have communicated through spoken language appeared

around 100 000 years ago. They have been named **(8)** _____ . About 35 000 years

ago, these disappeared from the fossil record as a group called **(9)** _____ evolved.

Understanding Main Ideas (Part A)

In the space at the left, write the letter of the word or phrase that best completes the statement or answers the question.

_____ 1. Which is the oldest hominid species to be unearthed?

    a. *Homo habilis*   **b.** *Homo erectus*

    c. *Australopithecus afarensis*   **d.** *Australopithecus africanus*

_____ 2. The skeleton of the hominid nicknamed "Lucy" gave anthropologists evidence that

    a. cavemen coexisted with dinosaurs.

    b. Neanderthals coexisted with *Homo habilis.*

    c. upright walking evolved after large brains.

    d. upright walking evolved before large brains.

_____ 3. Most early hominid fossils have been found in

    a. Egypt.   **b.** France.   **c.** Africa.   **d.** North America.

_____ 4. The earliest primate identifiable from the fossil record is

    a. *Purgatorius.*   **b.** *Australopithecus.*   **c.** *Neanderthalus.*   **d.** *Afarensis.*

_____ 5. The first hominids to make and use simple stone tools were

    a. *Homo sapiens.*   **b.** *Homo habilis.*

    c. *Australopithecus afarensis.*   **d.** *Australopithecus africanus.*

_____ 6. As primates evolved, they developed

    a. a good sense of smell and large lower vertebrae.

    b. good vision and large teeth.

    c. stereoscopic vision and rotating shoulder joints.

    d. large teeth and a well-developed collar bone.

_____ 7. The hominid that had the most advanced tool-making abilities and spoken language was

    a. Cro-Magnon.   **b.** Neanderthal.   **c.** *Purgatorius.*   **d.** *Homo habilis.*

_____ 8. Based on the fossil record, it has been determined the earliest primates probably lived in the

    a. grasslands.   **b.** mountains.   **c.** forests.   **d.** deserts.

_____ 9. Primates evolved approximately

    a. 200 000 years ago.   **b.** 2 million years ago.

    c. 8 million years ago.   **d.** 66 million years ago.

_____ 10. The anthropologists who discovered the skull of *Homo habilis* were

    a. the Leakeys.   **b.** the Darts.   **c.** the Johansons.   **d.** the Priestleys.

Chapter Assessment

Understanding Main Ideas (Part B)

In the space at the left, write the letter of the word or phrase that best completes the statement or answers the question.

_____ **1.** Which factor may have played a large role in human evolution?

    a. a geologic event that released much radiation into the environment, which in time resulted in an increased mutation rate

    b. climatic changes that caused existing primates to search for new food sources

    c. flooding due to melting glaciers causing primates to seek refuge in the trees

    d. massive grassland fires that caused existing primates to flee to the mountains

_____ **2.** Evidence that *Homo erectus* was more intelligent than its predecessors would include

    a. a small cranial capacity as indicated by their skeletal remains.

    b. involved messages they wrote on cave walls.

    c. signs of agriculture and tilled fields.

    d. tools, such as hand axes, that have been found near their fire pits.

_____ **3.** Some primate skeletons were located in a cave in association with these things: a variety of tools, the charred bones of some animals they had cooked and eaten, and numerous paintings on the walls. Carbon-14 dating techniques determined that the bones and other artifacts were about 35 000 years old. The skeletal remains probably belonged to

    a. *A. afarensis.*   **b.** *Homo habilis.*   **c.** Cro-Magnons.   **d.** *Homo erectus.*

_____ **4.** The jaw from the skull of the genus *Homo* and one from the genus *Australopithecus* are different in that the jaw from the genus *Homo* would

    a. be much heavier with large teeth and well-defined canines.

    b. be smaller with smaller teeth and not so much definition of tooth type.

    c. be larger with a multitude of small teeth with well-defined canines.

    d. be smaller with larger teeth that were all about the same.

_____ **5.** The nucleotide sequence of human and chimpanzee genes differs by about only 1.6%. This fact, along with the fossil record, reveals that

    a. humans descended from chimpanzees.

    b. chimpanzees descended from humans.

    c. humans and chimpanzees evolved from a common ancestor.

    d. convergent evolution has resulted in chimpanzees and humans becoming more alike.

_____ **6.** Evidence for the determination of bipedal locomotion in an animal could be found by an examination of the

    a. skull.   **b.** upper arm (humerous).

    c. finger (carpal).   **d.** jaw.

Chapter 16 **Primate Evolution,** *continued*

Thinking Critically

Answer the following questions.

1. Early primates spent most, if not all of their time in trees. How did their successful adaptations there eventually lead to important hominid adaptations?

_____

_____

_____

_____

_____

_____

_____

_____

_____

_____

2. Why is bipedal locomotion an important hominid trait?

_____

_____

_____

3. You are on an expedition searching for early hominid fossils. You unearth a jaw bone. What traits would indicate to you that you have discovered an ape jaw and not a hominid jaw?

_____

_____

_____

4. Why is it that we are still piecing together a picture of how human evolution occurred and how is it possible that our understanding of it might be flawed?

_____

_____

_____

_____

Chapter 16   Primate Evolution, *continued*

Applying Scientific Methods

It is speculated that environmental changes in the African habitat from warm, moist forest to cool, dry grassland exerted selection pressures on all native species, including prehumans. Of all the theories attempting to explain hominid evolution, the one presently receiving much attention links the emergence of humankind to wide-scale climatic change. Two such major events in human evolution occurred, the first 2.8 million years ago and the second, 1 million years ago.

Ocean-bottom core samples taken from the west coast of Africa, the Arabian Sea, and the Gulf of Aden off the east coast of Africa lend credibility to this theory. A thick layer of dust and silicate particles has been found in the cores at levels determined to have been deposited 2.8 million and 1 million years before the present. Scientists attribute the deposits to the fact that grasses draw large quantities of silicates from the soil and concentrate them in their tissues for structural use. In a grassland environment, as grasses live, die, and decompose over many years, quantities of silicates accumulate in the surface soil.

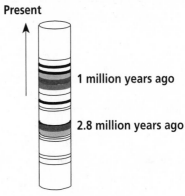

Segment of Ocean-Bottom Core

Deposits of dust and silicates also coincide with ice sheet formation and the onset of two ice ages in the Northern Hemisphere. Computer models show that the cooling and ice sheet formation influenced weather in both hemispheres. The models illustrate how cool, dry winds would have been diverted toward Africa as the ice sheets grew.

Another important piece of information has been obtained from the Gulf of Aden core. It contains volcanic ash, along with dust and silicates blown by monsoon winds from the Rift Valley. This type of ash is also found in association with some hominid fossils discovered in the Rift Valley.

1. What does the above information tell us about the African environment that existed approximately 2.8 million and 1 million years ago? Explain.

_____

_____

_____

_____

2. Describe what the African environment might have been like 2 million years ago.

_____

_____

_____

_____

_____

Chapter 16 Primate Evolution, *continued*

Applying Scientific Methods   continued

3. In what way does the presence of volcanic ash in the Gulf of Aden cores and in the Rift Valley help in tracing human evolution?

_____

_____

_____

_____

When African forests declined and were replaced with vast areas of grassland, competition for food among animal species intensified. In an attempt to survive, hominids radiated outward from small forested areas. A vegetarian group, the australopithecines, emerged a few thousand years after the cooling period 2.8 million years ago. These hominids had to rely on seeds and tubers during the harsher seasons and on dense vegetation along river banks during the remainder of the year. Exploiting a variety of habitats at about the same time as the australopithecines was the first representative of the genus *Homo*. Members of this group consumed many kinds of food, including meat.

4. How would a diet of meat improve the chances of this group's survival, compared to australopithecines?

_____

_____

_____

_____

5. How would a diet of meat select for a different jaw and tooth structure than is seen in earlier primates?

_____

_____

_____

_____

_____

_____

_____

Chapter 17 Organizing Life's Diversity

Reviewing Vocabulary

Match the definition in Column A with the term in Column B.

	Column A		Column B
_____	**1.** Group of related phyla		**a.** class
_____	**2.** Classification system based on phylogeny		**b.** family
_____	**3.** Group of related orders		**c.** genus
_____	**4.** Evolutionary history of a species		**d.** kingdom
_____	**5.** Group of related genera		**e.** cladistics
_____	**6.** Group of related species		**f.** order
_____	**7.** Group of related classes		**g.** phylum
_____	**8.** Group of related families		**h.** phylogeny

In the space at the left, write the letter of the word or phrase that best completes the statement.

_____ **9.** The branch of biology that groups and names organisms is

    a. classification.   **b.** phylogeny.   **c.** nomenclature.   **d.** taxonomy.

_____ **10.** A group of related classes of plants is a(n)

    a. order.   **b.** kingdom.   **c.** division.   **d.** phylum

_____ **11.** A heterotrophic eukaryote that absorbs nutrients from organic materials in the environment is a(n)

    a. bacterium.   **b.** herbivore.   **c.** fungus.   **d.** animal.

_____ **12.** The placing of information or objects into groups based on similarities is

    a. biochemical analysis.   **b.** classification.
    c. phylogeny.   **d.** speciation.

_____ **13.** The system for identifying organisms that uses two words to name the species is

    a. binomial nomenclature.   **b.** dichotomous keying.
    c. cladistics.   **d.** fan diagramming.

_____ **14.** Prokaryotes that live in most habitats are

    a. protists.   **b.** eubacteria.   **c.** archaebacteria.   **d.** fungi.

Chapter 17 **Organizing Life's Diversity,** *continued*

Understanding Main Ideas (Part A)

In the space at the left, write <u>true</u> if the statement is true. If the statement is false, change the italicized word or phrase to make the statement true.

_____ **1.** In Aristotle's system of classification, animals were classified on the basis of their *size and structure*.

_____ **2.** The greater the number of taxa two organisms have in common, the *more closely* related they are.

_____ **3.** Organisms that are similar in structure and form and successfully interbreed belong to the same *family*.

_____ **4.** A phylum is related to a class as a family is related to *an order*.

_____ **5.** In the scientific name of the white oak, *Quercus alba, Quercus* is the *species* name.

_____ **6.** Two groups of organisms that are farther from each other on a cladogram share *more* derived traits than groups that are closer to each other.

_____ **7.** In a fanlike diagram, groups represented by rays that begin *closer to* the edge of the fan evolved more recently.

_____ **8.** When organisms are classified within the same group, it can be assumed that they have a common *phylogeny*.

_____ **9.** *Escherichia coli*, a type of bacterium that lives in the small intestine, is classified in the Kingdom *Protista*.

_____ **10.** Linnaeus used similarities in *structure* to determine relationships among organisms.

Classify each of the following as a bacterium, protist, or fungus.

11.

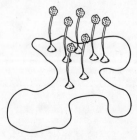

_____

12.

_____

13.

_____

Chapter
17   Organizing Life's Diversity, *continued*

Chapter Assessment

Understanding Main Ideas (Part B)

Answer the following questions.

1. What was one shortcoming of Aristotle's classification system?

_____

_____

_____

2. What are two advantages of using scientific names for organisms?

_____

_____

_____

_____

_____

_____

3. On what basis are members of one kingdom distinguished from those of another kingdom?

_____

_____

_____

Complete the following table of the characteristics of the six kingdoms.

	Characteristic	Eubacteria and Archaebacteria	Protista	Fungi	Plantae	Animalia
4.	Cell type					eukaryotic
5.	Body form				multicellular	
6.	Method of obtaining food	heterotrophic or autotrophic				
7.	Presence of complex organ systems			no		

Chapter 17 Organizing Life's Diversity, *continued*

Chapter Assessment

Thinking Critically

The table below shows the complete classification of several species of animals. Use the table to answer the questions that follow.

Organism	House cat	Red Fox	Dog	Wolf	Gopher	Fly
Kingdom	Animalia	Animalia	Animalia	Animalia	Animalia	Animalia
Phylum	Chordata	Chordata	Chordata	Chordata	Chordata	Arthropoda
Class	Mammalia	Mammalia	Mammalia	Mammalia	Mammalia	Insecta
Order	Carnivora	Carnivora	Carnivora	Carnivora	Rodentia	Diptera
Family	Felidae	Canidae	Canidae	Canidae	Geomyidae	Muscidae
Genus	*Felis*	*Vulpes*	*Canis*	*Canis*	*Thomomys*	*Musca*
Species	*F. domesticus*	*V. fulva*	*C. familiaris*	*C. lupus*	*T. bottae*	*M. domestica*

1. What kind of animal is *Vulpes velox*? How do you know?

   _____

   _____

2. What is the complete classification of *Vulpes velox*?

   _____

   _____

   _____

3. From the table, which two animals are most closely related? Explain.

   _____

   _____

   _____

4. At what classification level does the evolutionary relationship between gophers and house cats diverge?

   _____

   _____

5. How does the table indicate that a dog is more closely related to a red fox than to a house cat?

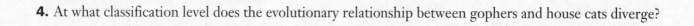

   _____

   _____

   _____

Chapter Assessment

Chapter 17 Organizing Life's Diversity, continued

Applying Scientific Methods

When a sample solution of DNA is heated to about 80°C, the DNA "melts," separating into single strands of nucleotides. If the sample is then cooled slightly and incubated, matching nucleotide sequences begin to reassociate. The solution can then be filtered to allow the single strands to pass through.

One technique for comparing DNA of different species involves the labeling of single strands of DNA with radioactive iodine and using the labeled DNA to form hybrid DNA. In this procedure, a small amount of labeled, single-stranded DNA from one species is mixed with a large amount of unlabeled, single-stranded DNA from another species and the mixture is incubated over time. A percentage of the strands form hybrid DNA consisting of one labeled and one unlabeled strand. (See Figure 1.)

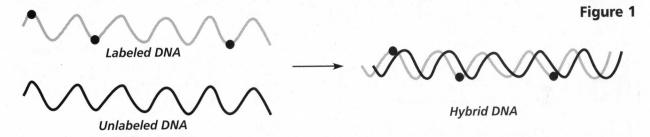

Figure 1

Labeled DNA

Unlabeled DNA

Hybrid DNA

The more closely related the two species are, the greater the number of matched sequences there will be in the hybrid DNA. (See Figure 2.) Hybrid DNA with a high proportion of matched sequences melts at higher temperatures than that with a low proportion of matched sequences.

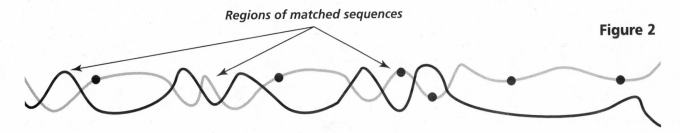

Regions of matched sequences

Figure 2

Use Figure 3 below to answer the questions that follow.

Figure 3

Hybrid A

Hybrid B

1. Which hybrid DNA was formed by DNA from two closely related species?

_____

2. Which hybrid DNA would melt at a lower temperature when heated?

_____

Applying Scientific Methods   continued

3. A solution containing Hybrid A is heated in stages, in 2.5-degree increments, from 55°C to 95°C and filtered at each stage to let single strands of DNA pass through. The radioactivity of the filtered material is measured at each stage. Would you expect to find a higher radioactivity level at 60°C or 85°C? Why?

_____

_____

_____

_____

A, B, and C are three groups of birds belonging to the same order. Birds in groups A and B show some structural similarities. Initially the two groups were classified together. However, recent microscopic comparisons of the vocal apparatus of birds in groups A and C show similarities in anatomy. Moreover, some birds in group A also exhibit many of the same behavioral patterns as birds in group C.

4. What is one hypothesis you could form about the relationships among bird groups A, B, and C, based on the given information?

_____

_____

5. How could you use the hybrid DNA technique to test your hypothesis?

_____

_____

_____

_____

_____

6. What would be the independent and dependent variables in your experiment?

_____

_____

_____

7. What control could you devise?

_____

_____

_____

Chapter 18 Viruses and Bacteria

Reviewing Vocabulary

Match the definition in Column A with the term in Column B.

Column A

_____ **1.** Poison produced by some bacteria

_____ **2.** Nonliving particle that replicates inside a living cell

_____ **3.** Process by which some bacteria convert nitrogen gas into ammonia

_____ **4.** Virus that infects only bacteria

_____ **5.** Process by which bacteria reproduce sexually

_____ **6.** Requires oxygen for respiration

_____ **7.** Process by which bacteria reproduce asexually

_____ **8.** Bacterial form produced under unfavorable environmental conditions

_____ **9.** Cell in which a virus reproduces

_____ **10.** Enzyme injected into a host cell, which copies viral RNA into DNA

Column B

a. bacteriophage

b. obligate aerobe

c. conjugation

d. endospore

e. host cell

f. nitrogen fixation

g. reverse transcriptase

h. binary fission

i. toxin

j. virus

Compare and contrast each pair of related terms.

11. archaebacteria, eubacteria

_____

_____

_____

_____

12. provirus, retrovirus

_____

_____

_____

_____

Understanding Main Ideas (Part A)

Study the diagram. Then in the space at the left, write the letter of the stage of the lytic cycle depicted that is described in each statement that follows.

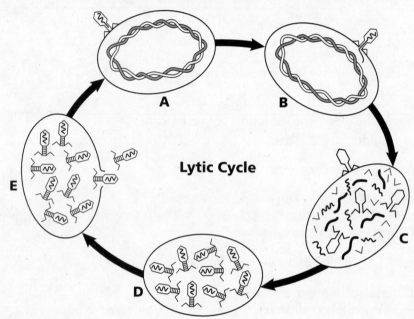

Lytic Cycle

_____ **1.** Viral nucleic acid and proteins are made.

_____ **2.** The host cell breaks open, and the new virus particles are released.

_____ **3.** The virus injects its nucleic acid into the host cell.

_____ **4.** New virus particles are assembled.

_____ **5.** The virus attaches to a host cell.

In the space at the left, write the letter of the word or phrase that best completes each statement.

_____ **6.** Bacteria that live in the roots of legumes

    a. change ammonia into nitrogen gas.   **b.** provide ATP for the plants.

    c. are autotrophic.   **d.** provide usable nitrogen for the plants.

_____ **7.** A bacterium's circular chromosome is copied during

    a. conjugation.   **b.** binary fission.   **c.** mitosis.   **d.** lysis.

_____ **8.** Penicillin kills bacteria by

    a. consuming them.   **b.** causing holes to develop in their cell walls.

    c. staining them.   **d.** depriving them of nutrients.

Chapter
18 **Viruses and Bacteria,** *continued*

Understanding Main Ideas (Part B)

Explain what happens in stages 1, 2, and 3 of the lysogenic cycle shown in the diagram.

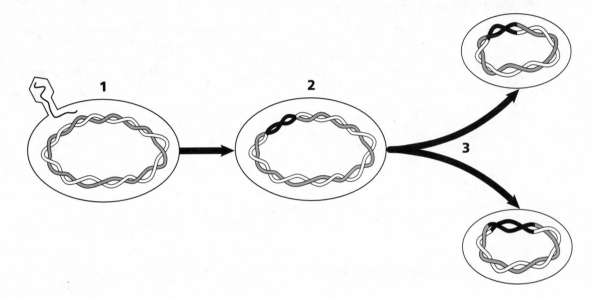

1. _____

2. _____

3. _____
   _____

Answer the following questions.

4. Why are viruses not considered to be living things?
   _____
   _____

5. How does a virus recognize its host?
   _____
   _____

6. Why is penicillin ineffective in destroying viruses or animal cells?
   _____
   _____

Chapter 18 Viruses and Bacteria, *continued*

Chapter Assessment

Thinking Critically

Study the table showing the percentages of deaths in developed and developing countries due to various causes. Then answer the questions.

Causes of death	Developed countries		Developing countries			
	Americas	Europe	Americas	Southeast Asia	Africa	Eastern Mediterranean
Infectious diseases	3.6	8.6	31.1	43.9	49.8	44.5
Cancer	21.5	18.1	9.0	4.4	2.9	4.2
Circulatory diseases	54.5	53.8	24.5	15.6	11.7	14.1
Accidents	8.4	5.6	6.3	4.3	3.8	4.1

1. What is the chief cause of death in developing countries? In developed countries? How does the table reflect the fact that the availability of antibiotics affects the number of deaths due to infectious diseases?

_____

_____

_____

_____

_____

2. What conditions in developed countries may check the spread of bacteria that cause disease?

_____

_____

3. Why do doctors sometimes advise patients who are taking antibiotics to eat yogurt?

_____

_____

_____

4. At one time, bacteria were classified as plants. Why do you think bacteria were classified this way? Give at least two reasons why bacteria should not be classified as plants.

_____

_____

_____

Chapter 18 Viruses and Bacteria, *continued*

Applying Scientific Methods

In 1957, Heinz Fraenkel-Conrat and his coworkers were studying two viruses that infect tobacco plants. One of the disease-causing viruses was called TMV and the other, HRV. Both viruses were similar in structure. (See the diagrams below.) It was easy to tell which virus had infected a tobacco plant because each virus caused different lesions on the leaves. Fraenkel-Conrat knew that TMV and HRV are RNA viruses. He wanted to find out which part of the virus—the protein coat or the RNA—was carrying the genetic information needed to specify the reproduction of these viruses. He decided that he would find the answer by producing hybrids of the viruses. A hybrid has the RNA of one virus and the protein coat of another virus. In this case, the two hybrids are denoted H-T and T-H, where the first letter indicates the virus from which the RNA was obtained.

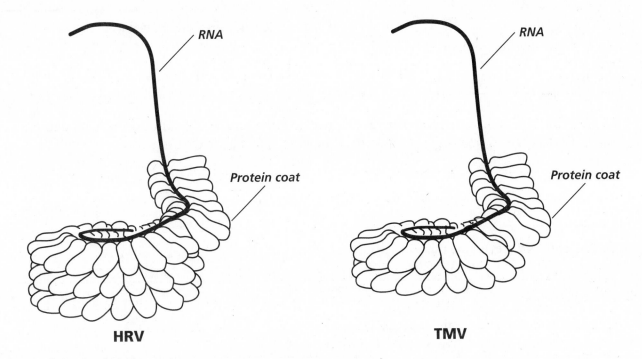

HRV   TMV

1. Suggest how Fraenkel-Conrat might produce the two hybrids.

_____

_____

_____

_____

_____

Chapter 18 — Viruses and Bacteria, *continued*

Applying Scientific Methods   continued

2. How might he determine whether the RNA or the protein coat of the H-T hybrid carried the genetic information of the virus?

_____

_____

_____

_____

_____

3. In lesions caused by the H-T hybrid on tobacco leaves, the new viruses produced were not hybrids. They were all HRV. Why would this be so?

_____

_____

_____

4. Hypothesize what kind of lesion the T-H hybrid will cause. Explain.

_____

_____

_____

5. What controls were used in this experiment?

_____

_____

6. What were the variables in the experiment?

_____

_____

7. What was the most convincing evidence in this experiment that showed which part of the virus carried the genetic information?

_____

_____

_____

Chapter 19 Protists

Reviewing Vocabulary

Match the definition in Column A with the term in Column B.

Column A

_____ **1.** An animal-like protist

_____ **2.** A protozoan that moves by beating hairlike parts that cover its cell

_____ **3.** A reproductive cell that can produce a new organism without fertilization

_____ **4.** Multicellular and unicellular photosynthetic protists

_____ **5.** A kind of reproduction that occurs when an individual breaks up into pieces, each of which grows into a new individual

_____ **6.** The haploid form of an alga that produces sex cells

_____ **7.** In slime molds, the mass of cytoplasm that contains many diploid nuclei but no cell walls or membranes

_____ **8.** A group of cells that live together in close association

_____ **9.** The diploid form of an alga that develops from a zygote and produces spores

_____ **10.** Extensions of an amoeba's plasma membrane, which function in locomotion

_____ **11.** Kind of reproduction in which a single parent produces offspring identical to itself

_____ **12.** Life cycle of organisms that have a haploid stage followed by a diploid stage

Column B

a. algae

b. alternation of generations

c. asexual reproduction

d. ciliate

e. colony

f. fragmentation

g. gametophyte

h. plasmodium

i. protozoan

j. pseudopodia

k. spore

l. sporophyte

Understanding Main Ideas (Part A)

In the space at the left, write the letter of the word or phrase that best completes the statement or answers the question.

_____ **1.** Many protozoans are classified according to

     a. their method of getting food.   **b.** the way that they move.

     c. their method of reproduction.   **d.** their habitats.

_____ **2.** An amoeba engulfs food by

     a. using its oral groove and the action of cilia.

     b. osmosis.

     c. surrounding the food with pseudopodia.

     d. forming cysts.

_____ **3.** Excess water is pumped out of a paramecium by means of

     a. its pellicle.   **b.** a micronucleus and macronucleus.

     c. its gullet.   **d.** a pair of contractile vacuoles.

_____ **4.** Which of the following forms a mass of amoeboid cells?

     a. amoeba   **b.** plasmodial slime mold

     c. water mold   **d.** cellular slime mold

_____ **5.** During the gametophyte generation, a green alga

     a. has the haploid number of chromosomes.

     b. has the diploid number of chromosomes.

     c. reproduces asexually.

     d. develops from a zygote.

_____ **6.** Dinoflagellates are able to spin by means of

     a. the cilia that emerge through their pellicle.

     b. two flagella at right angles to each other.

     c. a pillbox shell that opens and closes.

     d. a holdfast that attaches them to a rock.

_____ **7.** Slime molds are said to be like animals during much of their life cycle because they

     a. look like animals.   **b.** reproduce by making spores.

     c. move about and engulf food.   **d.** grow on rotting leaves or tree stumps.

_____ **8.** Which ancient protist group was probably the ancestor of plants?

     a. diatoms   **b.** green algae   **c.** red algae   **d.** slime molds

_____ **9.** A protozoan that moves by lashing one or more of its whiplike parts is a

     a. thallus.   **b.** sporozoan.   **c.** water mold.   **d.** flagellate.

Chapter 19 Protists, *continued*

Understanding Main Ideas (Part B)

Answer the following questions.

1. How do protists differ from bacteria?

_____

_____

2. Euglenoids have characteristics of both autotrophs and heterotrophs. Explain.

_____

_____

_____

_____

3. What is the relationship between the sporophyte and gametophyte stages of some algae?

_____

_____

_____

_____

4. What triggers sexual reproduction in diatoms?

_____

_____

_____

_____

5. What causes the dangerous red tides in the ocean?

_____

_____

6. What adaptation helps red algae to live in deep water?

_____

_____

_____

Chapter 19 Protists, *continued*

Thinking Critically

Answer the following questions.

1. Ciliates have specialized cilia whose motion sweeps particles and/or bacteria into the ciliates' oral groove. In an experiment, inert latex beads and bacteria of the same size were placed in water with ciliated protozoans. Equal numbers of latex beads and bacteria were ingested by the ciliates. Form a hypothesis to explain these results.

2. A study of the protozoan populations per gram of leaf litter in a deciduous forest provided the data in the table. Interpret the data.

Season	Ciliates	Testate Amoebas
Winter	1500/gm	7000/gm
Summer	400/gm	700/gm

3. Anemia is a condition in which the blood is deficient in red blood cells and in hemoglobin. Why does a person with malaria develop anemia?

4. In the 1840s, a famine killed hundreds of thousands of people in Ireland. The famine was caused by a downy mildew that destroyed the entire potato crop. Hypothesize why the downy mildew was able to do such damage.

5. Why is the relationship between some termites and the flagellates that live in their intestines said to be mutualistic?

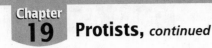

Chapter 19 Protists, *continued*

Applying Scientific Methods

It has been well-documented that populations of protozoans increase when water is polluted. The increase of protozoans may simply indicate that these organisms feed on the bacteria, the active decomposers of organic matter in the polluted water. Imagine that you are working with a team of scientists to determine if protozoans, like bacteria, would have any beneficial effects on a water purification system in which organic wastes are decomposed. The line at the top of the grid below shows the rate of decomposition of hay in water when bacteria are present alone. The lower line shows the rate of decomposition when both bacteria and protozoans are present.

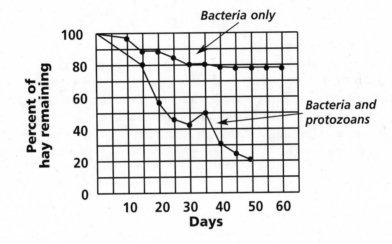

1. What does the graph show about the amount of decomposition that occurs when only bacteria are present?

_____

_____

2. What happens to the same amount of hay when protozoans also are present?

_____

_____

3. One member of the team hypothesizes that the protozoans are the decomposers in this case. Plan an experiment to prove whether this hypothesis is true or not.

_____

_____

_____

_____

Applying Scientific Methods   continued

4. Suppose that very little of the hay decomposed in 50 days when protozoans were present alone. What might you hypothesize then about the role of protozoans in decomposition?

_____

_____

_____

_____

_____

5. Suppose you have a vial of *Carchesium polypinum*, a species of ciliates found in waste water. You have just read that these protozoans produce a kind of mucus, which they secrete into the water. You want to develop a laboratory model of waste-water treatment. As your model, you drop some India ink into a beaker of tap water and add a vial of *Carchesium*. What effect might the mucus produced by the ciliates have on the India ink? How might you apply your results to the effect of the mucus on waste matter in water?

_____

_____

_____

_____

Chapter 20 Fungi

Reviewing Vocabulary

Match the definition in Column A with the term in Column B.

	Column A	Column B
_____	**1.** In parasitic fungi, specialized hyphae that penetrate cells and absorb nutrients	**a.** ascospore
_____	**2.** Case in which asexual spores are produced	**b.** ascus
_____	**3.** Thick-walled spore adapted to withstand unfavorable conditions	**c.** chitin
_____	**4.** Hyphae that grow horizontally along the surface of a food source	**d.** gametangia
_____	**5.** Complex carbohydrate in the cell walls of fungi	**e.** haustoria
_____	**6.** Mutualistic association between a fungus and a green alga or cyanobacterium	**f.** lichen
_____	**7.** Saclike structure in which sexual spores develop in some fungi	**g.** mycorrhiza
_____	**8.** Spore produced by sac fungi	**h.** sporangium
_____	**9.** Mutualistic association in which a fungus lives in close contact with the roots of a plant partner	**i.** stolons
_____	**10.** In zygomycotes, the haploid structures that fuse to form a diploid zygote	**j.** zygospore

Compare and contrast the following pairs of related terms.

11. hypha, mycelium

_____

_____

_____

12. basidium, basidiospore

_____

_____

_____

Understanding Main Ideas (Part A)

In the space at the left, write the letter of the word or phrase that best completes each statement.

_____ **1.** Fungi are classified into groups by their

    a. symbiotic relationships.   **b.** spore-producing structures.

    c. nutrition.   **d.** recycling ability.

_____ **2.** Fungi that break down complex organic substances into raw materials that other organisms can use are

    a. parasites.   **b.** mutualists.   **c.** decomposers.   **d.** autotrophs.

_____ **3.** In hyphae divided by septa, cytoplasm flows from one cell to the next through

    a. haustoria.   **b.** chitin.   **c.** spores.   **d.** pores.

_____ **4.** Yeasts usually reproduce asexually by

    a. budding.   **b.** meiosis.   **c.** fission.   **d.** fragmentation.

_____ **5.** The bread mold *Rhizopus* produces sexual zygospores when

    a. environmental conditions are unfavorable.

    b. environmental conditions are favorable.

    c. there is moist food.

    d. rhizoids are present.

_____ **6.** Fossils of fungi are rare due to fungi's

    a. late appearance on the Geologic Time Scale.

    b. lack of species diversity.

    c. composition of soft materials.

    d. ability to form protective zygospores.

In the space at the left, write <u>true</u> if the statement is true. If the statement is false, change the italicized word to make it true.

_____ **7.** During asexual reproduction, ascomycotes produce *ascospores*.

_____ **8.** Mycorrhizae increase the *reproductive* surface of plant roots.

_____ **9.** The four major divisions of fungi are Zygomycota, Ascomycota, *Basidiomycota*, and Deuteromycota.

_____ **10.** The fungus that produces penicillin is an example of a *basidiomycote*.

_____ **11.** Bread mold is able to penetrate bread by means of *zygospores*.

Understanding Main Ideas (Part B)

Answer the following questions.

1. How do fungi obtain nutrients? What is this process called?

_____

_____

_____

_____

2. What is the role of saprophytic fungi in food chains?

_____

_____

3. How does the symbiotic relationship of a lichen benefit both organisms?

_____

_____

_____

4. How is reproduction in deuteromycotes different from that in other fungi?

_____

_____

5. How is a zygospore formed?

_____

_____

_____

6. Why are mycorrhizae economically important?

_____

_____

Chapter Assessment

Thinking Critically

Answer the following questions.

1. A soil fungus is one of the sources of cyclosporine. This drug is given to patients who are about to receive an organ transplant. Cyclosporine suppresses the body's natural response to reject the organ transplant as a foreign substance. Hypothesize about how cyclosporine may be useful to the fungus that produces it.

_____

_____

2. Wheat rust is a fungus that causes enormous damage to wheat crops. The life cycle of wheat rust alternates between two different hosts: wheat plants and barberry bushes. The wheat rust needs both hosts to complete its sexual cycle. What could farmers do to protect their wheat crops?

_____

_____

3. Hypothesize about how mycorrhizal associations may have evolved.

_____

_____

_____

_____

_____

_____

4. Fossil plants often had mycorrhizal roots. How might the mycorrhizal association have played a role in the invasion of plants onto land?

_____

_____

_____

_____

5. A biologist proposes classifying fungi together with protists, rather than in a separate kingdom. Why might this suggestion be accepted? Why might the suggestion be rejected?

_____

_____

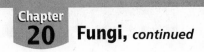

Chapter Assessment

20 Fungi, *continued*

Applying Scientific Methods

At first, it may seem that the fungus in a mycorrhizal association receives the greatest benefit. After all, the fungus uses the organic nutrients produced by the plant. However, the fungus is also useful to the plant. For example, the fungal hyphae increase the absorptive surface of the plant's roots. The table below records the inflow of phosphate in two kinds of onion plants—mycorrhizal and non-mycorrhizal.

Inflow of Phosphate in Onion Plants			
		Inflow (pmol/cm/s)	
Trials	Interval Duration (days)	Mycorrhizal	Non-mycorrhizal
1	14	0.17	0.050
2	7	0.22	0.016
3	10	0.13	0.042
Averages:		0.17	0.036

1. In each of the trials recorded, contrast the amount of phosphate that moved into an onion plant that is mycorrhizal with the amount that moved into a non-mycorrhizal onion plant. What conclusion do you reach?

_____

_____

_____

_____

_____

_____

_____

2. Explain why mycorrhizal and non-mycorrhizal plants take in different amounts of phosphate.

_____

_____

_____

_____

_____

_____

Chapter 20 **Fungi,** *continued*

Applying Scientific Methods   continued

To study the effect of mycorrhizal associations on plant growth, an investigator grew six seedlings in nutrient solution. The seedlings illustrated in the drawing on the left were then planted in soil that contained no mycorrhizal fungi. The seedlings illustrated on the right were grown first in forest soil rich in mycorrhizal fungi and then transferred to the soil without mycorrhizal fungi. All the plants grew for the same amount of time.

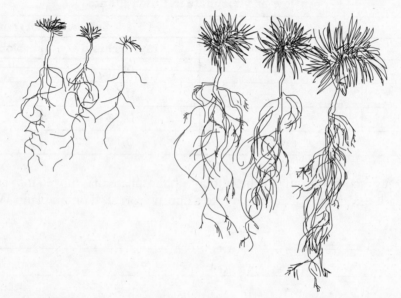

3. What was the variable in this investigation?

_____

4. What was the control in the investigation?

_____

_____

5. You have been given six healthy plants that were grown in soil with mycorrhizal fungi. Hypothesize what might happen to the mycorrhizae if you transplant the plants to soil that is phosphate-rich.

_____

_____

6. Plan an experiment to test your hypothesis.

_____

_____

_____

_____

_____

Chapter
21 **What Is a Plant?**

Reviewing Vocabulary

Match the definition in Column A with the term in Column B.

Column A	Column B
_____ **1.** A plant organ that absorbs water and minerals from the soil	**a.** cone
_____ **2.** Contains tissues of tubelike, elongated cells through which water and food are transported	**b.** frond
_____ **3.** Provides structural support for upright growth and contains tissues for transporting materials from one part of the plant to another	**c.** cuticle
_____ **4.** Structures that support male and female reproductive structures	**d.** leaf
_____ **5.** Structure that contains an embryo along with a food supply and is covered by a protective coat	**e.** root
_____ **6.** Protective, waxy layer covering most fruit, leaves, and stems	**f.** vascular plant
_____ **7.** Leaves found on ferns that vary in length from 1 cm to 500 cm	**g.** stem
_____ **8.** Broad, flat structure of a plant that traps light energy for photosynthesis	**h.** seed

Write a definition for each term listed below.

9. nonvascular plant

_____

_____

_____

10. vascular tissues

_____

_____

_____

Chapter
21 **What Is a Plant?,** *continued*

Understanding Concepts (Part A)

Complete the three tables by using the following list of words and phrases:

club mosses	mosses
ferns	needlelike or scaly leaves
flowering plants	only one living species
hornworts	palmlike trees with cones as long as 1 m
horsetails	three distinct genera
liverworts	whisk ferns

Phylogeny of Plants (based on division)

Non-seed nonvascular plant divisions

Division	Common Name
Hepatophyta	**a.**
Anthocerophyta	**b.**
Bryophytes	**c.**

Non-seed, vascular plant division

Division	Common Name
Psilophyta	**d.**
Lycophyta	**e.**
Spenophyta	**f.**
Pterophyta	**g.**

Seed Plants

Division	Common characteristics
Cycadophyta	**h.**
Gnetophyta	**i.**
Ginkgophyta	**j.**
Coniferophyta	**k.**
Anthophyta	**l.**

Chapter
21 **What Is a Plant?,** *continued*

Chapter Assessment

Understanding Concepts (Part B)

Answer the following questions.

1. Why do scientists think that plants probably evolved from green algae?

_____

_____

_____

_____

2. In what ways does vascular tissue provide an adaptive advantage for plants?

_____

_____

_____

_____

3. How does the cuticle prevent water loss?

_____

_____

_____

4. What major events highlight the evolution of plants?

_____

_____

_____

5. Compare the seeds of cycads, conifers, and flowering plants.

_____

_____

_____

_____

Thinking Critically

Use the graph to answer questions 1–3.

1. Investigators study the influence of light on spore germination in bryophytes. A spore has germinated when a small, green filament of cells is just protruding through the ruptured spore coat. Based on the graph, what wavelength of light appears to initiate spore germination?

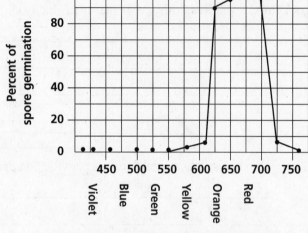

Wavelength of light (nm)

_____

_____

_____

_____

2. What is the optimum wavelength for spore germination?

_____

_____

3. What colors of light favor spore germination?

_____

Answer the following questions.

4. Aquatic bryophytes have been invaluable in monitoring pollution by heavy metals in contaminated water. However, the highest concentrations in the water do not always correspond to the highest values in the plants. Why might this be?

_____

_____

_____

_____

5. Some mosses that live in deserts dry out, and all their metabolic activities cease during a dry spell. At the next rainfall, however, they revive, grow, and reproduce. Why is this behavior adaptive?

_____

_____

_____

Chapter 21 **What Is a Plant,?** *continued*

Applying Scientific Methods

In an effort to understand alternation of generations in bryophytes, scientists have tried in the laboratory to develop moss sporophytes from gametophytes *without fertilization*. When filaments of cells that develop into haploid gametophytes were cultivated in a sugar-free medium, only gametophytes were produced. However, when botanists transferred these cell filaments to a medium supplemented with 2 percent sucrose, the filaments produced a large number of sporophyte sporangia.

1. Formulate a hypothesis to explain why a medium with 2 percent sucrose causes this change in the reproductive cycle. (Be creative in your thinking.)

_____

_____

_____

_____

_____

2. Plan an experiment to prove your hypothesis.

_____

_____

_____

_____

3. What will be your variable in this experiment?

_____

_____

4. What will be your control?

_____

_____

5. Some experimenters showed that the effect of sucrose is enhanced when lower light intensities are also present. How might less light affect the experiment?

_____

_____

_____

Chapter 21 **What Is a Plant?**, *continued*

Chapter Assessment

Applying Scientific Methods   continued

6. Scientists also discovered that after about 12 weeks of producing sporophytes, the plants stopped reproducing. However, if the gametophytes were transferred to a new sucrose medium, they began the formation of sporophytes again. In a medium lacking sucrose, the plants produced only gameto-phytes. How might these results be explained?

_____

_____

_____

_____

_____

7. Why would botanists perform an experiment like this, which seems to involve events that do not usually occur in nature?

_____

_____

_____

_____

Chapter
22 **The Diversity of Plants**

Reviewing Vocabulary

Match the definition in Column A with the term in Column B.

Column A	Column B
1. Cluster of sporangia	**a.** cotyledon
2. Leaf of a fern	**b.** embryo
3. Plants that lose all their leaves at one time	**c.** deciduous plant
4. Early gametophyte in lycophytes, sphenophytes, and pterophytes	**d.** frond
5. Organism at an early stage of development	**e.** fruit
6. Thick, underground stem	**f.** ovule
7. Food-storage organ of some plant embryos	**g.** pollen grain
8. The ripened ovary of a flower	**h.** prothallus
9. Structure in which the female gametophyte develops	**i.** rhizome
10. Structure that includes sperm cells, nutrients, and a protective outer covering	**j.** sorus

Compare and contrast each pair of terms.

11. antheridium, archegonium

_____

_____

_____

_____

12. annuals, perennials

_____

_____

_____

_____

Understanding Main Ideas (Part A)

In the space at the left, write the letter of the word or phrase that best completes the statement or answers the question.

_____ **1.** Horsetails are

    a. bryophytes.   **b.** sphenophytes.   **c.** lycophytes.   **d.** pterophytes.

_____ **2.** You can recognize that a plant is a dicotyledon if it has

    a. parallel veins.   **b.** branched veins.

    c. one seed leaf within the seed.   **d.** flower parts in multiples of three.

_____ **3.** Sphagnum, or peat moss, which is used in the horticultural industry, is a(n)

    a. bryophyte.   **b.** hepatophyte.   **c.** anthocerophyte.   **d.** lycophyte.

_____ **4.** In the fern life cycle, a spore germinates to form a(n)

    a. thallus.   **b.** antheridium.   **c.** prothallus.   **d.** archegonium.

_____ **5.** Which of the following divisions do *not* include nonvascular plants?

    a. Bryophyta   **b.** Hepatophyta   **c.** Anthocerophyta   **d.** Anthophyta

_____ **6.** In most seed plants, fertilization does not require

    a. a film of water to carry the sperm to the egg.

    b. alternation of generations.

    c. the production of eggs.

    d. a gametophyte generation.

_____ **7.** Which of these are vascular plants?

    a. club mosses   **b.** spike mosses   **c.** ferns   **d.** all of these

_____ **8.** The fronds of ferns are divided into

    a. rhizomes.   **b.** pinnae.   **c.** cycads.   **d.** sori.

_____ **9.** Which of the following is *not* a characteristic of a non-seed vascular plant?

    a. These plants exhibit alternation of generations.

    b. The gametophyte generation is dominant.

    c. They have vascular tissues through which water and sugars are transported.

    d. Plants are found in a variety of habitats.

_____ **10.** Most conifers

    a. lose all their leaves when water is unavailable.

    b. lose most of their water through the leaves.

    c. are deciduous trees.

    d. never lose all their leaves at one time.

Chapter
22   **The Diversity of Plants,** *continued*

Chapter Assessment

Understanding Main Ideas (Part B)

Answer the following questions.

1. Describe the major characteristics of nonvascular plants.

_____

_____

_____

_____

2. What advantages does a seed plant have over a non-seed plant?

_____

_____

_____

_____

_____

_____

3. What are the advantages of fruit-enclosed seeds?

_____

_____

_____

_____

_____

4. What advantages does an evergreen tree have?

_____

_____

_____

_____

_____

Chapter 22 **The Diversity of Plants,** *continued*

Thinking Critically

Refer to the graph to answer questions 1 and 2.

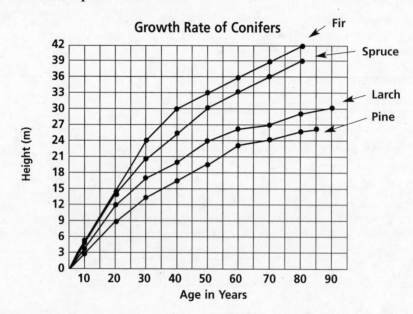

Growth Rate of Conifers

1. In the table, write the correct information about the patterns of growth of certain conifers.

	Age at maximum growth	Maximum height	Height at 45 years
Fir	_____	_____	_____
Spruce	_____	_____	_____
Larch	_____	_____	_____
Pine	_____	_____	_____

2. How does the graph show that these conifers grow according to their own growth pattern?

_____

_____

_____

3. The ginkgo, with its broad leaves that turn yellow in autumn, looks more like a flowering plant than a gymnosperm. Why is the ginkgo classified as a gymnosperm?

_____

_____

Chapter
22 The Diversity of Plants, *continued*

Applying Scientific Methods

Bracken ferns are one of the most widely distributed species of ferns. Brackens occur in all but hot and cold desert regions of the world. In many regions, this species invades the grasslands, where it becomes a troublesome weed that is difficult to eradicate because of its persistent underground rhizome. The problem is worsened because bracken is a poisonous plant. It causes thyamine deficiency, which results in the death of certain animals.

1. What circumstances might arise in your community such that you might need to find out how to control the growth of brackens?

   _____

   _____

   _____

2. Bracken spores will germinate in lava, mortar of brickwork, abandoned building sites, bomb sites, and fire-damaged natural habitats. However, they will not germinate within a bracken colony. Hypothesize as to what the limiting factor in the germination of bracken spores might be.

   _____

   _____

   _____

   _____

3. Plan an experiment to test your hypothesis. Decide the conditions under which you will grow the bracken fern.

   _____

   _____

   _____

4. What will be the variable in this experiment?

   _____

   _____

   _____

   _____

Applying Scientific Methods   continued

5. What will be the control?

_____

_____

6. If you found that when bracken spores grew into ferns, the other plant in the pot flourished, what might you conclude?

_____

_____

7. How could you prove that the conclusion you came to in question 6 was correct?

_____

_____

_____

_____

8. If you found that the plant did not flourish or even died when it was grown with bracken spores, what would you conclude?

_____

_____

_____

9. How could you prove that the conclusion you came to in question 8 was correct?

_____

_____

_____

_____

Chapter Assessment

Chapter 23 Plant Structure and Function

Reviewing Vocabulary

Match the definition in Column A with the term in Column B.

Column A	Column B
_____ **1.** Plant tissue that transports water and minerals from the roots to the rest of the plant	**a.** apical meristem
_____ **2.** Tubular cell that is tapered at each end and that transports water throughout a plant	**b.** companion cell
_____ **3.** Tissue that gives rise to lateral roots	**c.** epidermis
_____ **4.** A responsive movement of a plant that is not dependent on the direction of the stimulus	**d.** guard cell
_____ **5.** Stalk that joins the leaf blade to the stem	**e.** hormone
_____ **6.** Any portion of the plant that uses or stores sugars	**f.** mesophyll
_____ **7.** Flattened parenchyma cells that cover all parts of the plant	**g.** nastic movement
_____ **8.** Tissue composed of living cells that transport sugars from the leaves to all parts of the plant	**h.** cortex
_____ **9.** Growth tissue that remains just behind the root tip	**i.** pericycle
_____ **10.** Contains a nucleus and helps control movement through the sieve cell	**j.** petiole
_____ **11.** A plant's response to an external stimulus that comes from a particular direction	**k.** phloem
_____ **12.** A chemical that is produced in one part of an organism and transported to another part, where it causes a physiological change.	**l.** sink
_____ **13.** Cell that surrounds and controls the opening of the stomata	**m.** tracheid
_____ **14.** Photosynthetic tissue of a leaf	**n.** tropism
_____ **15.** Tissue in the root that can act as a storage area for food and water	**o.** xylem

Understanding Main Ideas (Part A)

In the space at the left, write the letter of the word or phrase that best completes the statement or answers the question.

_____ **1.** To control water loss, the size of the stomata is reduced by the

      a. xylem.   **b.** phloem.   **c.** cambium.   **d.** guard cells.

_____ **2.** Xylem is vascular tissue that

      a. is alive.

      b. transports sugar from the leaves to all parts of the plant.

      c. transports water and dissolved minerals from the roots to the leaves.

      d. transports sperm to the eggs.

_____ **3.** Cells in the apical meristem that cause a root to grow longer are found

      a. just behind the root tip.   **b.** along the sides of the root.

      c. at the top of the root.   **d.** in the center of the root.

_____ **4.** What area is responsible for producing the cells that allow the roots and stems to increase in length?

      a. apical meristem   **b.** vascular meristem   **c.** pericycle   **d.** endodermis

_____ **5.** What is the primary function of plant leaves?

      a. to support the plant   **b.** to produce flowers

      c. to take in water   **d.** to trap sunlight for photosynthesis

_____ **6.** Where does most photosynthesis take place?

      a. in the cells of the cortex   **b.** in the spongy mesophyll

      c. in the palisade mesophyll   **d.** in the stomata

_____ **7.** The petiole and veins of a leaf contain the

      a. apical meristem.   **b.** epidermis.   **c.** endodermis.   **d.** vascular tissue.

In the space at the left, write <u>true</u> if the statement is true. If the statement is false, change the italicized word or phrase to make it true.

_____ **8.** A *root cap* is a tiny extension of a single epidermal cell that increases the surface area of the root and absorbs water, oxygen, and dissolved minerals.

_____ **9.** The loss of water from the stomata of the leaves is called *perspiration*.

_____ **10.** A *vessel element* is a tubular cell that transports water throughout the plant.

Understanding Main Ideas (Part B)

Answer the following questions.

  1. What causes tree rings to form?

_____

_____

_____

_____

  2. How do auxims promote cell elongation?

_____

_____

_____

_____

_____

  3. Explain why fruit kept in a closed container ripens more quickly than fruit left out in an open bowl.

_____

_____

_____

  4. How do guard cells prevent a plant from drying out?

_____

_____

_____

_____

_____

  5. What are the functions of a root?

_____

_____

_____

Thinking Critically

Answer the following questions.

1. A researcher performed an experiment to determine the function of xylem and phloem. He removed the bark, including the phloem, in a complete ring around a tree. The xylem was left intact. After doing this, the researcher noticed a swelling just above the stripped ring; a sweet fluid leaked from this swollen area. The leaves of the tree remained green for several weeks. Eventually, however, they died; the entire tree died soon after. What could the researcher conclude from this experiment? Explain.

_____

_____

_____

_____

_____

_____

2. The table at the right shows the transpiration rate of some plants measured in liters per day. Why would the transpiration rate of the cactus be so much lower than that of the other plants?

Plant	Liters/Day
Cactus	0.02
Tomato	1.00
Apple	19.00

_____

_____

_____

3. When he was 12 years old, Joe carved his initials into the bark of a tree in the forest behind his house. The tree was 7 m tall and 20 cm in diameter, and the initials were 1.5 m above the ground. When Joe was 22 years old, he went back to see the tree; it had grown to a height of 10 m and was now 27 cm in diameter. How far above the ground were Joe's initials? Explain.

_____

_____

_____

_____

_____

Applying Scientific Methods

Students often perform a simple experiment to verify the fact that water is transported upward from the roots of a plant to its leaves. You may remember that, when you place a celery stalk in colored water, after a few hours, the color reaches the leaves at the top of the celery stalk.

1. Why might you infer that water also reaches the leaves?

_____

_____

This experiment may lead you to formulate a question about water transport in plants. What causes the water to rise from the roots to the leaves against the force of gravity? The answer is that some other force, greater than the gravitational pull on the water, must pull the water upward. In the tallest sequoias, for example, water must rise about 107 m from roots to top leaves. Quite a pull is needed to get the water up to that height.

   The answer lies in transpiration. Transpiration occurs as water evaporates from the stomata in the leaves. Scientists think that it is transpiration that provides the force that pulls the water upward against the force of gravity. As water at the stomata evaporates, the water in the leaf just below the stomata is drawn up to replace the vaporized water. Through this process, water slowly and continuously rises to the leaves.

2. Formulate a hypothesis about how temperature could affect the flow of water upward.

_____

_____

3. Plan an experiment to prove your hypothesis.

_____

_____

_____

_____

4. What will be your control in this experiment?

_____

_____

_____

5. What is the variable in this experiment?

_____

_____

Chapter
23 **Plant Structure and Function,** *continued*

Applying Scientific Methods   continued

6. Transpiration occurs only during the day. Hypothesize why this might be.

_____

_____

_____

7. How would you verify your hypothesis?

_____

_____

_____

8. What will be your control in this experiment?

_____

_____

_____

9. What is the variable in this experiment?

_____

_____

Chapter 24 Reproduction in Plants

Reviewing Vocabulary

Write the word or phrase that best completes each statement. Use these choices:

anther	pistil	stamen	germination
day-neutral plant	megaspores	ovary	petals
endosperm	microspores	micropyle	photoperiodism
protonema			

1. The response of flowering plants to the difference in the duration of light and dark periods in a day is called _____ .

2. The _____ is food-storage tissue that supports development of the embryo.

3. The _____ is the part of the flower in which ovules containing eggs are formed.

4. The _____ is a small green filament of cells that develops into either a male or a female gametophyte.

5. Leaflike, usually colorful, structures arranged in a circle around the tip of a flower stem are called _____ .

6. The beginning of the development of the embryo into a new plant is called _____ .

7. The _____ is the female structure of the flower.

8. _____ are female spores that eventually become female gametophytes.

9. The male cones have sporangia that undergo meiosis to produce males spores called _____ .

10. The _____ , at the tip of the stamen, produces pollen that contains sperm.

11. The flowering time of a _____ is controlled by temperature, moisture, or other environmental factors, rather than by day length.

12. The _____ is the male reproductive structure of a flower.

13. The _____ is a tiny opening in the ovule through which a sperm cell moves through the pollen tube into the ovule.

Chapter 24 **Reproduction in Plants,** *continued*

Understanding Main Ideas (Part A)

Label the parts of a flower in the diagram below.

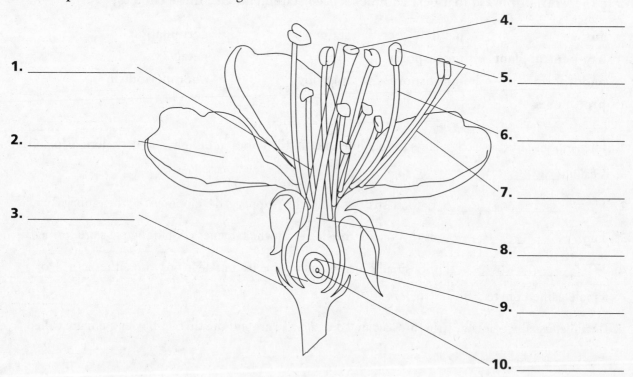

1. _____

2. _____

3. _____

4. _____

5. _____

6. _____

7. _____

8. _____

9. _____

10. _____

In the space at the left, write the letter of the word or phrase that best completes the statement or answers the question.

_____ **11.** Where does the process of double fertilization occur?
    a. in the pollen tube   **b.** in the stigma
    c. in the central nucleus   **d.** in the ovule

_____ **12.** The fertilization of the central cell produces a
    a. triploid nucleus.   **b.** zygote.
    c. diploid nucleus.   **d.** haploid egg.

_____ **13.** After fertilization, the central cell develops into the
    a. zygote.   **b.** endosperm.   **c.** pollen tube.   **d.** fruit.

_____ **14.** Which of the following plants has a prothallus that forms archegonia and antheridia and has a dominant sporophyte?
    a. mosses   **b.** ferns   **c.** conifers   **d.** flowering plants

_____ **15.** Which of the following plants produce separate male and female cones that produce microspores and megaspores that develop into male and female gametophytes?
    a. mosses   **b.** ferns   **c.** conifers   **d.** flowering plants

Chapter 24 **Reproduction in Plants,** *continued*

Understanding Main Ideas (Part B)

Answer the following questions.

1. What is the dominant generation?

_____

_____

_____

_____

2. Give at least three of the special requirements that some seeds may have before they germinate.

_____

_____

_____

_____

3. What steps are involved in fruit and seed formation?

_____

_____

_____

_____

_____

4. What is a photoperiodism? Differentiate between short-day plants and long-day plants.

_____

_____

_____

_____

_____

_____

Chapter
24 **Reproduction in Plants,** *continued*

Chapter Assessment

Thinking Critically

Answer the following questions.

1. Hypothesize why vegetative reproduction is an adaptive advantage for most plants.

_____

_____

_____

_____

_____

_____

_____

2. Flower production uses up large quantities of sugar in a plant. Sugarcane growers try to delay flowering as long as possible in order to allow time for the sugar content of the cane to increase. If sugarcane is a short-day plant, hypothesize as to how they might achieve their goal.

_____

_____

_____

_____

_____

3. Investigators tried an experiment with short-day plants in the laboratory to find out how the day/night stimulus is carried throughout the plant. Immediately after exposing the plants to light during what was normally a dark period, investigators removed all the leaves from the plant. Flowering did not occur in the plants. However, if they waited and removed the leaves several hours after the light stimulus was given, flowering did occur. Hypothesize as to the function of the leaves in the flowering process. Why did flowering occur when there was a delay before removing the leaves?

_____

_____

_____

_____

_____

_____

Applying Scientific Methods

Plant physiologists have for a number of years been investigating the stimuli that initiate flowering in plants. They have concluded that some plants are short-day plants. These plants produce flowers in early spring or late summer when days are shorter than nights. Other plants are long-day plants that bloom in summer when days are longer than nights. In still other plants, flowering is controlled by temperature, moisture, or other environmental factors.

1. How does each of these adaptations benefit the plant?

_____

_____

_____

Investigators have known about the day/night length effect on flowering for many years. However, some investigators were unsure as to whether it is the day length or the night length that actually causes flowers of a certain species to bloom.

2. Hypothesize about which of these is the stimulus that causes blooming. You must support your hypothesis with valid reasons for your choice.

_____

_____

_____

_____

_____

_____

3. In planning an experiment to investigate the effect of day/night length on flowering, it is best to use plants whose flowering pattern you know. Why?

_____

_____

_____

Chapter 24 **Reproduction in Plants,** *continued*

Chapter Assessment

Applying Scientific Methods *continued*

4. Use either short-day or long-day plants. Plan an experiment to support your hypothesis.

_____

_____

_____

_____

_____

5. What will be your control during your experiment?

_____

_____

6. What is the variable in this experiment?

_____

_____

7. If the results of your experiment do *not* support your hypothesis, what would you do next?

_____

_____

_____

_____

Chapter 25 What Is an Animal?

Reviewing Vocabulary

Match the definition in Column A with the term in Column B.

Column A	Column B
_____ **1.** Third cell layer formed in the developing embryo	**a.** acoelomate
_____ **2.** Body plan of an organism that can be divided along any plane, through a central axis, into roughly equal halves	**b.** bilateral symmetry
_____ **3.** Animal that has three cell layers, with a digestive tract but no body cavities	**c.** blastula
_____ **4.** Single layer of cells surrounding a fluid-filled space that forms during early development	**d.** coelom
_____ **5.** Animal in which the mouth does not develop from the opening in the gastrula	**e.** deuterostome
_____ **6.** Layer of cells on the outer surface of the gastrula	**f.** ectoderm
_____ **7.** Body plan of an organism that can be divided down its length into right and left halves that form mirror images	**g.** endoderm
_____ **8.** Body cavity completely surrounded by mesoderm	**h.** gastrula
_____ **9.** Layer of cells lining the inner surface of the gastrula	**i.** mesoderm
_____ **10.** Body cavity partly lined with mesoderm, such as found in roundworms	**j.** pseudocoelom
_____ **11.** Describes organisms that don't move from place to place	**k.** protostome
_____ **12.** Embryonic structure in animals that consists of two cell layers	**l.** radial symmetry
_____ **13.** Animal with a mouth that develops from the opening in the gastrula	**m.** sessile

Chapter 25 **What Is an Animal?,** *continued*

Understanding Main Ideas (Part A)

Match the number of each location on the drawing of the flatworm with the correct descriptive term for the location. Use these choices: ventral, posterior, dorsal, anterior.

1. _____

2. _____

3. _____

4. _____

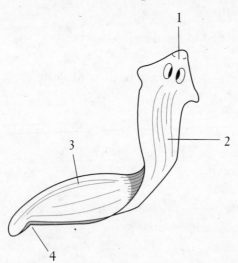

In the space at the left, write the letter of the word or phrase that best completes each statement or answers the question.

_____ **5.** The embryonic layer that forms the skin and nervous tissue is the

    a. endoderm.   **b.** mesoderm.   **c.** ectoderm.   **d.** protostome.

_____ **6.** The animal's digestive tract forms from the

    a. endoderm.   **b.** mesoderm.   **c.** ectoderm.   **d.** protostome.

_____ **7.** Which of the following applies to a sponge?

    a. adult is sessile   **b.** has a gastrula stage

    c. bilateral symmetry   **d.** develops three embryonic layers

_____ **8.** What type of symmetry does a penny have?

    a. bilateral symmetry   **b.** radial symmetry

    c. no symmetry   **d.** biaxial symmetry

_____ **9.** Which of these animals has bilateral symmetry?

    a. sponge   **b.** hydra   **c.** jellyfish   **d.** flatworm

_____ **10.** Animals with bilateral symmetry find food and mates and avoid predators more efficiently because they have

    a. body cavities.   **b.** more muscular control.

    c. tails.   **d.** the ability to see in all directions.

Chapter
25 **What Is an Animal?,** *continued*

Understanding Main Ideas (Part B)

Answer the following questions.

1. What are the main characteristics of an animal?

_____

_____

_____

2. In what way does a sponge qualify as a heterotroph?

_____

_____

_____

3. How do the structures of the digestive tracts of a flatworm and an earthworm differ?

_____

_____

_____

4. What are the early stages of development from zygote to gastrula?

_____

_____

_____

5. In flatworms, different types of tissues are organized into organs, but unlike earthworms, flatworms lack a coelom in which their internal organs are suspended. Where are the internal organs of the flatworms located?

_____

_____

6. Briefly identify the three cell layers formed during embryonic development and give examples of the body organs and tissues that each layer gives rise to.

_____

_____

_____

_____

_____

Thinking Critically

Answer the following questions.

Answer questions 1–4, using the table below, which shows the amount of oxygen required for animals of different body mass to move a given distance.

Animal	Body Mass Moved	mL O$_2$ Required per 1 g of Body Mass
Mouse	10 g	4.00 mL
Kangaroo rat	45 g	2.00 mL
Ground squirrel	140 g	0.80 mL
Dog	13 kg	0.40 mL
Horse	500 kg	0.04 mL

1. How many mL of O$_2$ does a kangaroo rat require per 1 g of body mass? _____

2. How many mL of O$_2$ would a mouse require in all? _____

3. After studying the table, what generalization can you make about the amount of oxygen used by animals of different body mass?

_____

_____

_____

_____

4. Where in the table do you think a 90 kg human adult would fall? Estimate about how many mL of O$_2$ the human would require per 1 g of body mass.

_____

_____

_____

5. Simpler animals are small in size. As large animals evolved, they tended to become more complex. Hypothesize as to why this was necessary.

_____

_____

_____

_____

_____

Chapter Assessment

Applying Scientific Methods

The scientific team you are working with wishes to demonstrate that animals become more efficient in interacting with their external environment when the body plan that evolved included bilateral symmetry. You have chosen to work with mealworms, the larvae of grain beetles (Tenebrio molitor).

1. You watch the mealworms moving along the sides of the box in which they are housed. State which factors other than the body plan of the mealworms might affect their behavior.

_____

_____

_____

2. Hypothesize how a mealworm's moving along the sides of a box is related to its bilateral body plan.

_____

_____

_____

_____

3. Plan an experiment to prove your hypothesis.

_____

_____

_____

_____

_____

_____

_____

_____

_____

_____

_____

4. What will be your control in this experiment?

_____

_____

_____

Chapter 25

What Is an Animal?, *continued*

Applying Scientific Methods   continued

5. How could you prove that mealworms are equally sensitive on both the right and left sides of their body?

_____

_____

_____

6. Hypothesize what would happen if you were to provide the mealworm with a vertical pane or wall on both its left and right sides.

_____

_____

_____

_____

7. Is this behavior seen in other animals? Explain your answer.

_____

_____

_____

_____

_____

Copyright © Glencoe/McGraw-Hill, a division of The McGraw-Hill Companies, Inc.

Chapter 26 — Sponges, Cnidarians, Flatworms, and Roundworms

Chapter Assessment

Reviewing Vocabulary

Write the word or phrase that best completes each statement. Use these choices:

external fertilization	internal fertilization	pharynx
filter feeding	medusa	polyp
gastrovascular cavity	nematocysts	proglottids
hermaphrodites	nerve net	scolex

1. Sponges get their food by _____ , in which small particles of food are removed from the water during passage through a part of their body.

2. Cnidarians capture prey by means of _____ which are coiled, threadlike tubes that are sticky or barbed or that contain toxins.

3. Digestion in cnidarians takes place in the _____ .

4. During feeding, planarians extend a tubelike, muscular organ, called the _____ , out of their mouths.

5. A parasitic tapeworm has a knob-shaped head, called a _____ , by which the worm attaches itself to the host's intestinal wall.

6. In _____ , fertilization occurs outside the animal's body after eggs and sperm are released.

7. In _____ , eggs remain inside the animal's body and sperm are carried to the eggs.

8. Sponges are considered _____ because an individual sponge can produce both eggs and sperm.

9. A _____ is the tube-shaped body form with a mouth surrounded by tentacles, which serves as the asexual stage in some cnidarians.

10. A _____ is the sexual form of a cnidarian that has a body form like an umbrella with tentacles hanging down.

11. A tapeworm has reproductive organs in segments called _____ .

Chapter 26 Sponges, Cnidarians, Flatworms, and Roundworms, *continued*

Chapter Assessment

Understanding Main Ideas (Part A)

In the space at the left, write the letter of the word or phrase that best completes each statement or answers the question.

_____ 1. The collar cells of sponges are similar to
  a. flagellated protists.   **b.** amoebas.
  c. ciliated paramecia.   **d.** sessile sporozoans.

_____ 2. Because sponges are sessile, they get their food through
  a. scavenging the sea floor.   **b.** filter feeding.
  c. the spicules.   **d.** tentacles.

_____ 3. A group of cnidarians that provide food and shelter for many kinds of animals are the
  a. jellyfish.   **b.** hydras.   **c.** sea anemones.   **d.** corals.

_____ 4. A _____ has a muscular tube called the pharynx, which can be extended outside its body to suck in food.
  a. jellyfish   **b.** sponge   **c.** planarian   **d.** tapeworm

_____ 5. In a cnidarian, digestion occurs in the
  a. proglottids.   **b.** gastrovascular cavity.
  c. digestive tract.   **d.** tentacles.

_____ 6. Uncooked or undercooked pork may contain
  a. trichina worms.   **b.** hookworms.
  c. pinworms.   **d.** free-living roundworms.

_____ 7. Which is an acoelomate animal?
  a. sponge   **b.** cnidarian   **c.** flatworm   **d.** roundworm

_____ 8. A Portugese man-of-war is an example of
  a. an anthozoan.   **b.** a large scyphozoan.
  c. a hydrozoan colony.   **d.** a sea anemone.

_____ 9. Nematocysts discharge when
  a. salt concentration in the ocean drops.   **b.** tentacles touch a source of food.
  c. a cnidarian regenerates.   **d.** cnidarians reproduce.

Write the numbers 1 to 3 to show the structures through which water passes through a sponge, in order.

_____ 10. collar cells   _____ 11. osculum   _____ 12. pore cells

Chapter 26 Sponges, Cnidarians, Flatworms, and Roundworms, *continued*

Understanding Main Ideas (Part B)

Answer the following questions.

1. How is a sponge's food-gathering technique adapted to its sessile lifestyle?

_____

_____

_____

2. Describe the process by which sponges reproduce sexually by internal fertilization.

_____

_____

_____

_____

_____

_____

3. Compare and contrast the sexual and asexual phases of jellyfish reproduction.

_____

_____

_____

_____

4. The body of the planarian is an advance over the cnidarian body. Explain.

_____

_____

_____

_____

_____

5. How do parasitic roundworms keep from being digested by their host organisms?

_____

Chapter 26 Sponges, Cnidarians, Flatworms, and Roundworms, *continued*

Chapter Assessment

Thinking Critically

Answer the following questions.

1. A biologist places a single, live sponge in a saltwater tank. After several weeks, the biologist observes other, smaller sponges living in the tank. Since the biologist is certain that no other sponge had been introduced into the tank, what other explanation could you provide to explain the observation?

_____

_____

2. When you see a sponge passed through a sieve and separated into cells, you may think a sponge is simply a colony of individual cells. What makes you realize that it is more than this?

_____

_____

3. When it brushes the tentacles of a sea anemone, a clownfish is recognized by the anemone, which does not trigger the release of nematocysts. One experiment has shown that the slime on the scales of the clownfish inhibits the release of stinging cells. Hypothesize how the slime might work.

_____

_____

_____

_____

4. What advantage is there to the extracellular digestion of cnidarians over the digestion of sponges?

_____

_____

_____

5. Hypothesize why medusae that live in the midwaters where bioluminescent prey are abundant have dark pigmentation.

_____

_____

_____

_____

Chapter 26 Sponges, Cnidarians, Flatworms, and Roundworms, *continued*

Applying Scientific Methods

In an experiment about possible factors that cause the differentiation and growth of cells in hydra larvae, a proportion-altering factor (PAF) was discovered and isolated in a specific colonial cnidarian known as Eudendrium sp. In the experiment, hydra larvae were placed in solutions, one with 10 drops of PAF/mL of water, one with 15 drops, one with 20 drops, one with 30 drops, and a control solution. The experiment showed that PAF factor caused parts of the hydra to grow out of normal proportions. The following table and illustration show the differences in tentacle development that result from varying concentrations of PAF. Study the illustration and the table and answer the questions that follow.

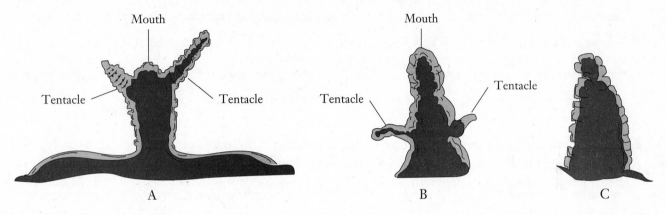

Amount of PAF (drops/10 mL of water)	Number of Hydras		
	tentacles near mouth	tentacles near base	no tentacles formed
0	197	0	0
10	90	119	0
15	74	130	5
20	30	145	26
30	0	160	44

Copyright © Glencoe/McGraw-Hill, a division of The McGraw-Hill Companies, Inc.

Applying Scientific Methods   *continued*

1. What was the control in the experiment?

_____

_____

2. After 48 hours, hydras from the control group looked like polyp A in the figure; most hydras from the 15-drop solution looked like polyp B. How does polyp A differ from polyp B?

_____

_____

_____

_____

_____

3. After 48 hours, most of the hydras treated with 30 drops of PAF/10 mL of water looked like polyp B, but some looked like polyp C. Describe the hydras that looked like polyp C.

_____

_____

_____

4. What conclusions can you draw from the results shown in the table?

_____

_____

_____

_____

Chapter 27 Mollusks and Segmented Worms

Reviewing Vocabulary

Write the word or phrase that best completes the statement. Use these choices:

closed circulatory system   open circulatory system

gizzard   radula

mantle   setae

nephridia

1. Annelids have a digestive organ called a(n) _____ that grinds organic matter, or food, into small pieces so that it can be absorbed as it passes through the animal's intestine.

2. In bivalves, the _____ is a thin membrane that sticks to both shells and forms siphons that are used for drawing in and expelling water.

3. The excretory structures that remove metabolic wastes from the bodies of animals such as mollusks and annelids are called _____ .

4. You dissect an animal and observe pools of blood surrounding its internal organs. This animal has a(n) _____ .

5. The _____ is a tongue-like organ with rows of teeth that is used by gastropods to scrape, grate, or cut food.

6. An animal whose blood moves throughout its body within blood vessels has a(n) _____ .

7. Tiny bristles protruding from each segment of a segmented worm are called _____ .

Understanding Main Ideas (Part A)

Identify each numbered part of the burrowing earthworm shown in the diagram, using the letter of each appropriate term.

A. ventral nerve cord   C. simple brain   E. blood vessels
B. setae   D. hearts   F. gizzard

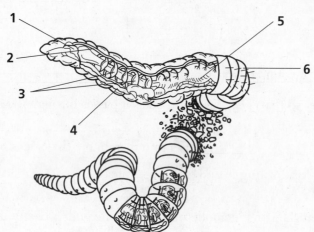

1. _____ 2. _____ 3. _____ 4. _____ 5. _____ 6. _____

In the space at the left, write **true** if the statement is true. If the statement is false, change the italicized word or phrase to make it true.

_____ **7.** In shelled mollusks, the *radula* secretes the shell.

_____ **8.** Bivalves obtain food by *predation*.

_____ **9.** The excretory structures in mollusks are called *nephridia*.

_____ **10.** *Gastropods* have two shells.

_____ **11.** The respiratory organs in aquatic gastropods are *primitive lungs*.

_____ **12.** Earthworms are *hermaphrodites* because each worm produces both eggs and sperm.

_____ **13.** Based on their pattern of early development and other evidence, earthworms and *cnidarians* are thought to be closely related.

_____ **14.** The first animals to have evolved respiratory organs are the *mollusks*.

_____ **15.** The most complex and most recently evolved mollusks are *gastropods*.

Understanding Main Ideas (Part B)

Answer the following questions.

1. What adaptations help the octopus and the squid escape their predators?

_____

_____

_____

_____

2. What are some of the functions of the mantle in mollusks?

_____

_____

_____

_____

3. What is the role of the radula?

_____

_____

4. Compare the circulatory system of gastropods, bivalves, and cephalopods.

_____

_____

_____

5. How do sea slugs improve their survival opportunities by feeding on jellyfishes?

_____

_____

_____

6. List and give examples of the three major types of segmented worms.

_____

_____

_____

Thinking Critically

Answer the following questions.

1. Most cephalopods lack an external shell. What is the adaptive advantage of this feature?

_____

_____

_____

_____

2. Most cephalopods have eyes that are remarkably like vertebrate eyes and fully capable of forming a good image. However, the cephalopod eye develops wholly from the surface ectoderm, whereas the vertebrate eye develops from the neural tube. What does this information indicate about whether or not the vertebrate eye evolved from the cephalopod eye?

_____

_____

_____

_____

3. An oyster produces a natural pearl when a parasite or a bit of sand lodges between the shell and the mantle. The oyster then grows layers of pearl around the foreign body. What is the advantage of pearl-making to the oyster?

_____

_____

4. The Greek philosopher Aristotle called worms "the intestines of the soil." What did he mean?

_____

_____

_____

_____

5. Suppose you are given an unknown mollusk to identify. The specimen does not have a shell. How could you decide whether the mollusk is an unshelled gastropod or a cephalopod?

_____

_____

_____

_____

Chapter 27 Mollusks and Segmented Worms, *continued*

Applying Scientific Methods

Alvin, and other submersible vehicles used by oceanographers to study the ocean floor, have also proved invaluable in studying populations of deep-sea mollusks and segmented tube worms. The invertebrates in question live where hot seawater circulates through cracks in the ocean floor called deep-sea vents.

Suppose that you are an invertebrate biologist studying these animals. Your studies show that clams that live near the vents may grow as much as 3.8 cm per year, far more rapidly than other deep-water clams.

1. Form a hypothesis to explain why vent clams grow more rapidly than other clams at the same depth.

_____

_____

_____

2. Plan an experiment to prove your hypothesis.

_____

_____

_____

_____

_____

3. Why wouldn't you choose water depth as an independent variable?

_____

_____

4. Suppose your data show that the temperature is the same in samples taken close to the vents or some distance away from the vents. However, the size of the clams is smaller the farther they are from the vents. What would this indicate?

_____

_____

_____

_____

Chapter 27 **Mollusks and Segmented Worms,** *continued*

Applying Scientific Methods   continued

5. Segmented tube worms that live near the vents grow to lengths of 1.5 m in contrast to the growth of related tube worms living in other environments, whose growth is measured only in centimeters at most. You hypothesize that the food that the worms eat is more abundant at the vents. When you collect samples of the worms, you discover that they have no mouth or other means of taking in food. Hypothesize how the tube worms are obtaining nutrients.

_____

_____

_____

_____

_____

_____

_____

6. Some researchers have hypothesized that life may have begun at deep-sea vents. Why might this be?

_____

_____

_____

_____

_____

Chapter
28 **Arthropods**

Reviewing Vocabulary

Match the definition in Column A with the term in Column B.

Column A	Column B
	a. appendage
_____ **1.** Branching networks of hollow passages that carry air throughout the body	**b.** book lung
_____ **2.** Chemical odor signal given off by an animal	**c.** cephalothorax
_____ **3.** Form of asexual reproduction in which an organism develops from an unfertilized egg	**d.** Malpighian tubule
_____ **4.** Openings through which air enters and leaves the tracheal tubes	**e.** mandible
_____ **5.** Any structure, such as a leg, that grows out of the body of an animal	**f.** molting
_____ **6.** Fused head and thorax region in some arthropods	**g.** parthenogenesis
_____ **7.** Excretory organ of terrestrial arthropods	**h.** pheromone
_____ **8.** Air-filled chamber containing leaflike plates that serve for gas exchange	**i.** spinneret
_____ **9.** Shedding of the old exoskeleton	**j.** spiracles
_____ **10.** Jaw of an arthropod	**k.** tracheal tubes
_____ **11.** Movable structure used by a spider to turn silk into thread	

Compare or contrast each pair of related terms.

12. simple eye, compound eye

_____

_____

13. chelicerae, pedipalps

_____

_____

_____

Chapter 28 **Artropods,** *continued*

Understanding Main Ideas (Part A)

In the space at the left, write the letter of the word or phrase that best completes the statement or answers the question.

_____ **1.** The characteristic that most distinguishes arthropods from other invertebrates is

    a. the coelom.   **b.** the endoskeleton.

    c. jointed appendages.   **d.** bilateral symmetry.

_____ **2.** Before an arthropod molts, a new exoskeleton

    a. grows on top of its old one.   **b.** must be found.

    c. cannot grow.   **d.** grows beneath its old one.

_____ **3.** Aquatic arthropods exchange gases through

    a. tracheal tubes.   **b.** gills.

    c. their exoskeleton.   **d.** book lungs.

_____ **4.** How many pairs of jointed appendages do arachnids have?

    a. two   **b.** four   **c.** three   **d.** six

_____ **5.** When a spider bites, it uses its

    a. chelicerae.   **b.** mandibles.   **c.** pedipalps.   **d.** silk glands.

_____ **6.** In spiders, the exchange of gases takes place in

    a. book lungs.   **b.** lungs.   **c.** gills.   **d.** spiracles.

_____ **7.** Most insects have one pair of _____ that are used to sense vibrations, food, and pheromones in the environment.

    a. pedipalps   **b.** wings   **c.** antennae   **d.** eyes

_____ **8.** The typical tick body consists of _____ segment(s).

    a. one   **b.** two   **c.** three   **d.** four

_____ **9.** Crabs, lobsters, shrimps, and pill bugs are members of the class

    a. Insecta.   **b.** Chilopoda.   **c.** Crustacea.   **d.** Arachnida.

_____ **10.** The stages of incomplete metamorphosis are

    a. egg, larva, pupa, adult.   **b.** larva, pupa, nymph.

    c. egg, larva, adult.   **d.** egg, nymph, adult.

_____ **11.** Grasshoppers have

    a. two compound eyes and three simple eyes.

    b. three compound eyes and two simple eyes.

    c. two compound eyes and two simple eyes.

    d. none of these.

Chapter 28 **Arthropods,** *continued*

Understanding Main Ideas (Part B)

Answer the following questions.

1. How are insects adapted to living on land?

_____

_____

_____

_____

_____

2. What are four uses of the jointed appendages of arthropods? Give examples.

_____

_____

_____

3. How do compound eyes aid arthropods?

_____

_____

4. How do web-spinning spiders create their webs?

_____

_____

_____

5. It is believed that arthropods evolved from the annelids. What differences, present in the arthropod structure, make arthropods better adapted to their environment?

_____

_____

_____

_____

_____

Chapter 28 **Arthropods,** *continued*

Thinking Critically

Answer the following questions.

1. Fossils reveal that the horseshoe crab has remained almost unchanged for 500 million years. Why would an arthropod such as the horseshoe crab fail to evolve? What can you infer about the rate of change of its seaside environment?

_____

_____

_____

2. How are insects' different modes of feeding reflected in their mouthparts?

_____

_____

_____

3. Why do arthropods lack muscle strength after molting?

_____

_____

_____

4. Barnacles are primarily sessile, filter-feeding crustaceans that live on rocks in the ocean. Many barnacles, however, live on the backs of gray whales. Compare and contrast these two environments with regard to barnacle survival.

_____

_____

_____

_____

5. Suppose a new species of insect is introduced into an area as a natural control to rid the area of other insect pests. What are some possible advantages and disadvantages of doing this?

_____

_____

_____

_____

Chapter 28 Arthropods, *continued*

Applying Scientific Methods

Many invertebrates, from hydrozoans to mollusks and arthropods, have specialized sense organs for monitoring gravity. This sensitivity is related to their sense of equilibrium. Arthropods can sense when they are upright and when they are turned over. The organ that senses changes with respect to gravity is the statocyst, located at the base of each antennule of the crayfish. A statocyst is a chamber that contains sensory neurons with hairlike fibers and a solid mass of sand grains or hardened calcium salts. These grains push against the hair cells, which then trigger signals in associated sensory neurons.

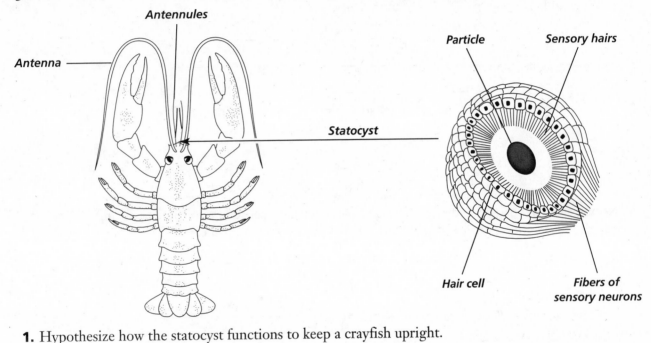

1. Hypothesize how the statocyst functions to keep a crayfish upright.

_____

_____

_____

_____

2. Suppose that scientists on board a space shuttle wanted to investigate the effects of microgravity on the uprighting reflex of crayfish. What experiment might they propose?

_____

_____

_____

_____

_____

_____

Chapter 28 Arthropods, continued

Applying Scientific Methods   continued

3. Which variable would be tested?

_____

_____

_____

4. What would be the control?

_____

_____

_____

5. What could scientists do if their hypothesis was not supported by the data?

_____

_____

6. Noting that hydrozoans and mollusks also have specialized sense organs for monitoring gravity, what experiment might be proposed to compare this mechanism among species?

_____

_____

_____

_____

_____

Chapter 29 Echinoderms and Invertebrate Chordates

Reviewing Vocabulary

Write the word or phrase that best completes each statement. Use these choices:

ampulla	madreporite	regeneration
notochord	tube feet	dorsal hollow nerve cord
pedicellariae	gill slits	water vascular system
rays	sea squirt	

1. Echinoderms have _____, which are hollow, thin-walled structures that each have a suction cup on the end.

2. The sievelike, disc-shaped opening in an echinoderm's body through which water enters and leaves is called the _____.

3. _____, the replacement or regrowth of missing body parts, is a common feature in echinoderms.

4. The _____, paired openings located in the pharynx behind the mouth, are present only during embryonic development in some chordates.

5. The _____ is a round, muscular structure that is located on the opposite end from the suction cup on the tube feet.

6. Another name for a tunicate is a(n) _____.

7. The long, spine-covered, tapered arms of sea stars are called _____.

8. The _____ regulates locomotion, gas exchange, food capture, and excretion in an echinoderm.

9. The _____ is a semirigid, rodlike structure in chordates that is replaced by the backbone in vertebrates.

10. In chordates, the _____ is a hollow tube of cells surrounding a fluid-filled canal that lies above the notochord.

11. Pincerlike appendages called _____ are modified spines found on sea stars.

Chapter 29 Echinoderms and Invertebrate Chordates, *continued*

Understanding Main Ideas (Part A)

Match each letter on the drawing of the sea star with the appropriate term that follows.

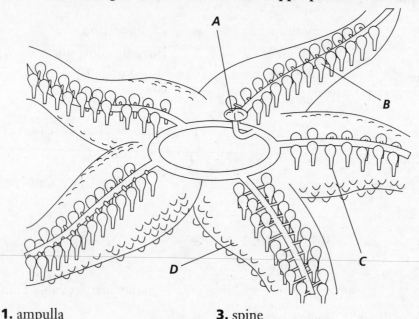

_____ **1.** ampulla   _____ **3.** spine

_____ **2.** madreporite   _____ **4.** tube foot

5. Write the names of the structures listed above that are part of the water vascular system.

_____

_____

In the space at the left, write the letter of the word or phrase that best completes the statement.

_____ **6.** A sea star can hold tightly to the surface it is touching because of the

        a. sieve in the madreporite.   **b.** endoskeleton.

        c. suction in the tube feet.   **d.** eyespots.

_____ **7.** You could recognize an adult sea squirt as a chordate by its

        a. notochord.   **b.** dorsal hollow nerve cord.

        c. gill slits.   **d.** spines.

_____ **8.** An animal that retains its chordate features throughout life is the

        a. sea star.   **b.** sand dollar.   **c.** sea squirt.   **d.** lancelet.

_____ **9.** The type of symmetry found in adult echinoderms is

        a. horizontal.   **b.** radial.   **c.** bilateral.   **d.** regional.

Chapter 29 Echinoderms and Invertebrate Chordates, *continued*

Chapter Assessment

Understanding Main Ideas (Part B)

1. Describe two characteristics that set echinoderms apart from other organisms in the animal kingdom.

_____

_____

_____

2. What are the functions of the water vascular system?

_____

_____

_____

3. What three methods do echinoderms use to get food?

_____

_____

_____

_____

4. Describe the nervous system of echinoderms.

_____

_____

_____

_____

5. Why are echinoderms thought to be related to chordates?

_____

_____

_____

_____

6. Describe how a sea star feeds on a clam.

_____

_____

_____

_____

Chapter 29 — Echinoderms and Invertebrate Chordates, continued

Thinking Critically

Answer the following questions.

1. When a fossil sea urchin is found with a large number of tube feet specialized for gas exchange, a paleoecologist infers that the sea urchin once lived in warm, tropical water. What would be the reasoning behind such an inference?

_____

_____

_____

_____

_____

_____

2. Fertilization in echinoderms may occur in areas where ocean currents are strong or in calm tide pools. Which of these areas would result in a higher rate of fertilization? Explain.

_____

_____

_____

3. Researchers induced male sea urchins to spawn out of season by placing them in an isotonic solution of potassium chloride. They recorded the number of males induced to spawn at different lunar phases: half moon (H), full moon (F), and new moon (N). From the table shown at the right, what can you conclude about the influence of the lunar cycle on spawning?

_____

_____

_____

_____

_____

Lunar phase	Total No.	No. induced to spawn	% induced to spawn
H	15	12	80
H	8	8	100
H	7	4	57
H	15	14	93
F	12	10	83
F	22	15	68
F	25	16	64
F	18	16	88
N	12	12	100
N	22	10	45
N	16	7	44

Chapter 29 **Echinoderms and Invertebrate Chordates,** *continued*

Applying Scientific Methods

Sand dollars have a system of food grooves on their underside. When food-containing sediment passes over their upper surface, fine particles of food in the sediment drop between the spines on that surface and are carried to the underside. There the fine matter passes to the food grooves. Food particles are captured by the tube feet that border the grooves and are helped along to the mouth.

Suppose that you are a taxonomist confronted with the task of determining the relationship among several families of the order Clypeasteroida, to which the sand dollars belong. You have many fossil sand dollars and are studying the differences in the arrangement of their food grooves. Refer to the diagrams.

1. Plan a way to show the relationships among the six families of sand dollars shown below, all of which belong to the order Clypeasteroida illustrated in the phylogenetic diagram to the right. Base your relationships on the arrangement of the food grooves. Show where each family belongs in the phylogenetic tree. Write the letter of the correct position of each family in the blank below each diagram. (Hint: Consider the number of grooves and the number and position of branches in relation to the mouth or the outer edge of the organism.)

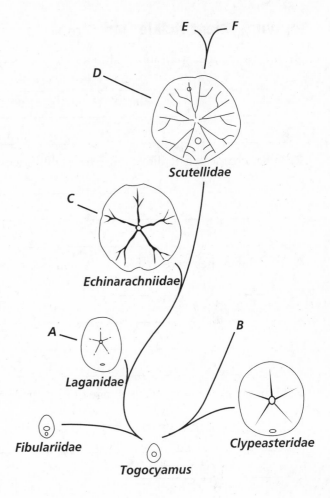

Scutellidae

Echinarachniidae

Laganidae

Fibulariidae

Togocyamus

Clypeasteridae

Arachnoididae

Astriclypeidae

Dendrasteridae

Mellitidae

Rotulidae

Scutellaster

_____ _____ _____ _____ _____ _____

Chapter 29 Echinoderms and Invertebrate Chordates, *continued*

Applying Scientific Methods continued

2. Which families were most difficult to place? Explain.

_____

_____

_____

3. What characteristic did you use to establish where to place the Mellitidae?

_____

_____

_____

4. Which families were easiest to place in side branches that did not further evolve? Explain.

_____

_____

_____

_____

5. Hypothesize about the advantage of food grooves on the underside of sand dollars.

_____

_____

_____

_____

_____

6. Why would taxonomists use food grooves to trace the evolution of sand dollars?

_____

_____

_____

_____

7. Which characteristic of the food grooves seems to have survived variations in the sand dollars' environment?

_____

_____

_____

Chapter 30 Fishes and Amphibians

Reviewing Vocabulary

Write the word or phrase that best completes the statement. Use these choices:

cartilage	scales	ectotherms
spawning	fins	swim bladder
lateral line system	vocal cords	

1. All classes of fishes possess a(n) _____ , composed of fluid-filled canals arranged along the sides of the body, which permit fishes to detect movement and vibrations in the water.

2. Many bony fishes possess a(n) _____ , which is a thin-walled, internal sac found just below the backbone. By altering the amount of gas in this structure, a fish can control its depth in the water.

3. The skeletons of lampreys, hagfishes, and sharks are made of a tough, flexible material called

   _____ .

4. Amphibians are _____ because their body temperature changes with the temperature of the surroundings.

5. Frogs and toads have bands of tissue in their throats called _____ , which are capable of producing a wide range of sounds.

6. The _____ of a fish can be toothlike, diamond-shaped, cone-shaped, or round. These structures are thin bony plates formed from the skin.

7. Breeding in fishes is called _____ .

8. Fishes depend on their _____ for balance, steering, and swimming. These structures are fan-shaped membranes supported by the endoskeleton.

Chapter 30 **Fishes and Amphibians,** *continued*

Understanding Main Ideas (Part A)

In the space at the left, write the letter of the word or phrase that best completes the statement.

_____ **1.** Lampreys are parasites that attach themselves to other fishes by suckerlike mouths because they lack

    a. teeth.   **b.** fins.   **c.** jaws.   **d.** a skeleton.

_____ **2.** A fish can detect movement and vibrations in the water by means of its

    a. keen sense of smell.   **b.** scales.

    c. excellent vision.   **d.** lateral line system.

_____ **3.** Fishes have great flexibility when they swim because they have

    a. separate vertebrae.   **b.** no limbs.

    c. scales.   **d.** no skin.

_____ **4.** Frogs have a tympanic membrane that

    a. allows water to pass into cells.

    b. picks up vibrations from water or air and transmits them to the inner ear.

    c. protects cells from harmful chemicals.

    d. allows nutrients to enter the body.

_____ **5.** Scientists believe that amphibians evolved from

    a. sharks.   **b.** aquatic tetrapods.

    c. lampreys.   **d.** salmon.

_____ **6.** Bony fishes belong to the class

    a. Agnatha.   **b.** Osteichthyes.   **c.** Amphibia.   **d.** Chondrichthyes.

Write the word or phrase that best completes the statement.

7. Fish have a _____ -chambered heart.

8. Blood flow in fishes is slow because most of the pumping action is used to _____

_____ .

9. Sharks have _____ fertilization.

10. Amphibians live mostly in warm environments because they are ectotherms whose body temperature

changes with the _____ .

11. In amphibians, the _____ is the most important organ for gas exchange.

Understanding Main Ideas (Part B)

Answer the following questions.

1. Why was the evolution of jaws an important event in vertebrate history?

_____

_____

2. How do members of class Osteichthyes differ from members of class Chondrichthyes and class Agnatha?

_____

_____

3. How does blood circulate in a fish?

_____

_____

_____

_____

4. What is the function of the swim bladder in bony fishes?

_____

_____

_____

5. What were the advantages of life on land for early amphibians? What were the disadvantages of living on land?

_____

_____

_____

_____

6. How does the three-chambered heart equip amphibians for life on land?

_____

_____

_____

Thinking Critically

Answer the following questions.

1. What may have been the selective pressures that favored the evolution of amphibians?

_____

_____

_____

_____

2. How might being able to jump have been a factor in the success of frogs on land?

_____

_____

_____

3. In what way does metamorphosis in frogs represent a shortened version of evolution that took place over countless generations?

_____

_____

_____

_____

_____

_____

4. In what way is hearing in humans similar to lateral-line reception in fish?

_____

_____

_____

5. Removing the thyroid gland from a tadpole will prevent it from undergoing metamorphosis. If the gland is reimplanted, the tadpole will then undergo metamorphosis. Make a hypothesis to explain this observation.

_____

_____

_____

Applying Scientific Methods

Many investigators would like to know whether sleep has an adaptive function. Some of the studies of sleep focus on fishes. Do fishes sleep? Although fishes cannot close their eyes because they lack eyelids, they do remain immobile for a period of time. At these times, the fishes are less sensitive to disturbances. To an investigator, this means they are asleep. Fish exhibit other signs that are indicative of sleep, such as a decreased rate of respiration, a decreased reaction to sound, and a lessened response to the approach of foreign objects.

1. Propose a hypothesis explaining the adaptive value of sleep for fish.

_____

_____

_____

_____

2. Plan an experiment to test whether fishes sleep. Because 24-hour observations are not feasible, you may want your plan to include recordings by infrared videos, electromechanical sensors, ultrasound telemetry, or infrared photo cells. Another approach might be to change the fishes' sleep patterns by reversing the patterns of light and darkness during a 24-hour period. You could then monitor oxygen consumption as an indicator of the level of the fishes' activity. Make sure that there is a shelter for the fish to go to during the rest phase. Not all fish use a shelter, but many do. Plan a chart or graph to show your findings.

_____

_____

3. What will be the variable in this investigation?

_____

_____

4. What will be the control?

_____

_____

5. What kind of correlation would you expect to find between any of the variables that you test and the depth of sleep or degree of insensitivity to disturbances?

_____

_____

_____

Applying Scientific Methods   continued

6. One nocturnal fish, *Tinca tinca*, has been observed to lie at the bottom of a tank for periods of 15–20 minutes during the day without moving. Its respiratory rate at that time is 65 percent of its nocturnal respiratory rate. What would you expect to happen to the respiratory rate of *Tinca tinca* if lights were left on at night and the tank was darkened during the day?

_____

_____

Name   Date   Class

Chapter 31 Reptiles and Birds

Reviewing Vocabulary

Complete the paragraphs by writing the correct term on the appropriate line. A term may be used more than once. Use these choices.

amniotic egg	feathers	sternum
endotherms	incubate	Jacobson's organ

Although amphibians preceded reptiles in living on land, amphibians retained their dependence on water for reproduction and the early part of their life cycle. Reptiles completely broke their ties to water. For example, the **(1)** _____ was an adaptation that liberated reptiles from their reliance on water for reproduction. The **(2)** _____ contains membranes that protect the embryo and provide it with nourishment while it develops in a terrestrial environment.

Reptiles also developed sense organs that allowed them to receive important information about their environment. The heads of some snakes have heat-sensitive organs that allow them to detect the presence of warm-blooded animals. Snakes and lizards also have a keen sense of smell. These reptiles flick their tongues to sense chemicals in the air. When the tongue is drawn back into the mouth, it is inserted into a structure called **(3)** _____ , where the chemical molecules are analyzed.

Unlike reptiles, which are ectotherms, birds are **(4)** _____ .
(5) _____ maintain a constant body temperature that is not dependent on the environmental temperature. Birds **(6)** _____ , or sit on their eggs to keep them warm, turning the eggs periodically so that they develop properly.

Other adaptations of birds aid in flight. The **(7)** _____ of a bird, which looks like the keel of a sailing boat, is a large breastbone to which powerful flight muscles are attached.
(8) _____ are lightweight, modified scales that provide insulation and enable flight. A bird uses its beak to rub oil from a gland near its tail onto the **(9)** _____ to waterproof them.

Chapter Assessment

Understanding Main Ideas (Part A)

Match each letter that appears on
the diagram of the amniotic egg
with the appropriate term below.

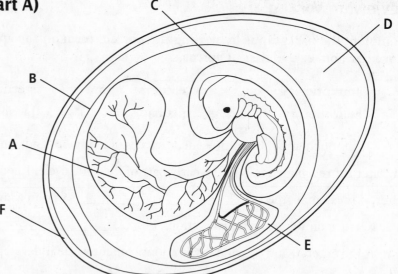

_____ **1.** albumen

_____ **2.** allantois

_____ **3.** amnion

_____ **4.** chorion

_____ **5.** shell

_____ **6.** yolk

Match each of the terms above with its function in the amniotic egg.

 7. The main food supply for the embryo is the _____ .

 8. The _____ is a membrane filled with fluid that cushions the embryo.

 9. The _____ is the outer membrane surrounding the yolk, allantois, and amnion
    that allows for gas exchange.

10. The embryo excretes nitrogenous wastes into the _____ .

11. The clear part of the egg is the _____ .

**In the space at the left, write the letter of the word or phrase that best completes the statement or
answers the question.**

_____ **12.** A rattlesnake detects your presence by means of its
         a. rattle.   **b.** heat-sensitive organs.
         c. sharp eyesight.   **d.** keen hearing.

_____ **13.** A snake flicks its tongue as a
         a. sign of aggression.   **b.** way of breathing.
         c. warning.   **d.** way to test chemicals in the air.

_____ **14.** Which structures do birds share with no other animals?
         a. shelled eggs   **b.** clawed toes
         c. feathers   **d.** scales on their feet

Understanding Main Ideas (Part B)

Answer the following questions.

1. How does a reptile's scaly skin make it suited to life on land?

_____

_____

2. In what way did the skeletal changes in which the legs became positioned beneath the body allow reptiles to exploit resources and niches on land?

_____

_____

_____

3. How did the amniotic egg liberate reptiles from a dependence on water for reproduction?

_____

_____

4. How do birds resemble reptiles?

_____

_____

5. How is a bird's body adapted for flight?

_____

_____

_____

_____

_____

_____

6. How is being endothermic both an advantage and a disadvantage for birds?

_____

_____

_____

_____

Thinking Critically

Answer the following questions.

1. At times, the only fossil remains of a dinosaur biped are its footprints. Scientists use footprints to estimate the dinosaur's size. In bipeds, the footprint length is about one-quarter to one-fifth the length of the dinosaur's leg. If the track of a dinosaur measures 30 cm in length, estimate the range of the length of the dinosaur's leg.

   _____

   _____

   _____

2. The feet of Canada geese and other birds that walk on ice have been found to have a much lower temperature than their bodies. Hypothesize why this is a useful adaptation for these birds.

   _____

   _____

   _____

   _____

3. Why did the discovery of the fossil *Archaeopteryx* support the view that birds evolved from reptiles?

   _____

   _____

   _____

4. A large, sluggish turkey has a heart that is about 0.12 percent of its body weight. A tiny, active hummingbird has a heart that is 2.4 percent of its body weight. What generalization might you make from this information?

   _____

   _____

   _____

5. An old saying states, "Birds of a feather flock together." What are at least three advantages of birds flocking together?

   _____

   _____

Applying Scientific Methods

Each species of reptile has a high and a low body temperature beyond which the animal will die. Between these high and low temperatures, there is a critical maximum and a critical minimum temperature, above which and below which, respectively, the reptile loses its powers of locomotion. Temperature also influences a reptile's ability to digest food, as the table below shows.

Temperature	Rate of Digestion
35°C	normal or slightly below normal
25°C	normal
15°C	far below normal
5°C	zero

1. Interpret the table. What is the optimal temperature at which the reptile would feed? Explain.

_____

_____

_____

2. Propose a hypothesis explaining why digestion depends on body temperature.

_____

_____

_____

_____

Plan an experiment in which you will determine the critical minimum and critical maximum temperatures of a species of lizard. For example, to find the critical minimum temperature, you might slowly cool the area where the lizards are detained, continuously recording their temperatures and that of the environment.

3. How will you know when the critical minimum temperature for this species has been reached?

_____

_____

_____

Chapter
31 **Reptiles and Birds,** *continued*

Applying Scientific Methods   continued

4. How will you find the lizards' critical maximum temperature?

_____

_____

_____

5. Why would it be a bad idea to leave the lizards at the critical minimum or the critical maximum temperature?

_____

_____

_____

6. What is the independent variable in this experiment?

_____

_____

7. What control would you plan?

_____

_____

8. In summer, certain lizards have a critical minimum temperature of 2.5°C. In winter, these same lizards have a critical minimum temperature of –1.2°C. The lizards do not freeze at the winter critical minimum temperature, even though it is below the freezing point for their blood. Propose a hypothesize explaining how the lizards can avoid freezing at temperatures below 0°C.

_____

_____

_____

9. The critical minimum temperature can be used to distinguish between two species. Explain how this characteristic may be an adaptive factor in lizards.

_____

_____

_____

_____

_____

_____

_____

Chapter

32 Mammals

Reviewing Vocabulary

Write the word or phrase that best completes the statement. Use these choices:

cud chewing	gland	monotreme	therapsids
diaphragm	mammary glands	placenta	uterus
gestation	marsupial	placental mammal	

1. A _____ is the sheet of muscle located beneath the lungs that is used to expand and contract the chest cavity of mammals.

2. A _____ is a group of cells that secretes substances needed by an animal for temperature regulation, reproduction, or other life processes.

3. _____ is an adaptation that enables many hoofed mammals to break down the cellulose of plant cell walls into nutrients that they can use and absorb.

4. Female mammals have _____ , which secrete milk, enabling mammals to nourish their young until the young are mature enough to find food.

5. Scientists can trace the origins of the first mammals back to _____ , a group of reptilian ancestors that had features of both reptiles and mammals.

6. The _____ is a hollow muscular organ in female mammals in which the development of offspring takes place.

7. In most mammals, nourishment of the young inside the uterus occurs through an organ called the _____ , which develops during pregnancy. This organ is instrumental in passing oxygen to and removing wastes from the developing embryo.

8. The time during which young placental mammals develop inside their mother is called _____ .

9. A _____ is a mammal in which the young have a second period of development inside a pouch made of skin and hair found on the outside of the mother's body.

10. A _____ is a mammal that reproduces by laying eggs.

11. A mammal that carries its young inside the uterus until birth is a _____ .

Understanding Main Ideas (Part A)

In the space at the left, write the letter of the word or phrase that best completes the statement or answers the question.

_____ 1. The main advantage of hair is that it

    a. protects the skin.   **b.** provides mucus.

    c. conserves body heat.   **d.** can be shed.

_____ 2. A jaw that has small incisors and canines but large premolars and molars may belong to a

    a. beaver.   **b.** dolphin.   **c.** horse.   **d.** wolf.

_____ 3. The folds in the mammalian brain

    a. increase the brain's surface area.

    b. secrete necessary fluids.

    c. form ridges for storing learned behavior.

    d. transfer heat from the body to the environment.

_____ 4. Most marsupials are found in

    a. America.   **b.** Antarctica.   **c.** Australia.   **d.** Africa.

_____ 5. Which of these mammals is a monotreme?

    a. opossum   **b.** kangaroo   **c.** chimpanzee   **d.** platypus

In the space at the left, write <u>true</u> if the statement is true. If the statement is false, change the italicized word to make it true.

_____ 6. Marsupials in continents other than Australia lost out in competition with *monotremes.*

_____ 7. Teeth called *incisors* are used to puncture and tear the flesh of prey.

_____ 8. *Molars* are used for crushing and grinding food.

_____ 9. The most intelligent mammals are *carnivores.*

_____ 10. The golden age of mammals was the *Mesozoic* era.

_____ 11. In most mammals, the nourishment of young inside the uterus occurs through the *placenta.*

_____ 12. Both mammals and reptiles share one aspect of their reproductive cycle: *external* fertilization.

Understanding Main Ideas (Part B)

Answer the following questions.

1. How do a mammal's sweat glands help regulate body temperature?

_____

_____

2. How does the diaphragm aid a mammal in taking in oxygen?

_____

_____

3. Why is cud chewing beneficial to some hoofed animals?

_____

_____

_____

_____

4. What reproductive strategies help mammals to be successful?

_____

_____

5. List three features that characterize mammals.

_____

_____

_____

6. What characteristics do mammals and birds have in common?

_____

_____

_____

Thinking Critically

Use the table to answer the questions that follow.

Mammal	Body Mass (kg)	Average Heart Rate (beats/minute)
Sheep	50	70–80
Harbor porpoise	170	40–110
Horse	380–450	34–55
Elephant	2000–3000	25–50

1. Which animal has the highest body mass?

_____

2. Which animal has the lowest heart rate?

_____

3. Based on the table, what happens to heart rate as body mass decreases?

_____

_____

4. Would you expect a squirrel's heart rate to be higher or lower than a sheep's? Explain.

_____

_____

Answer the following question.

5. The fat content of the milk produced in the mammary glands of humans differs from that of marine mammals. In human milk, fat makes up 3 to 5 percent of total nutrients. In the milk of marine mammals, fat makes up 30 to 40 percent of total nutrients. How would you account for this difference in fat content?

_____

_____

_____

_____

Chapter 32 Mammals, *continued*

Applying Scientific Methods

Some mammals have a wide range of heart rates. For example, a resting brown bat has a heart rate of a little more than 450 beats per minute. The graph at the right shows what happens to a bat's heart rate during flight and at the end of flight.

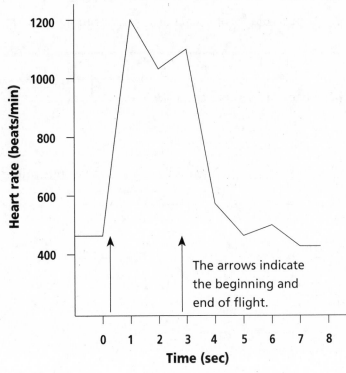

Heart Rate of Brown Bat During Flight

The arrows indicate the beginning and end of flight.

1. What initial change occurs in the bat's heart rate during flight?

_____

_____

2. How long does it take for the heart rate to reach its maximum?

_____

_____

_____

_____

_____

3. How long does the bat fly?

_____

_____

4. After the flight, how long does it take the bat's heart rate to stabilize at its resting value?

_____

5. Hypothesize why there is such a wide range between the resting heart rate and the flight heart rate.

_____

_____

_____

_____

6. Plan an experiment in which you could determine a bat's heart rate at rest and during flight. Be sure to include the instruments you would use and how you would record your data.

_____

_____

_____

Applying Scientific Methods   continued

7. What would be the dependent variable in this experiment?

_____

_____

8. What would be the control?

_____

_____

9. What other experiments dealing with heart rate might you carry out on bats?

_____

_____

_____

Chapter
33 Animal Behavior

Reviewing Vocabulary

Match the definition in Column A with the term in Column B.

Column A	Column B
_____ **1.** Complex pattern of innate behavior	**a.** aggressive behavior
_____ **2.** Physical space that contains the breeding area, feeding area, or potential mates of an animal	**b.** behavior
_____ **3.** Learning in which an animal uses previous experience to respond to a new situation	**c.** communication
_____ **4.** Behavior that is used to intimidate another animal of the same species	**d.** courtship behavior
_____ **5.** Learning by association	**e.** fight-or-flight response
_____ **6.** Anything an animal does in response to a stimulus	**f.** imprinting
_____ **7.** Use of symbols to represent ideas	**g.** insight
_____ **8.** State of reduced metabolism that occurs in mammals living under intense heat	**h.** instinct
_____ **9.** Exchange of information that results in a change of behavior	**i.** language
_____ **10.** Behavior that mobilizes the body for greater activity	**j.** motivation
_____ **11.** Inherited behavior	**k.** territory
_____ **12.** Form of behavior in which an animal, soon after hatching or birth, forms a social attachment to another object	**l.** innate behavior
_____ **13.** A form of social ranking within a group in which some individuals are more subordinate than others	**m.** dominance hierarchy
_____ **14.** Behavior that males and females of a species carry out before mating	**n.** conditioning
_____ **15.** An internal need that causes an animal to act	**o.** estivation

Understanding Main Ideas (Part A)

In the space at the left, write the letter of the word or phrase that best completes the statement or answers the question.

_____ 1. When a male sea lion patrols the area of beach where his female sea lions rest, he is displaying

       a. habituation.   **b.** pecking order.

       c. territorial behavior.   **d.** circadian rhythm.

_____ 2. When a bird sings to signal others of the same species to keep away, it is showing signs of

       a. cheerfulness.   **b.** insight.

       c. conditioning.   **d.** aggressive behavior.

_____ 3. Which biologist first demonstrated conditioning in dogs?

       a. Dimitri Mendeleev   **b.** Bruno Huber

       c. Ivan Pavlov   **d.** Gregor Mendel

_____ 4. Which of the following is *not* an example of the use of a pheromone?

       a. Wolves mark their territories by urinating at the boundaries.

       b. Hyenas give off an odor that keeps different clans of hyenas apart.

       c. Poisonous snakes wind around each other and butt heads.

       d. Skunks release a rotten odor when they are threatened.

_____ 5. Owls sleep during the day and are awake at night because of their kind of

       a. estivation.   **b.** habituation.   **c.** circadian rhythm.   **d.** conditioning.

_____ 6. For trial-and-error learning to take place, an animal must receive

       a. a dose of imprinting.   **b.** a reward for a particular response.

       c. conditioning.   **d.** habituation.

_____ 7. Which of these is an example of imprinting?

       a. Young ducklings follow their mother.

       b. A bird makes a nest of grasses and twigs.

       c. Your cat rubs against your ankles when you open a can of cat food.

       d. A chimpanzee searches for a longer pole to reach for a distant fruit.

_____ 8. Animal communication can occur through

       a. sounds.   **b.** touches.   **c.** smells.   **d.** all of these.

_____ 9. Solving math problems is an example of

       a. insight.   **b.** conditioning.

       c. innate behavior.   **d.** rhythmic response.

Understanding Main Ideas (Part B)

Answer the following questions.

1. How does courtship behavior aid survival?

_____

_____

_____

_____

2. Explain the role genes play in animal behavior.

_____

_____

_____

_____

3. In what way does an instinct differ from a reflex?

_____

_____

_____

4. In a fight between two males of a species, how does the defeated male avoid serious injury?

_____

_____

5. What are three effects of setting up territories?

_____

_____

6. Which external and internal cues stimulate an animal to migrate?

_____

_____

7. Birds are frightened away by a scarecrow at first, but after a few days, they ignore it and come back to feed. Explain this behavior.

_____

_____

_____

Chapter 33 Animal Behavior, continued

Thinking Critically

Answer the following questions.

Black-headed gulls carry away eggshells of their already-hatched chicks. The animal behaviorist, Niko Tinbergen, hypothesized that this behavior makes it less likely that crow predators will discover nests and attack eggs that still contain live chicks. Tinbergen carried out an experiment to test his hypothesis. Refer to the table below to answer the questions.

Distance from eggshell to egg (cm)	Crow predation		Risk of predation (%)
	Eggs taken	**Eggs not taken**	
15	63	87	42
100	48	102	32
200	32	118	21

1. How do the data support Tinbergen's hypothesis?

_____

_____

_____

2. Some eggs were still taken by crows even when the eggshells were 200 cm from the eggs. Hypothesize what this shows.

_____

_____

_____

3. Do you think the gulls' behavior is instinctive or learned? Give reasons for your choice.

_____

_____

_____

_____

_____

Chapter 33 Animal Behavior, *continued*

Applying Scientific Methods

An animal behaviorist confronted with a particular behavior will try to determine its usefulness to the animal. One such behavior is exhibited by the Thomson's gazelle. In the presence of a predator, the gazelle jumps about a half meter off the ground with all four legs held straight and stiff and with the white rump patch clearly visible. This behavior is called stotting.

One behaviorist, Timothy M. Caro, devised eleven hypotheses that might explain stotting in gazelles. Here are a few of them.

A. Stotting warns other gazelles, particularly offspring, that a predator is near.

B. Stotting signals other gazelles to flee as a group, lessening the predator's chances of isolating a victim from the herd.

C. Stotting confuses the predator, keeping it from focusing on one animal.

D. Stotting communicates to the predator that it has been seen by the gazelle.

1. Which of these four hypotheses do you think is most plausible? Give reasons for your choice.

_____

_____

_____

Caro then set about eliminating some of the hypotheses. First, he made predictions about how the gazelles would behave if a certain hypothesis were correct. In the table below, write <u>Yes</u> or <u>No</u> in each empty box after you consider each of the hypotheses and how it would affect the gazelles' behavior.

Questions to Be Answered	Predictions Based on Hypotheses			
	A	B	C	D
Would solitary gazelles stott?				
Would groups of gazelles stott?				
Would gazelles display the white rump to predators?				
Would they display the white rump to other gazelles?				

2. Caro continued his investigation to try to eliminate some of the hypotheses. He discovered that a solitary gazelle sometimes stotts when a cheetah approaches. Which hypotheses does this eliminate? Why?

_____

_____

_____

Chapter 33 Animal Behavior, *continued*

Applying Scientific Methods continued

3. Caro found that all stotting gazelles turn their rumps toward the predator. Which hypotheses does this eliminate?

_____

_____

_____

4. Explain which hypothesis now appears to be the most plausible.

_____

_____

_____

5. How would letting the predator know that it has been seen benefit the gazelle?

_____

_____

_____

_____

Chapter 34 Protection, Support, and Locomotion

Reviewing Vocabulary

Match the definition in Column A with the term in Column B.

Column A	Column B
_____ **1.** Where two or more bones meet	**a.** ligament
_____ **2.** Fluid-filled sac between bones	**b.** marrow
_____ **3.** Potential bone cell found in cartilage of embryo	**c.** melanin
_____ **4.** Soft tissue that fills center cavities of bones	**d.** osteoblast
_____ **5.** Protein in dead epidermal cells that protects underlying cells and gives skin its elasticity	**e.** bursa
_____ **6.** Cell pigment that colors skin and protects it from solar radiation	**f.** sarcomere
_____ **7.** Band of tissue connecting bone to bone	**g.** keratin
_____ **8.** Smaller fiber in a muscle fiber	**h.** joint
_____ **9.** The functional unit of a myofibril	**i.** myofibril

Compare and contrast each pair of related terms.

10. compact bone, spongy bone

_____

_____

11. axial skeleton, appendicular skeleton

_____

_____

_____

12. voluntary muscle, involuntary muscle

_____

_____

13. epidermis, dermis

_____

Chapter 34 Protection, Support, and Locomotion, *continued*

Chapter Assessment

Understanding Main Ideas (Part A)

Write the word or phrase that best completes the statement.

1. Beneath the scab of a wound, _____ begin to multiply to fill in the gap.

2. _____ produces red blood cells, some white blood cells, and cell fragments involved in blood clotting.

3. The mineral _____ , found in dairy products, is a critical part of the diet for healthy, strong bones.

4. Contraction of _____ muscle, the muscle of internal organs, is slow and prolonged.

5. Bones grow in length at the _____ of the bone. They grow in diameter on the _____ surface of the bone.

6. Muscle strength depends on the _____ of the fibers and the number of fibers that _____ at one time.

7. When an inadequate supply of oxygen is available to meet a muscle cell's oxygen needs, _____ respiration becomes the primary source of ATP.

Answer the following questions.

8. Why is the skin considered an organ? Name two important functions of skin.

_____

_____

_____

_____

9. Explain what causes a sprain and what the effects are.

_____

_____

_____

Understanding Main Ideas (Part B)

In the space at the left, write the letter of the word, phrase, or sentence that best completes the statement or answers the question.

_____ **1.** The skin regulates the temperature of the body on a hot day by

    a. closing the pores.   **b.** dilating the capillaries.

    c. constricting the blood.   **d.** reducing access to the exterior.

_____ **2.** After suffering widespread third-degree burns, the burn victim

    a. is unlikely to incur bacterial infection.

    b. recovers in a short time.

    c. has a harder time regulating body temperature.

    d. has slight damage to cells of the dermis.

_____ **3.** Which of the following examples illustrates a pivot joint in use?

    a. You wind up to pitch a baseball.   **b.** You wave good-bye to a friend.

    c. You kick a football.   **d.** You look behind you.

_____ **4.** By age 20, a person's bones stop growing because

    a. bone-forming cells are no longer present.

    b. less calcium is present in the body.

    c. hormones cause the growth centers at the ends of bones to degenerate.

    d. bone cells receive less oxygen and nutrients at that time.

Answer the following questions.

5. How does the sliding filament theory explain muscle contraction?

_____

_____

_____

6. How does the buildup of lactic acid in muscle cells result in more oxygen being delivered to your cells?

_____

_____

_____

7. Explain one beneficial and one harmful effect of exposure to sunlight.

_____

_____

Thinking Critically

Because it usually goes unnoticed until back pain or a spontaneous fracture occurs, osteoporosis is often referred to as the silent disease. This skeletal disease is characterized by a decrease in bone mass resulting in bones so porous they break as a result of even everyday activities. Though most prevalent after the age of 50, intervention before the age of 30 can significantly decrease the risk of developing osteoporosis later in life. The table below shows some of the risk factors associated with developing osteoporosis later in life. Use the table to answer questions 1 and 2.

Risk Factors	Description
Age	After the middle or later forties, bone mass begins to decrease.
Alcohol Intake	Excessive alcohol intake increases the risk of osteoporosis, especially in men.
Body frame/weight	Small-framed women and men are at greater risk for developing osteoporosis.
Cigarette Smoking	Smokers generally have lower bone densities than nonsmokers.
Diet	Calcium intake below the RDA throughout life increases the risk of osteoporosis.
Genetics	Having a close relative with osteoporosis or an osteoporotic fracture increases the risk of developing the disease.
Gender	Though both men and women develop osteoporosis, women are about four to five times more likely to develop the disease.
Physical Activity	Regular physical activity, especially weight-bearing exercise, increases bone density.

1. Which of the factors listed in the table are controllable? Which are not controllable?

_____

_____

2. Why would weight-bearing exercises increase bone density? _____

_____

_____

Answer the following questions.

3. Bone fractures in children are often different from fractures in adults. Explain why this may be so.

_____

_____

_____

4. A paramedic at an accident is aware of pressure points, areas where a major blood vessel crosses a bone close to the body surface. How might the paramedic use these points to stop bleeding?

_____

Applying Scientific Methods

The different function of skeletal, smooth, and cardiac muscle is reflected in the way each of the muscles contracts. Study the graphs below to see how the contractions compare. The black line indicates the electrical impulse that stimulates the muscle. The dotted line represents the muscle contraction.

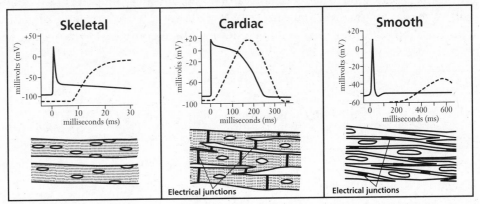

1. Study the graphs. Which of the three muscle types contracts most quickly following electrical impulse? Slowest? Explain the basis for your answer.

_____

_____

_____

_____

2. Compare the electrical impulses in each of the muscle types. How does the electrical impulse for cardiac muscle reflect the function of the heart?

_____

_____

_____

_____

3. Using the graphs and the illustrations, compare the contraction in smooth muscle to skeletal muscle.

_____

_____

_____

_____

4. Explain how the structure of cardiac muscle helps to stimulate muscle cells more quickly than in other muscle types.

_____

_____

_____

Chapter 34 **Protection, Support, and Locomotion,** *continued*

Applying Scientific Methods continued

Two muscles in your leg, the gastrocnemius and soleus muscles, help you to extend your foot. The gastrocnemius is used in jumping and performing other rapid movements of the foot. The soleus is used principally for support against gravity. In the laboratory, you can study muscle contraction by causing "muscle twitch" in these two muscles. You can apply a single stimulus to the nerve of an excised frog muscle. The time of contraction for these two muscles may be recorded, as seen in the graph below.

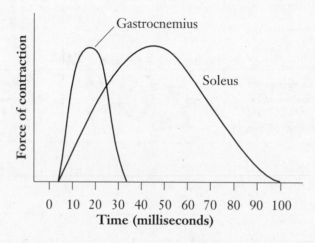

5. Use the graph to decide whether the gastrocnemius or the soleus has the longer duration of contraction. About how many times longer is this contraction than the other?

_____

_____

_____

_____

6. Why do you suppose the one leg muscle contracts so much more quickly than the other one?

_____

_____

_____

_____

Chapter 35 The Digestive and Endocrine Systems

Reviewing Vocabulary

Match the definition in Column A with the term in Column B.

Column A	Column B
_____ **1.** Digestive enzyme that breaks down starch into smaller molecules	**a.** epiglottis
_____ **2.** Muscular tube that connects the mouth to the stomach	**b.** pepsin
_____ **3.** Series of involuntary muscle contractions along the walls of the digestive tract	**c.** rectum
_____ **4.** Flap of cartilage that covers the opening to the respiratory tract during swallowing	**d.** amylase
_____ **5.** Muscular, pouchlike enlargement of the digestive tract	**e.** stomach
_____ **6.** Digestive enzyme that begins the chemical digestion of proteins	**f.** target tissue
_____ **7.** Chemical that breaks down fats into small droplets	**g.** esophagus
_____ **8.** Last section of the digestive system from which feces are eliminated	**h.** endocrine gland
_____ **9.** Regulates metabolism, growth, and development	**i.** small intestine
_____ **10.** Specific cells in the body to which hormones convey information	**j.** liver
_____ **11.** Unit of heat used to measure the energy content of food	**k.** thyroid gland
_____ **12.** Narrow, muscular tube in which digestion is completed	**l.** bile
_____ **13.** Organ that releases hormones directly into the bloodstream	**m.** peristalsis
_____ **14.** Organ that produces bile	**n.** Calorie

Chapter 35 The Digestive and
Endocrine Systems, *continued*

Chapter Assessment

Understanding Main Ideas (Part A)

In the space at the left, write the letter of the word or phrase that best completes the statement or answers the question.

_____ **1.** Starches are large

    a. fats.   **b.** proteins.   **c.** polysaccharides.   **d.** monosaccharides.

_____ **2.** Which of the following is *not* mechanical digestion?

    a. chewing food   **b.** breakdown of fats by bile

    c. churning of the stomach   **d.** action of pepsin on proteins

_____ **3.** The surface area of the small intestine is greatly increased by

    a. a large number of villi.   **b.** chemical digestion.

    c. peristalsis.   **d.** mechanical digestion.

_____ **4.** Which of the following is part of the digestive tract?

    a. liver   **b.** small intestine   **c.** gallbladder   **d.** pancreas

_____ **5.** Which of the following occurs in the large intestine as the work of anaerobic bacteria?

    a. absorption of water

    b. synthesis of vitamin K and some B vitamins

    c. change of glucose to glycogen

    d. elimination of indigestible matter

_____ **6.** Vitamins are used by the body to

    a. provide energy.   **b.** maintain growth and metabolism.

    c. supply building materials.   **d.** digest proteins.

_____ **7.** Which is the most abundant substance in the body?

    a. fat   **b.** water   **c.** sugar   **d.** protein

_____ **8.** The body's preferred energy source is

    a. carbohydrates.   **b.** vitamins.   **c.** proteins.   **d.** minerals.

_____ **9.** As a result of digestion, proteins are broken down into

    a. monosaccharides.   **b.** amino acids.

    c. triglycerides.   **d.** glycerol.

_____ **10.** Cellulose is important in the diet as a source of

    a. energy.   **b.** protein.   **c.** fat.   **d.** fiber.

_____ **11.** Pepsin works best in the presence of

    a. amylase.   **b.** protein.

    c. saliva.   **d.** hydrochloric acid.

Chapter 35 **The Digestive and Endocrine Systems,** *continued*

Understanding Main Ideas (Part B)

Answer the following questions.

1. Name and describe the type of feedback mechanism that controls most endocrine glands.

_____

_____

_____

_____

_____

_____

2. How do glucagon and insulin affect blood glucose levels?

_____

_____

_____

3. Describe how a steroid hormone affects its target tissue.

_____

_____

_____

_____

4. Describe how an amino acid hormone affects its target tissue.

_____

_____

_____

5. Describe the relationship among the hypothalamus, the pituitary gland, and the endocrine glands that are under the control of the pituitary gland.

_____

_____

6. Explain why the pituitary gland is considered the master gland of the endocrine system.

_____

_____

Thinking Critically

Answer the following questions.

1. One cause of diabetes mellitus is the failure of the pancreas to secrete insulin. Describe the blood glucose levels of a person who has diabetes and goes untreated for the disease. How might a doctor test a person that he or she suspects might have diabetes?

_____

_____

_____

2. Cholesterol, secreted by the liver, may cause the gallbladder to produce gallstones. At times, the gallstones block the common bile duct that leads to the duodenom. How might these gallstones affect the patient's digestion?

_____

_____

_____

3. Many people have their gallbladder removed, but the absence of the gallbladder has little effect on their ability to digest fats. Explain why this is so.

_____

_____

_____

4. Vitamin C is a water-soluble vitamin. Is eating a large amount of vitamin C once a week sufficient to keep the body healthy? What happens to excess amounts of vitamin C that may be consumed to prevent a cold?

_____

_____

_____

5. A person suffering from diarrhea may become dehydrated. How might this cause problems in the body?

_____

_____

_____

_____

Chapter 35 The Digestive and
Endocrine Systems, *continued*

Applying Scientific Methods

Although fats are an essential part of your diet, it is important to keep total fat intake at or below
30 percent of all the Calories you consume in a day. The fatty acids in fats vary in length and in the degree
to which they are saturated by hydrogen atoms. Fats that are saturated are usually solid at room temperature. Most saturated fats, such as those in butter, dairy products, and meats, come from animal sources.
However, coconut oil and palm oil are highly saturated fats from plants. A diet high in saturated fat can
result in high blood cholesterol levels, which can lead to heart disease. You should limit your intake of
saturated fats to no more than 10 percent of your total Calories. Most of your fat Calories should come
from unsaturated fats. These fats do not have all the hydrogen atoms they can carry.

1. Calculate the percentage of fat Calories in each food in the table below. (Round answers to the
   nearest percent.) 1 g of fat provides 9 Calories.

   Notice that a hamburger contains 21 g of fat. To find the Calories from fat in the hamburger,
   multiply 21 g by 9 Calories = 189 Calories from fat. Divide the Calories from fat by the total
   Calories in a hamburger:

   189 Calories ÷ 289 Calories = 0.65 or 65 percent

Food Source (100 g)	Calories	Fat (g)	% of Calories from Fats	Saturated Fats (g)
Regular hamburger	289	21		8
Beef loin	184	7		3
Chicken breast with skin	197	8		2
Chicken breast, skinless	165	4		1
Drumstick with skin	216	11		3
Drumstick, skinless	172	6		1
Bacon	576	49		17
Ham, canned, extra lean	136	5		2
Tuna, yellowfin	145	1		<1
Shrimp	99	1		<1
Sour cream	214	21		13
Whole milk	61	3		2
Low-fat milk	50	2		1
Cottage cheese	72	1		<1
Cheddar cheese	403	33		21

Applying Scientific Methods *continued*

2. Which food has the highest percentage of fat Calories?

_____

_____

3. Which food has the lowest percentage of fat Calories?

_____

_____

4. It is recommended that a female student who regularly consumes 2100 Calories per day eat only 70 g of fat per day. How many of the Calories eaten by the female student should be fat Calories?

_____

5. A male student who consumes 2800 Calories per day should eat only 93 g of fat per day. How many fat Calories is this?

_____

6. If a student ate a hamburger with a slice of Cheddar cheese and a glass of whole milk, how many grams of fat could the student still safely eat at the rest of his or her meals?

_____

_____

_____

7. Which foods have less than one-third of their fat grams as saturated fats?

_____

_____

Chapter 36 The Nervous System

Reviewing Vocabulary

Match the definition in Column A with the term in Column B.

Column A	Column B
_____ 1. Medicine that acts on the central nervous system to relieve pain	**a.** neutrotransmitters
_____ 2. Any drug that slows down the activities of the central nervous system (CNS)	**b.** semicircular canals
_____ 3. Psychological and physical dependence on a drug	**c.** cochlea
_____ 4. Automatic response to a stimulus	**d.** addiction
_____ 5. Single extension of a neuron that carries impulses away from the cell body	**e.** hallucinogen
_____ 6. Occurs when a person needs larger and/or more frequent doses of a drug to achieve the same effect	**f.** rods
_____ 7. Layer of nerve tissue made up of sensory neurons that respond to light	**g.** depressant
_____ 8. Light receptors adapted for vision in dim light	**h.** narcotic
_____ 9. Structure in the inner ear that helps maintain balance	**i.** retina
_____ 10. Controls involuntary activities such as breathing and heart rate	**j.** synaptic space
_____ 11. Tiny space between the axon of one neuron and the dendrites of another neuron over which nerve impulses must travel	**k.** medulla oblongata
_____ 12. Fluid-filled, snail-shaped structure in the inner ear	**l.** tolerance
_____ 13. Drug that affects the CNS, altering moods, thoughts, and sensory perceptions	**m.** reflex
_____ 14. Chemicals that diffuse across the synapse and stimulate changes in a neuron	**n.** axon

Understanding Main Ideas (Part A)

In the space at the left, write the letter of the word or phrase that best completes the statement or answers the question.

_____ **1.** Sensory neurons

    a. process incoming impulses and pass them on to motor neurons.

    b. carry impulses from around the body to the brain and spinal cord.

    c. carry response impulses away from the brain and spinal cord.

    d. carry impulses across synapses.

_____ **2.** A nerve impulse travels from one cell to another by passing from

    a. one axon to another axon.

    b. one dendrite to an axon.

    c. one axon to a dendrite.

    d. one dendrite to another dendrite.

_____ **3.** Which controls involuntary activities of the body such as breathing and heart rate?

    a. cerebrum   **b.** cerebellum   **c.** medulla oblongata   **d.** none of these

_____ **4.** You can see the colors in a picture because you are aided by the

    a. rods of the retina.   **b.** right visual field.

    c. cones of the retina.   **d.** left visual field.

_____ **5.** A person who is addicted to a drug is experiencing withdrawal when he or she

    a. needs more of the drug to achieve the same effect.

    b. becomes ill after stopping its use.

    c. needs to take the drug more often.

    d. feels better when stopping its use.

_____ **6.** Cocaine is a stimulant because it

    a. causes blood pressure to drop.

    b. causes heart rate to slow down.

    c. relieves anxiety.

    d. causes levels of neurotransmitters in the brain to increase.

_____ **7.** Alcohol may act on the brain by

    a. dissolving through the membranes of neurons.

    b. speeding up the movement of sodium and calcium ions.

    c. increasing anxiety.

    d. increasing oxygen content.

Understanding Main Ideas (Part B)

Answer the following questions.

1. How is a nerve impulse transmitted through a neuron?

_____

_____

_____

_____

2. How does a nerve impulse pass from neuron to neuron?

_____

_____

_____

_____

3. How is the eye adapted for vision in a dimly lit place?

_____

_____

_____

4. How do the semicircular canals help you to keep your balance?

_____

_____

_____

_____

5. What is the role of the somatic nervous system in your body?

_____

_____

_____

_____

_____

Thinking Critically

If you enter a darkened room from a lighted area, you cannot see well at first. The retina of the eye lacks the light-sensitive pigment, called rhodopsin, in the rods. However, as the graph at the right shows, the concentration of rhodopsin builds up quickly, and the eyes adapt to the change in the amount of light.

Use the graph to answer questions 1–4.

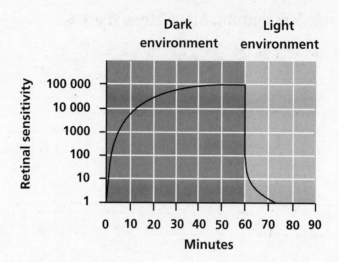

1. How long does it take for the sensitivity of the retina to improve from 1 to 10 000 arbitrary units?

_____

_____

2. After how many minutes does the retina have a sensitivity of 100 000 units?

_____

3. How is the response of the retina to changes in light an adaptation?

_____

_____

_____

_____

4. Upon entering a bright room after being in the dark, what happens to the levels of rhodopsin in the rods?

_____

_____

The utricle and saccule are organs of the inner ear. Each of these organs contains a patch of epithelium called the *macula*. The macula is covered with tiny hairs, each of which is weighted by a small mineral grain. As the grains pull on the hairs, impulses are sent from the hair cells to the brain, alerting it to the head's position. The strength with which a mineral grain pulls a hair depends on the force of gravity.

5. In terms of the utricle and saccule, why might an astronaut in zero gravity experience space sickness?

_____

_____

_____

_____

Chapter
36 **The Nervous System,** *continued*

Applying Scientific Methods

Scientists in western countries have been searching for a chemical that will help curb an alcoholic's appetite for alcohol. Recently, some scientists have been looking at a treatment used in China for over 2000 years. Chinese healers have given alcoholics an extract made from the root of the kudzu vine, which they claim is about 80 percent effective in reducing alcohol craving in patients who have been treated for two to four weeks. Dr. Wing-Ming Keung of Harvard Medical School in Boston visited China to find out what modern researchers thought of the herbal remedy. He spoke to physicians who claimed to have treated 300 human alcohol abusers with the extract. They were convinced that the chemicals in the extract effectively suppressed the patient's appetite for alcohol.

After returning to Harvard, Dr. Keung and Dr. Bert L. Vallee decided to try the drug on a group of Syrian golden hamsters in their laboratory. These hamsters were specifically selected because they are known to drink large amounts of alcohol when it is available to them. Suppose you are a member of the Harvard Medical School research team. Your job is to design an experiment that will demonstrate the effectiveness of the kudzu root extract to suppress the hamsters' craving for alcohol.

1. Describe the experimental procedure you will follow.

_____

_____

_____

_____

_____

2. What will you use as your control?

_____

_____

3. What will be the variable in your experiment?

_____

_____

4. Predict the results of your experiment.

_____

_____

5. How might you follow up on your experiment?

_____

_____

_____

_____

Applying Scientific Methods   continued

6. Dr. Keung and Dr. Vallee discovered two active ingredients in the root extract, each of which had the effect of lessening alcohol use in the hamsters by 50 percent. The two compounds appeared to interfere with the metabolism, or breakdown, of alcohol in the body. Hypothesize what this discovery may tell us about the nature of alcoholism.

_____

_____

_____

_____

7. How might Dr. Keung and Dr. Vallee's discovery help alcoholics overcome their addition?

_____

_____

_____

_____

Chapter 37 Respiration, Circulation, and Excretion

Reviewing Vocabulary

Match the definition in Column A with the term in Column B.

Column A

_____ **1.** Passageway leading from the larynx to the lungs

_____ **2.** Sacs of the lungs where exchange of oxygen and carbon dioxide takes place

_____ **3.** Fluid portion of blood in which blood cells move

_____ **4.** Iron-containing protein that picks up oxygen after it enters the blood vessels in the lungs

_____ **5.** Cell fragments that help blood to clot after an injury

_____ **6.** A substance that stimulates an immune response in the body

_____ **7.** Microscopic blood vessel

_____ **8.** Protein that reacts with an antigen

_____ **9.** A kind of large, muscular, thick-walled elastic vessel that carries blood away from the heart

_____ **10.** A kind of large blood vessel that carries blood from the tissues to the heart

_____ **11.** An upper chamber of the heart

_____ **12.** A lower chamber of the heart

_____ **13.** Largest blood vessel in the body

_____ **14.** Regular surge of blood through an artery

_____ **15.** Solution of body wastes consisting of excess water, waste molecules, and excess ions

_____ **16.** A filtering unit in the kidney

Column B

a. alveoli

b. antibody

c. antigen

d. aorta

e. artery

f. atrium

g. urine

h. capillary

i. hemoglobin

j. nephron

k. plasma

l. platelets

m. pulse

n. trachea

o. vein

p. ventricle

Understanding Main Ideas (Part A)

In the space at the left, write <u>true</u> if the statement is true. If the statement is false, change the italicized word or phrase to make it true.

_____ **1.** Red blood cells are produced in the *spleen*.

_____ **2.** The blood in the veins is prevented from flowing backward because of *pressure* in these blood vessels.

_____ **3.** The only veins that carry oxygen-rich blood are the *venae cavae*.

_____ **4.** When blood first enters the heart, it passes into the *ventricles*.

_____ **5.** As the liquid passes through the *U-shaped tubule* in the nephron, most of the ions and water and all of the glucose and amino acids are reabsorbed into the bloodstream.

_____ **6.** The major waste products of the cells are ammonia and the wastes from the breakdown of *carbohydrates*.

_____ **7.** The urine of a person who has diabetes may contain excess *salts*.

_____ **8.** Carbon dioxide and *oxygen* are the waste products of cellular respiration.

_____ **9.** When your diaphragm *contracts*, the space in the chest cavity becomes larger.

_____ **10.** Breathing is controlled by changes in the chemistry of the blood, which cause the *medulla oblongata* to react.

_____ **11.** Your pulse represents the pressure that blood exerts as it pushes the walls of a(n) *vein*.

_____ **12.** If you have type A blood and *anti-A* is added during a transfusion, no clumps will form.

_____ **13.** *External respiration* uses oxygen in the breakdown of glucose in cells in order to provide energy in the form of ATP.

Chapter 37   **Respiration, Circulation, and Excretion,** *continued*

Understanding Main Ideas (Part B)

Answer the following questions.

1. How does the respiratory system prevent most of the foreign matter in urban air from reaching your lungs?

_____

_____

_____

2. Distinguish between systolic pressure and diastolic pressure.

_____

_____

_____

3. What problem may arise when a woman with Rh⁻ blood is pregnant with an Rh⁺ fetus?

_____

_____

_____

_____

4. How does a pacemaker set the heart rate?

_____

_____

_____

5. How does the urinary system maintain homeostasis?

_____

_____

_____

Chapter 37 Respiration, Circulation, and Excretion, *continued*

Thinking Critically

A marathon runner is able to increase the amount of blood pumped by the heart (cardiac output) from 5 L/min while resting to 30 L/min while competing. The runner's stroke volume (pumping capacity per heartbeat) measured in mL/beat, and heart rate, measured in beats/min, are also increased.

Use the graph to answer questions 1–3.

1. When the runner's cardiac output is 20 L/min, what is the heart rate?

   _____

2. What is the stroke volume when the cardiac output is 20 mL/min?

   _____

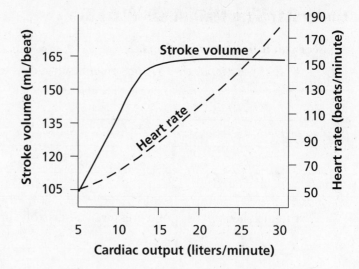

3. Which has the greater effect on cardiac output, stroke volume or heart rate?

   _____

   _____

   _____

   _____

Answer the following questions.

4. When a person has pneumonia, the alveoli become inflamed and the air spaces become clogged. What effect will these symptoms have on a pneumonia patient?

   _____

   _____

5. Arteriosclerosis slowly reduces blood flow through the arteries to the brain. Explain how this may affect a patient who has this condition.

   _____

   _____

   _____

6. The antidiuretic hormone (ADH) stimulates the reabsorption of water in the kidneys. Alcohol inhibits ADH secretion. Predict the effect of drinking alcoholic beverages on urine production.

   _____

   _____

Chapter 37 Respiration, Circulation, and Excretion, *continued*

Applying Scientific Methods

The vertebrate heart can beat spontaneously. If the heart of a vertebrate is removed and placed in a balanced salt solution with nutrients, it will continue to beat for hours. In fact, the muscle from each part of the heart beats at its own rate if it is not under the control of the pacemaker.

In a physiology laboratory experiment, a frog is anaesthetized and the heart is exposed. Recall that the frog has a three-chambered heart, with right and left atria and a single ventricle. It also has a sinus venosus, which receives oxygen-depleted blood from all parts of the body except the lungs. The sinus venosus is where contraction begins. (This role is assumed by the pacemaker in the mammalian heart.) For this experiment, the nerve connections to the heart are blocked. The sinus venosus, the right atrium, and the ventricle are each attached to a stylus for marking on a kymograph (an instrument that records changes in pressure). In the graphs, rises represent contractions.

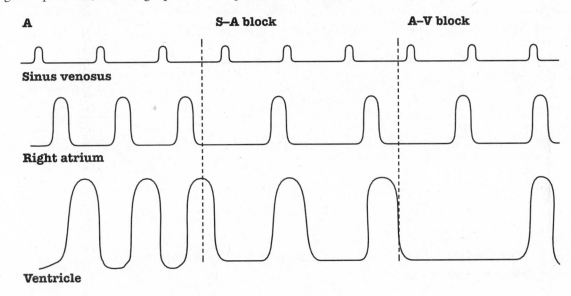

1. Interpret the data in A.

_____

_____

_____

2. To understand how the heart beats when the impulse from the sinus is blocked, a string is tied tightly around the heart between the sinus and the atrium. This is called an "S-A block." How does the S-A block affect the rate of the beat of the sinus?

_____

3. How does blocking the sinus affect the rate at which the atrium and ventricle beat?

_____

_____

Applying Scientific Methods *continued*

4. What could you do to find out the effect of blocking the atrium?

_____

_____

5. How does blocking the action between the atrium and the ventricle, which is called an "A-V block," affect the beat of the sinus, the atrium, and the ventricle?

_____

_____

6. What can you conclude about the rate of beat of the different parts of the heart from this experiment?

_____

_____

_____

_____

_____

Chapter 38 **Reproduction and Development**

Reviewing Vocabulary

Match the definition in Column A with the term in Column B.

Column A

Column B

_____ **1.** Group of epithelial cells that surround a developing egg

a. semen

_____ **2.** Information provided by trained professionals about the probabilities of hereditary disorders in a developing fetus

b. first trimester

c. puberty

_____ **3.** Period of development in pregnancy during which all the organ systems of the embryo begin to form

d. pituitary

_____ **4.** Combination of sperm and fluids in which they are transported

e. genetic counseling

_____ **5.** Refers to the time when secondary sex characteristics begin to develop

f. implantation

_____ **6.** Attachment of the blastocyst to the lining of the uterus

g. umbilical cord

_____ **7.** Ropelike structure that attaches the embryo to the wall of the uterus

h. follicle

_____ **8.** Gland that secretes hormones that influence many physiological processes of the body

Compare and contrast each pair of related terms.

9. bulbourethral gland, prostate gland

_____

_____

_____

10. epididymis, vas deferens

_____

_____

_____

_____

Understanding Main Ideas (Part A)

Label the diagram. Use these choices: ovary, implantation, blastocyst, ovulation, fertilization, uterus, zygote, vagina, oviduct.

1. _____

2. _____

3. _____

4. _____

5. _____

6. _____

7. _____

8. _____

9. _____

Sperm enter

In the space at the left, write the letter of the word or phrase that best completes the statement.

_____ **10.** The fluid that provides energy for the sperm cells comes from the
   a. bulbourethral glands.   **b.** seminal vesicles.
   c. prostate gland.   **d.** urethra.

_____ **11.** When FSH reaches the testes, it causes the production of
   a. testosterone.   **b.** LH.
   c. sperm cells.   **d.** secondary sex characteristics.

_____ **12.** In the female, FSH stimulates the
   a. production of eggs.   **b.** production of progesterone.
   c. blastocyst.   **d.** development of a follicle in the ovary.

_____ **13.** All the body systems of the fetus are present by the
   a. third week.   **b.** sixth week.   **c.** eighth week.   **d.** first month.

Understanding Main Ideas (Part B)

Use the diagram of the negative feedback system in the male to complete the following statements.

1. The release of LH by the pituitary is stimulated by a hormone secreted by the _____ .

2. LH stimulates the production of _____ .

3. _____ and testosterone affect sperm production.

4. An increase of testosterone inhibits _____ production.

5. Cells that produce sperm send signals to the pituitary and hypothalamus to stop releasing _____ .

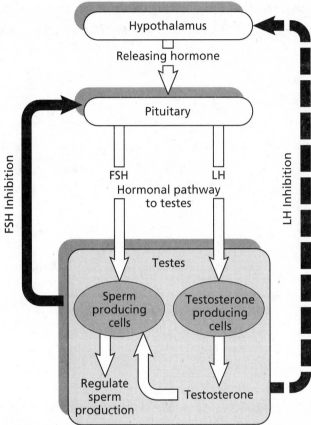

Answer the following questions.

6. Why is the scrotum located outside the male body?

_____

_____

7. What happens to the lining of the uterus if fertilization does not occur?

_____

_____

8. What is the function of the corpus luteum?

_____

_____

_____

_____

Chapter Assessment

Thinking Critically

Answer the following questions.

1. Although the incidence is less than 1 percent, an ectopic pregnancy may occur, in which the implantation takes place in an oviduct or in the pelvic cavity. When would implantation in the oviduct be fatal for the developing fetus?

_____

_____

_____

2. How could it happen that implantation could take place in the pelvic cavity? What must happen for the fetus to be nourished there?

_____

_____

_____

_____

3. Why would an ectopic fetus have to be removed by surgery, not by delivery through the birth canal?

_____

_____

4. Two groups of married women, about the same age and weight, participated in a test. The women in Group A were given a placebo, a sugar pill, each morning of their menstrual cycle. The women in Group B were given a pill containing estrogen and progesterone each morning of their menstrual cycle. The LH levels before, during, and after ovulation of both groups were recorded.

Group	Four Days Before	Day of Ovulation	Four Days After
A	17 mg/100mL	299 mg/100 mL	16 mg/100mL
B	20 mg/100mL	156 mg/100 mL	14 mg/100mL

The number of pregnancies during the year of the test in Group A was 25 times the number of pregnancies in Group B. What would you conclude, based on these data?

_____

_____

_____

Chapter 38 Reproduction and Development, *continued*

Applying Scientific Methods

The Smiths would like to have a baby. Mrs. Smith has begun to keep a record of her temperature readings during her menstrual cycle. She knows that she is fertile, or capable of beginning pregnancy, only for a period of about 24 hours from the time of ovulation. She also knows that her temperature rises about 0.3°C when she ovulates. She keeps a record of her temperature every day at the same time. The dates that are shaded on the calendars are the dates when Mr. Smith is away for National Guard duty. Use the temperature charts and the calendars to find out when Mrs. Smith has the best opportunity of becoming pregnant. (Note that sperm are able to survive inside the oviducts and uterus for several days.)

March

S	M	T	W	T	F	S
		1	2	3	4	5
6	7	8	9	10	11	12
13	14	15	16	17	18	19
20	21	22	23	24	25	26
27	28	29	30	31		

April

S	M	T	W	T	F	S
					1	2
3	4	5	6	7	8	9
10	11	12	13	14	15	16
17	18	19	20	21	22	23
24	25	26	27	28	29	30

May

S	M	T	W	T	F	S
1	2	3	4	5	6	7
8	9	10	11	12	13	14
15	16	17	18	19	20	21
22	23	24	25	26	27	28
29	30	31				

June

S	M	T	W	T	F	S
			1	2	3	4
5	6	7	8	9	10	11
12	13	14	15	16	17	18
19	20	21	22	23	24	25
26	27	28	29	30		

March Temp.
19   36.7 (°C)
20   37.0
21   37.0

April Temp.
16   36.7 (°C)
17   37.0
18   37.0

May Temp.
14   36.6 (°C)
15   36.9
16   37.0

June Temp.
11   36.7 (°C)
12   37.0
13   37.0

1. During which month or months do the Smiths have the best chance of producing a baby? Explain your answer.

_____

_____

_____

_____

_____

Applying Scientific Methods *continued*

2. Would changing Mr. Smith's National Guard weekend to the second Saturday of every month have helped the Smiths in their efforts to have a baby?

_____

_____

_____

3. Some researchers have noted slight physical variations in X and Y sperm. They postulate that because Y sperm are lighter than X sperm, the Y sperm travel more quickly. Hypothesize how this may affect the sex of the Smiths' baby, providing reasons on which your hypothesis is based.

_____

_____

_____

4. What if the Smiths tried for their baby the day before ovulation. How might this affect the sex of their baby?

_____

_____

_____

_____

Chapter
39 Immunity from Disease

Reviewing Vocabulary

Match the definition in Column A with the term in Column B.

Column A

_____ **1.** Disease caused by the presence of pathogens in the body

_____ **2.** Substance produced by a microorganism, which kills or inhibits the growth and reproduction of other microorganisms

_____ **3.** Type of white blood cell that defends the body against foreign substances

_____ **4.** Disease-producing agents such as bacteria, protozoa, fungi, viruses

_____ **5.** Proteins that protect cells from viruses

_____ **6.** Defense against a specific pathogen by gradually building up resistance to it

_____ **7.** Small mass of tissue that filters pathogens from lymph

_____ **8.** Procedure used to determine which pathogen causes a specific disease

_____ **9.** Weakened, dead, or parts of pathogens or antigens that, when injected into the body, causes immunity

Column B

a. interferons

b. acquired immunity

c. lymph node

d. lymphocyte

e. pathogens

f. vaccine

g. infectious disease

h. Koch's postulates

i. antibiotic

Contrast and compare each pair of related terms.

10. T cell, B cell

_____

_____

_____

_____

11. phagocyte, macrophage

_____

_____

_____

Chapter
39 **Immunity from Disease,** *continued*

Chapter Assessment

Understanding Main Ideas (Part A)

In the space at the left, write the letter of the word or phrase that best completes the statement.

_____ **1.** A bacterial disease becomes difficult to cure when the bacteria

    a. die off.   **b.** make interferons.

    c. develop resistance to antibiotics.   **d.** produce antibodies.

_____ **2.** Toxins produced by invading bacteria

    a. are always harmless unless released in vary large amounts.

    b. can, in some cases, cause fever and cardiovascular disturbances.

    c. rarely attack the nervous or circulatory systems.

    d. are the same as those produced by HIV.

_____ **3.** Interferons are a body cell's defense against

    a. all pathogens.   **b.** bacteria.   **c.** viruses.   **d.** lymphocytes.

_____ **4.** Immunity occurs when the system recognizes a foreign substance and responds by producing

    a. lymphocytes that make antibodies.   **b.** antigens.

    c. toxins.   **d.** all of these.

_____ **5.** HIV can be transmitted by

    a. intimate sexual contact.   **b.** contaminated food.

    c. air.   **d.** shaking hands.

_____ **6.** A person with AIDS is susceptible to all kinds of infectious diseases because HIV

    a. destroys pathogens.   **b.** weakens the immune system.

    c. causes an increase of antigens.   **d.** causes antibody production.

_____ **7.** The symptoms of an infectious disease are caused by

    a. macrophages.   **b.** toxins produced by pathogens.

    c. interferons.   **d.** phagocytes.

_____ **8.** Active immunity is obtained when a person is exposed to

    a. antigens.   **b.** injected antibodies.

    c. macrophages.   **d.** antibiotics.

_____ **9.** Koch's postulates cannot be carried out on viral diseases because the viruses

    a. do not have hosts.   **b.** are not pathogens.

    c. cannot be grown outside of cells.   **d.** are too deadly.

Chapter 39 Immunity from Disease, *continued*

Understanding Main Ideas (Part B)

Answer the following questions.

1. How do researchers identify the specific cause of an infectious disease?

_____

_____

_____

_____

2. How do interferons provide a defense against viruses?

_____

_____

_____

3. How does a nonspecific defense mechanism differ from a specific defense mechanism?

_____

_____

_____

_____

4. What role do B cells play in immunity?

_____

_____

_____

_____

5. How does cellular immunity protect the body?

_____

_____

_____

6. Why is AIDS considered a disease of the immune system?

_____

_____

Thinking Critically

Answer the following questions.

1. You get a splinter in your finger, which becomes sore and swollen. In a few days, pus forms around the splinter. Explain.

_____

_____

_____

_____

2. Antibodies produced by the body to combat the pathogen that causes rheumatic fever may begin to attack the patient's own cardiac muscle cells. How might such a mixup occur?

_____

_____

_____

_____

_____

3. Organ-transplant patients are given a drug called cyclosporine to suppress the body's defenses against the transplanted organ. Why is this necessary?

_____

_____

_____

_____

4. Unlike earlier drugs that suppressed the entire immune system, cyclosporine does not significantly suppress the bone marrow where lymphocytes are formed. What was the danger of taking the earlier drugs?

_____

_____

_____

5. Suppose parents hear that a neighbor's child has chicken pox, and they take their young child over to their neighbor's house. Why would they do this?

_____

_____

_____

_____

Copyright © Glencoe/McGraw-Hill, a division of The McGraw-Hill Companies, Inc.

Chapter
39 Immunity from Disease, *continued*

Applying Scientific Methods

Vincent Fischetti is a professor of bacterial pathogenesis and immunology at New York's Rockefeller University. His team of researchers has been studying why some Group A streptococcal bacteria manage to slip by the defenses of the human body. Group A streptococci cause strep throat, which often leads to acute rheumatic fever, a disease that damages heart valves.

First, Fischetti's team looked at Group A streptococci under an electron microscope. They noticed that some of these bacteria have long, hairlike filaments on their surfaces. The filaments were found to consist of a protein called M protein. They decided to find out if the M protein has anything to do with Group A's ability to resist ingestion by human phagocytes. They placed streptococci in a drop of human blood on a microscope slide. The phagocytes in the blood moved away from the bacteria that had M proteins on their surfaces. The phagocytes attacked any streptococci that lacked M-protein filaments.

Fischetti next wanted to know how the M protein resists the body's defenses. The team began a study of the protein sequence of M protein. Figure 1 shows what they found. Four different repeated amino acid sequences (A, B, C, and D) make up 80 percent of the protein.

Almost immediately a discovery slowed the study. Fischetti found that there are 80 different varieties of M protein! He realized that M-proteins must be affected by rapid mutations. Further study of different varieties of M protein showed that most of the mutations occur in the numbers of repeated A and B amino acid sequences, as shown in Figure 2. Mutated streptococci show deleted copies of the amino acid repeat blocks normally found in the parent.

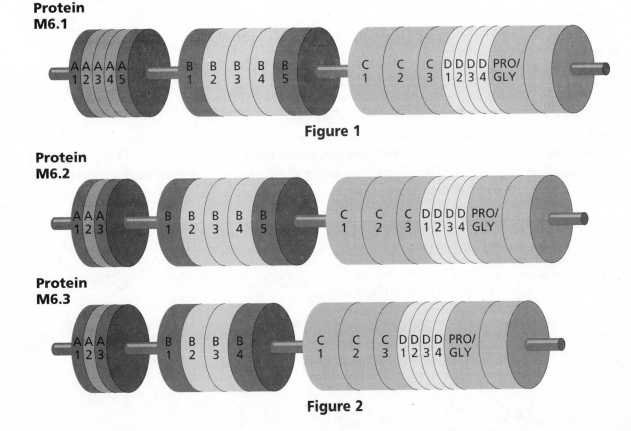

Figure 1

Figure 2

Chapter
39 **Immunity from Disease,** *continued*

Applying Scientific Methods   continued

Suppose that you are a new member of Fischetti's team. After observing the experiments just described, you are asked the following questions about the work being done.

1. Which experiment provided evidence that the M protein protects streptococci?

_____

_____

_____

2. Having mutations in the numbers of repeated amino acid sequences in the M protein is extremely helpful to the bacteria. How might this adaptation help them to survive?

_____

_____

_____

3. Figure 2 shows two mutations of the M protein. What differences do you observe between M6.1 and M6.2? Between M6.1 and M6.3?

_____

_____

_____

4. How might rapid mutation thwart the human immune system?

_____

_____

_____

5. The M protein has an excess of negatively charged amino acids. This results in a net negative charge on the bacterial surface. Mammalian cells also have a negative charge on their surfaces. How might this affect the ability of mammalian phagocytes to ingest the bacteria?

_____

_____

_____

ANSWER PAGES

Chapter Assessment

Chapter 1 — Chapter Assessment

Biology: The Study of Life

Reviewing Vocabulary

Match the definition in Column A with the term in Column B.

	Column A	Column B
f	1. The process whereby an organism produces more of its own kind	a. adaptation
b	2. The part of an experiment in which all conditions are kept the same	b. control
d	3. An organism's tendency to maintain a stable internal environment	c. evolution
a	4. Any structure, behavior, or internal process that enables an organism to better survive in an environment	d. homeostasis
e	5. A testable explanation for a question or problem	e. hypothesis
c	6. The gradual change in the characteristics of a species over time	f. reproduction

Compare and contrast each pair of related terms.

7. stimulus, response
A stimulus is any environmental condition that requires an organism to adjust. A response is the adjustment.

8. independent variable, dependent variable
An independent variable is the factor in an experiment that is changed. A dependent variable is a condition that results from making the change in the independent variable.

9. organism, species
An organism is an individual living thing. A species is a group of organisms that can interbreed to produce fertile offspring.

Chapter 1 — Chapter Assessment

Biology: The Study of Life, *continued*

Understanding Concepts (Part A)

Match the definition in Column A with the term in Column B.

	Column A	Column B
d	1. Scientists commonly use these steps in gathering information to test hyphotheses and solve problems.	a. energy
b	2. Over time, gradual changes in structures, behaviors, and internal processes of organisms result in diversity of species.	b. evolution
e	3. Scientists use this system of measurement because of its ease of understanding.	c. homeostasis
c	4. A variety of structural and behavioral adaptations help organisms regulate their internal environment.	d. scientific methods
a	5. Its flow through ecosystems determines how organisms interact and powers all life processes.	e. SI (metric)

In the space at the left, write **true** if the statement is true; if the statement is false, change the italicized word or phrase to make it true.

true	6. Biologists discover problems by *observing the world around them*.
conclusion	7. A *natural law* is based on the analysis of data collected in a controlled experiment.
experimental	8. In an experiment, the *control* group is used to test the effect of the independent variable.
quantitative	9. Counts or measurements are examples of data produced by *descriptive* research.
ethics	10. Whether applications of science to everyday life are considered good, bad, right, or wrong comes under the category of *technology*.
true	11. The *liter* is a metric unit of volume.

Name _____ Date _____ Class _____

Biology: The Study of Life, *continued*

Understanding Concepts (Part B)

Identify the characteristic of life illustrated in each picture

1.

2.

Shell
Mantle edge (collar)
Eyes
Anus
Tentacles
Mouth Foot

organization

3.

reproduction

4.

growth/development **adaptation**

Identify the independent variable and the dependent variable that would be used in testing each hypothesis below.

5. An electromagnet can be made by wrapping insulated wire around an iron nail and connecting the ends of the wire to a 6-volt battery. HYPOTHESIS: Increasing the number of coils of wire wrapped around the nail increases the strength of the electromagnet, as measured by the number of paper clips the magnet can pick up.

independent variable: number of coils of wire; dependent variable: number of paper clips lifted by magnet

6. Sugar dissolves in, or mixes completely with, water. The solubility of a substance in water is determined by measuring the maximum amount of the substance that dissolves in a given amount of water at a given temperature. HYPOTHESIS: The solubility of sugar in water increases as the temperature of the water decreases.

independent variable: temperature of water; dependent variable: amount of sugar that dissolves

---

Name _____ Date _____ Class _____

Biology: The Study of Life, *continued*

Thinking Critically

One hundred pregnant women and their developing fetuses were monitored over the course of pregnancy in a study designed to compare the average weight gain of a woman during pregnancy with the average weight gain of the developing fetus. (Note that the weight gain of the developing fetus is its actual weight.) The averages for the group are recorded in the table below.

1. Graph the data for the mother and the fetus on the same grid. Decide on a method to distinguish the sets of data. Be sure to label each graph.

Week of pregnancy	Weight gain of mother (kg)	Weight gain of fetus (kg)
8	1.5	not measureable
12	1.8	0.25
16	3.0	0.25
20	4.0	0.50
24	5.5	0.75
28	8.0	1.25
32	10.0	2.00
36	13.0	2.25
40	15.0	3.00

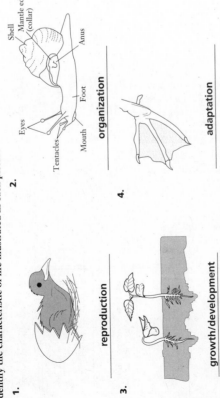

Weight gain (kg): 15, 12, 9, 6, 3, 0
Mother
Fetus
Week of pregnancy: 8 12 16 20 24 28 32 36 40

2. How would you describe the weight gain of the developing fetus? **Answers may vary. The developing fetus gains very little weight during the first 24 weeks of pregnancy; during the last 16 weeks, its weight triples.**

3. During the last 16 weeks of pregnancy, how does the mother's total weight gain compare with the total weight gain of the developing fetus? **The mother's gain is about 5 times as much as the total weight gain of the developing fetus.**

4. Overall, how does the mother's rate of weight gain compare with the rate of weight gain of the developing fetus? How can you determine this by looking at the graphs? **The mother gains weight much more rapidly than the developing fetus. The graph for the mother rises more steeply than the graph for the fetus.**

Chapter 1

Biology: The Study of Life, *continued*

Chapter Assessment

Applying Scientific Methods

Paramecia are single-celled, microscopic organisms that live in fresh water. Like other living things, paramecia respond to changes in their environment. For example, if a paramecium encounters an obstacle in its path, it will avoid it by swimming away from or around the obstacle.

A paramecium may respond positively or negatively to a stimulus, or it may not respond at all. A positive response is indicated by movement toward the stimulus; a negative response is indicated by movement away from the stimulus.

A student prepared several covered slides of paramecia in fresh water. The student added different stimuli and observed the behavior of the organisms under the microscope. The diagrams below show what the student viewed.

In fresh water

Reaction to drop of dilute salt water (0.5% solution)

Reaction to drop of vinegar

Reaction to piece of food

Reaction to air bubble

Reaction to carbon dioxide bubble

Chapter 1

Biology: The Study of Life, *continued*

Chapter Assessment

Applying Scientific Methods *continued*

Compare the data chart. Use + for a positive response; – for a negative response, and 0 for no response.

Stimulus	Response (+, –, 0)
1. fresh water	0
2. 0.5% salt solution	–
3. vinegar	+
4. food	+
5. air bubble	0
6. carbon dioxide bubble	+

7. Which stimulus represents the natural environment of paramecia?
fresh water

8. What purpose does observing the response to this stimulus serve?
It acts as a baseline, or control, against which the other responses can be compared.

9. To which substance(s) did the paramecia have the strongest positive response? Explain your reasoning.
They seem to respond most positively to the piece of food because the entire population of paramecia moved toward the piece of food.

10. Predict how a population of paramecia would respond to the addition of a drop of 10% salt solution. Give reasons for your prediction.
Answers may vary. The paramecia would respond more negatively to 10% salt solution than to 0.5% salt solution because it represents a greater change from their natural environment.

Name _____ Date _____ Class _____

Principles of Ecology

Reviewing Vocabulary

Match the definition in Column A with the term in Column B.

Column A

c 1. Tiny organisms that break down and absorb nutrients from dead organisms

f 2. Obtains energy by feeding on other organisms

i 3. Step in the passage of energy and matter through an ecosystem

j 4. Place where an organism lives out its life

g 5. Relationship between species in which one species benefits at the expense of another

a 6. Manufactures nutrients using energy from the sun or from chemical compounds

k 7. Collection of interacting populations

d 8. Simple model for showing how matter and energy move through an ecosystem

h 9. Eats dead organisms

l 10. Portion of Earth that supports life

b 11. Relationship between species in which one species benefits and the other is neither harmed nor benefited

e 12. Network of interconnected food chains

n 13. Relationship between species in which both species benefit

m 14. Study of interactions among organisms and their environments

Column B

a. autotroph

b. commensalism

c. decomposer

d. food chain

e. food web

f. heterotroph

g. parasitism

h. scavenger

i. trophic level

j. habitat

k. community

l. biosphere

m. ecology

n. mutualism

Name _____ Date _____ Class _____

Principles of Ecology, *continued*

Understanding Main Ideas (Part A)

In the space at the left, write the word or phrase in parentheses that correctly completes the statement.

rocks 1. Wind, humidity, and (mosses, rocks) would be considered abiotic factors in a terrestrial ecosystem.

decomposers 2. The size of a population does not directly depend on the availability of (food, decomposers).

biomass 3. To show how the weight of living material at each trophic level of a food chain changes, you could use a pyramid of (numbers, biomass).

lightning 4. In the nitrogen cycle, bacteria and (lightning, decomposers) convert atmospheric nitrogen into nitrogen compounds usable by plants.

heat 5. Some energy that passes through a food chain is lost to the environment as (heat, matter).

decomposition 6. Carbon and nitrogen are released back into the atmosphere during (symbiosis, decomposition).

mutualism 7. Both the alga and the fungus of a lichen benefit from their relationship. This relationship is one of (mutualism, commensalism).

In the space at the left, write the word or phrase that includes all the rest.

food web 8. trophic level, food web, food chain

symbiosis 9. parasitism, commensalism, mutualism, symbiosis

ecosystem 10. organism, ecosystem, population, community

biosphere 11. ecosystems, biotic factors, biosphere, abiotic factors

consumers 12. omnivores, consumers, carnivores, herbivores, scavengers, decomposers

water cycle 13. evaporation, precipitation, water cycle, condensation, urination

Understanding Main Ideas (Part B)

Questions 1–5 refer to the food chain pictured below. In the space at the left, write the letter of the word or phrase that best completes the statement or answers the question.

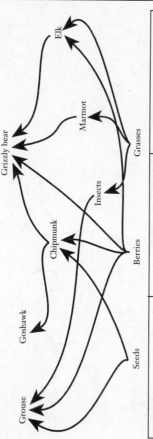

__c__ 1. Energy flows from
 a. coyotes to grasses.   b. cats to mice.
 c. mice to cats.   d. coyotes to cats.

__b__ 2. The coyotes are
 a. herbivores.   b. third-order heterotrophs.
 c. second-order heterotrophs. d. decomposers.

__a__ 3. How many trophic levels does the food chain include?
 a. four   b. one
 c. three   d. two

__c__ 4. As matter and energy move from grasses to coyotes, the amount of available energy
 a. always decreases and population size always increases.
 b. always increases and population size always decreases.
 c. always decreases but population size may increase or decrease.
 d. increases or decreases but population size remains the same.

__d__ 5. Suppose 10 000 units of energy are available at the level of the grasses. What is the total number of energy units lost by the time energy reaches the coyote?
 a. 90 units   b. 990 units   c. 9900 units   d. 9990 units

Thinking Critically

Use the diagram to complete the table below. Classify each member of the food web as *autotroph* or *heterotroph* and identify each heterotroph as *herbivore*, *carnivore*, or *omnivore*. Then answer the questions that follow.

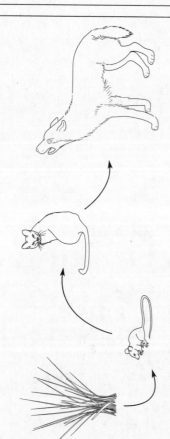

Autotrophs	Heterotrophs	Type of Heterotroph
1. seeds	4. insects	11. herbivore
2. berries	5. elk	12. herbivore
3. grasses	6. marmot	13. herbivore
	7. chipmunk	14. herbivore
	8. grouse	15. omnivore
	9. grizzly bear	16. omnivore
	10. goshawk	17. carnivore

18. How would you describe the marmot's habitat and its position in the food chain? **The marmot's habitat is a forest community. It gets energy from grasses and provides energy for omnivores—bears are omnivores.**

19. When a grouse eats berries, the berry seeds are eliminated as waste and may be dropped in another part of the forest where they may sprout and eventually grow into new berry plants. How would you classify the relationship between the berry plant and the grouse? Explain your reasoning. **The relationship is one of mutualism—the grouse benefits by getting food energy from the berries, and the berry plant benefits by having its seeds dispersed, thereby aiding its reproduction.**

Copyright © Glencoe/McGraw-Hill, a division of The McGraw-Hill Companies, Inc.

Chapter 2 | **Chapter Assessment**

Principles of Ecology, *continued*

Applying Scientific Methods

Milkweed is a plant commonly found throughout fields and pastures and along roadsides in eastern and central North America. It gets its name from the milky white sap that oozes when the plant is broken or cut. Milkweed plants bloom in June and July. When fertilized, the flowers form large seedpods that open in the fall. The following observations were taken from a scientist's field study of milkweed plants from spring through fall.

In the summer, the sugary nectar secreted by the milkweed's flowers attracts many bees, butterflies, moths, and a variety of smaller insects that carry away pollen when they depart. Milkweed nectar seems to be the major source of nutrition for several species of small moths, flies, mosquitoes, and ants. Monarch butterflies, which visit in large numbers, lay their eggs on milkweed plants, and the hatching caterpillars feed on the leaves. As fall approaches, milkweed bugs begin to attack the developing seeds, and milkweed beetles eat the foliage.

Aphids, which suck milkweed sap, are found throughout the year. Crab spiders do not feed on the plant itself but on most of the insects that visit the plant. In the two to three weeks while the milkweed are in bloom, successful adult female crab spiders may increase ten times in mass before laying their eggs on the inner surface of leaves. Some species of flies and wasps, which feed on crab spider eggs, visit the plants periodically. Harvestmen, also known as daddy longlegs, eat the remains left by predators.

1. Did the scientist conduct quantitative or descriptive research?
descriptive research

Milkweed bugs
Bees
Caterpillar
Harvestman
Mosquito
Aphids
Monarch butterfly
Crab spider
Milkweed beetle
Mud-dauber wasp
Ichneumon wasp

Chapter 2 | **Chapter Assessment**

Principles of Ecology, *continued*

Applying Scientific Methods   continued

2. What level of organization in an ecosystem is represented by the milkweed and the organisms that visit or live on the plant?
The milkweed and the other organisms form a community.

3. Based on the scientist's observations, what is one food chain that begins with a milkweed plant?
Answers may vary. Milkweed → mosquito → crab spider → wasp.

4. What is the niche of the harvestmen?
The harvestmen act as scavengers.

5. How would you describe the symbiotic relationship between the milkweed plant and bees?
mutualism

6. Based on the scientist's observations, formulate two possible hypotheses about the effects of crab spiders on the survival of the milkweed plant.
Answers may vary. Because crab spiders feed on insects that help pollinate the milkweed plant, the spiders threaten the reproductive success of the plant. Because crab spiders feed on insects that eat milkweed, the spiders increase the chances of the plant's survival.

Communities and Biomes

Reviewing Vocabulary

In the space at the left, write **true** if the statement is true; if the statement is false, change the italicized word or phrase to make it true.

desert   1. The *taiga* is an arid region characterized by little or no plant life.

plankton   2. Small organisms that live in the sunlit regions of the ocean are *pioneer species*.

permafrost   3. *Humus* is a layer of soil that remains permanently frozen.

estuary   4. A body of water near the coast that is partly surrounded by land and contains both freshwater and salt water is known as an *intertidal zone*.

true   5. *Succession* is the replacement of species in a community as environmental conditions change.

true   6. The portion of the marine biome shallow enough for sunlight to penetrate is the *photic zone*.

intertidal zone   7. The portion of the shoreline that lies between high and low tide lines is the *abiotic zone*.

limiting factors   8. Conditions that restrict the existence, number, reproduction, or distribution of organisms are called *ranges of tolerance*.

true   9. A *climax* community is a stable, mature community that undergoes little or no change in species.

primary   10. The colonization of new sites by communities of organisms is *secondary* succession.

biome   11. A large group of ecosystems characterized by the same type of climax community is called a *taiga*.

true   12. The *temperate forest* is a region dominated by broad-leaved hardwood trees.

secondary   13. *Primary* succession is the sequence of changes that takes place after a community is disrupted.

Communities and Biomes, *continued*

Understanding Main Ideas (Part A)

Write the word or phrase that best completes the statement. Use these choices:

abiotic	optimum	soil	tundra
climax communities	pioneer species	taiga	
photic zone	salinity	tolerance	
grassland	secondary succession	tropical rain forest	

1. **Tolerance** is the ability of an organism to withstand changes in abiotic and biotic factors in an ecosystem.

2. The first species to live in an area are known as **pioneer species**.

3. Shallow marine environments along coastlines are part of the **photic zone**.

4. The **tropical rain forest** is the most species-rich biome.

5. The **grassland** biome occupies more area than any other terrestrial biome.

6. Natural disasters and human actions are possible causes of **secondary succession**.

7. Tropical rain forest and **tundra** biomes are both characterized by a thin layer of nutrient-poor topsoil that can support only shallow-rooted plants.

8. **Climax communities** are characterized by many different species of organisms and little or no succession.

9. Water temperature and light are two **abiotic** factors that affect organisms in a deep lake.

10. The tides affect the **salinity** of water in an estuary.

11. The presence of coniferous trees as the dominant climax plants characterizes the **taiga**.

12. During primary succession, the decay of pioneer species results in the formation of **soil**.

13. The greatest number of organisms is found within the **optimum** range of environmental conditions for a particular population.

Name _____ Date _____ Class _____

Chapter 3 Communities and Biomes, *continued*

Thinking Critically

The illustrations below show succession in a pond within a forest community. Use the illustrations to answer questions 1–5.

Figure 1   **Figure 2**   **Figure 3**

Figure 4   **Figure 5**

1. How is the pond in Figure 2 different from the pond in Figure 1?
Answers may vary. The pond in Figure 2 is slightly shallower than the pond in Figure 1. The land along the margins of the pond in Figure 2 extends farther out into the pond, making it narrower than the pond in Figure 1.

2. What might account for these differences?
Answers may vary. Soil washes into the pond; fallen leaves and other dead matter gradually build up on the bottom of the pond, increasing the nutrients in the pond. The increase in nutrients results in an increase in plant growth around the margins.

3. What changes are illustrated in Figure 4?
Answers may vary. The pond continues to fill in. In the filled-in areas, grasses begin to replace the cattails and reeds.

4. What type of succession is illustrated? Explain.
Primary succession; the pond area is an undisturbed site that underwent change from its original condition.

Name _____ Date _____ Class _____

Chapter 3 Communities and Biomes, *continued*

Understanding Main Ideas (Part B)

Identify the biomes on the map and then answer the questions that follow.

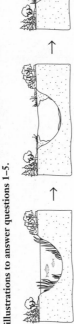

1. **grassland**
2. **taiga**
3. **desert**
4. **tundra**
5. **temperate forest**
6. **tropical rain forest**

7. Which biome has the warmest temperatures and the most rainfall? **tropical rain forest**
8. Which biome has the coldest temperatures? **tundra**
9. Which biome is the driest? **desert**

Study the diagram and then answer the questions.

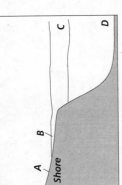

10. Identify the regions of the marine biome shown in the diagram. Use these choices: aphotic zone, photic zone, intertidal zone, shallow-water region.

A. **intertidal zone**
B. **shallow-water region**
C. **photic zone**
D. **aphotic zone**

11. Why are few producers found in region A?
Answers may vary. Crashing waves and tidal variations make it difficult for producers to float or take hold in one place.

12. In which regions are plankton found? **regions B and C**

Applying Scientific Methods

Epiphytes are plants that grow on other plants. In the tropical rain forest, epiphytes sprout from seeds or spores carried by the wind or animals and take root on the trunks and branches of the canopy trees. Epiphytes are not parasitic; they gain nothing from the trees except support and access to sunlight. Under favorable conditions, however, they may form dense, water-logged, tangled mats of roots and stems, weighing up to several thousand kilograms. This weight is often enough to break the limbs of the more fragile trees. Some tree species have developed adaptations to protect against the growth of epiphytes. Two known mechanisms are (1) the frequent shedding of bark layers that periodically removes young epiphytes and (2) the manufacturing of chemicals that inhibit the growth of other plants.

In his explorations of the Costa Rican tropical rain forest, Donald Perry developed an apparatus consisting of a platform base built on one tree and connected to two other trees by means of ropes. From this base, a system of ropes and pulleys attached to a harness allowed an investigator to access previously unexplored areas of the canopy and to move within the canopy with minimal contact or interference with organisms.

During his studies, Perry noticed that some trees were completely free of epiphytes, although the tree species were known not to shed bark or to manufacture plant-inhibiting chemicals. Other scientists speculated that *Azteca* ants, which live on certain species of tropical rain-forest trees, were responsible for the absence of epiphytes on those trees. These aggressive ants were known to swarm and attack other insects and mammals that might damage their trees. To test the effect of the ants on epiphytes, Perry tied some moss and other small epiphytes to the limbs of a tree inhabited by the ants. Perry found that the ants destroyed the epiphytes.

1. What problem did Perry try to solve regarding certain epiphyte-free trees that he observed in the tropical rain forest?
Perry tried to determine why those trees were epiphyte-free even though they did not shed their bark or manufacture plant-inhibiting chemicals.

2. What was Perry's hypothesis regarding those trees?
Perry's hypothesis was that *Azteca* ants prevented epiphytes from growing on the trees.

3. On what did Perry base his hypothesis?
Azteca ants were known to live on trees and to attack other animals that damaged the trees.

4. Why might the ants want to destroy the epiphytes?
Answers will vary. The epiphytes might restrict the movement of the ants on the trees or have a negative effect on the ants' food supply.

Applying Scientific Methods   continued

5. What kind of symbiotic relationship do the ants and trees have? Explain.
The ants and trees have a mutualistic relationship since they both benefit from each other's presence. The trees provide a habitat for the ants, while the ants protect the trees from the epiphytes.

6. How was Perry's rope-and-pulley apparatus helpful in the testing of his hypothesis?
Answers will vary. The apparatus allowed easier access to the ant-inhabited trees and minimized direct contact with the trees, ants, and epiphytes. Also, since the ants were known to attack mammals, the apparatus reduced the risk of the investigator being attacked by the ants.

7. In what other ways might Perry's apparatus be useful?
Answers will vary. With the aid of the apparatus, scientists can explore parts of the tropical rain forest previously unseen by humans, which may lead to the discovery of new species.

Copyright © Glencoe/McGraw-Hill, a division of The McGraw-Hill Companies, Inc.

Chapter Assessment

Chapter 4 Population Biology

Reviewing Vocabulary

In the space at the left, write the letter of the word or phrase that best completes the statement.

b 1. Limiting factors whose effects increase as the size of the population increases are
 a. abiotic factors.
 b. density-dependent factors.
 c. exponential in nature.
 d. density-independent factors.

d 2. The movement of individuals from a population is
 a. immigration.
 b. a reproductive pattern.
 c. a life-history pattern.
 d. emigration.

c 3. The proportions of a population that are at different age levels make up the population's
 a. fertility rate.
 b. growth rate.
 c. age structure.
 d. carrying capacity.

a 4. Unrestricted populations of organisms experience
 a. exponential growth.
 b. linear growth.
 c. infertility.
 d. biotic growth.

b 5. For a particular species, the carrying capacity is the maximum number of individual organisms that
 a. the species could reach in a given time period if all the offspring survive and reproduce.
 b. can be supported by a given environment.
 c. are in their post-reproductive years.
 d. can be supported if there are no limiting factors.

c 6. Density-independent factors are limiting factors whose effects are
 a. confined to the habitat of a population.
 b. determined by the degree of competition for resources.
 c. not influenced by population densities.
 d. determined by the difference between birthrate and death rate.

Chapter Assessment

Chapter 4 Population Biology, *continued*

Understanding Main Ideas (Part A)

In the space at the left, write the term in parentheses that correctly completes each statement.

J 1. A (J, S)-shaped curve describes the tendency of a population to grow without limit to its size.

less 2. If a population's death rate is (less, greater) than its birthrate, the population will grow.

Food availability 3. (Food availability, Earthquake damage) would be a density-dependent limiting factor on the growth of a population.

fertility 4. The number of offspring produced by a female during her reproductive years defines the (fertility, birth) rate.

rapid 5. The production of many offspring in a short period of time is characteristic of a (slow, rapid) life-history pattern.

carrying capacity 6. Instead of growing explosively, population growth tends to level off because the population reaches the (competitive limit, carrying capacity) of a particular environment.

Immigration 7. (Immigration, Emigration) can greatly increase the size of the population and create stresses within the population.

Label the graph below, which depicts the population growth for a sample of paramecium. Use these terms: beginning growth stage, exponential growth stage, leveling-off stage, carrying capacity.

8. **carrying capacity**

9. **leveling-off stage**

10. **exponential growth stage**

11. **beginning growth stage**

Understanding Main Ideas (Part B)

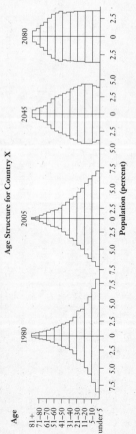

Age Structure for Country X

1980   2005   2045   2080

Age
81+
71–80
61–70
51–60
41–50
31–40
21–30
11–20
5–10
under 5

Population (percent)

The first age structure graph for country X shows the percent of the population in each age group for 1980. The remaining three graphs are projections of how the age structure of country X will change. Use the graphs to answer questions 1–5.

1. In 1980, does country X exhibit an age structure more typical of a developing nation or an industrialized nation? Explain.

The age structure is more typical of a developing nation, as indicated by the larger percentage of individuals in the pre-reproductive and reproductive years and a smaller percentage in the post-reproductive years.

2. How is the age structure expected to change by 2005?

Very little change is projected; a slight decrease in the proportion of pre-reproductive individuals and a slight increase in the proportion of reproductive individuals is indicated.

3. What can you conclude about the stage of population growth for country X from 1980 to 2005? Country X is in a rapid-growth, or exponential, stage.

Country X is in a rapid-growth, or exponential, stage.

4. Describe the overall trend in population growth predicted.

Population growth will begin to slow down by 2045, with little to no growth expected by 2080.

5. What might account for the age structure predicted for 2080?

Answers may vary. The carrying capacity of the environment will be reached; the country will have become more industrialized; the birthrates, death rates, and/or fertility rates will have changed.

Thinking Critically

The figures represent a population of bees occupying the same territory in the years 1990 and 1992. Each ■ represents 100 bees. Use the figures to answers questions 1–6.

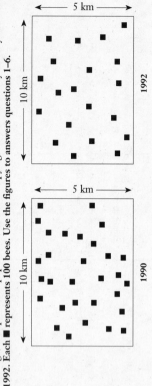

1990   1992

1. What is the area of the territory occupied by the bees?
area = 10 km × 5 km = 50 sq km

2. What was the size of the bee population in 1990?
30 × 100 = 3000 bees

3. What was the density per square kilometer of the bee population in 1990?
density = 3000 bees/50 sq km = 60 bees per sq km

4. How did the size and density of the bee population change by 1992? Describe the changes in numbers.
The number of bees decreased from 3000 to 2000; density decreased from 60 to 40 bees per sq km.

5. What environmental factors might explain this change?
Answers may vary. A decrease in population size may result from increased competition from other insects for the same flowers and plants the bees feed on; drought or other weather conditions resulting in fewer plants and flowers growing in the area; and human intervention, such as pesticide spraying.

6. Suppose in a population of 1000 wild horses, there are 400 births and 220 deaths. Also, 180 new horses join the population from an area that was destroyed by fire, and 380 horses are captured by park rangers. Describe the overall change in this horse population. What is the percentage of increase or decrease? Since a total of 580 horses are added and a total of 600 horses are lost, the population decreases by 20 individuals. The population decreased by 20/1000, or 2%.

Since a total of 580 horses are added and a total of 600 horses are lost, the population decreases by 20 individuals. The population decreased by 20/1000, or 2%.

Chapter Assessment

Chapter 4   Population Biology, *continued*

Applying Scientific Methods

A student grew a yeast culture on sterilized nutrient medium in a closed dish for 5 days. Each day, she took the same size sample from the dish and placed it on a special slide used for counting microorganisms. She examined the samples under a microscope and drew the following illustrations of her observations over the course of the investigation. Each dot represents 10 yeast cells.

Day 0   Day 1   Day 2   Day 3   Day 4   Day 5

1. Why did the student use sterilized medium and keep the dish closed?
to prevent the culture from being contaminated by yeast cells or other microorganisms in the medium or in the air

2. What problem was this student investigating?
The student was investigating the growth pattern of a yeast population.

3. During which two-day period was population growth most rapid?
Population growth was most rapid from day 1 to day 2, during which time the population more than tripled in size.

4. At what point did the population reach the carrying capacity of the culture dish?
The population reached its maximum number on day 3; after that, there were fewer yeast cells present.

5. What factors limited the growth of the yeast population?
available food and space

6. How could the student change the investigation so that the carrying capacity of the yeast's environment is increased?
Answers may vary. The student could use a larger culture dish and more nutrient medium so that the yeast have more available food and space.

Chapter Assessment

Chapter 4   Population Biology, *continued*

Applying Scientific Methods   *continued*

7. What steps could the student take to ensure the accuracy of her results?
Answers may vary. Grow more than one culture and average the results from each; have another student make counts using a second sample of equal size; and have other students repeat the investigation and use the average of all the results obtained.

8. Which graph best illustrates the growth of the student's yeast population?
graph C

Graph A — Number of yeast cells vs. Time (days)
Graph B — Number of yeast cells vs. Time (days)
Graph C — Number of yeast cells vs. Time (days)

Chapter 5 — Biological Diversity and Conservation

Chapter Assessment

Reviewing Vocabulary

In the space at the left, write true if the statement is true; if the statement is false, change the italicized term to make it true.

low   **1.** Acid precipitation is rain, snow, sleet, or fog with a *high* pH value.

true   **2.** Zoo animals are in *captivity.*

an edge effect   **3.** The different conditions along the boundaries of an ecosystem, caused by habitat fragmentation, are called *a boundary effect.*

true   **4.** *Conservation biology* studies methods and implements plans to protect biodiversity.

true   **5.** When an *exotic species* is introduced into an area, it can grow at an exponential rate due to a lack of competitors.

extinction   **6.** *Conservation* is the disappearance of a species when the last of its members dies.

degradation   **7.** Air, water, and land pollution cause habitat *fragmentation.*

true   **8.** The harvesting of food in a protected area is an example of *sustainable use.*

ultraviolet radiation   **9.** The ozone layer protects organisms from *CFCs.*

a threatened species   **10.** Because the number of African elephants is declining rapidly, the African elephant is *an endangered species.*

true   **11.** The greater the number of species in a certain area, the greater is the area's *biodiversity.*

true   **12.** *Habitat corridors* allow organisms to migrate from one protected area to another.

true   **13.** *Reintroduction* programs release organisms into areas where their species once lived.

Chapter 5 — Biological Diversity and Conservation, *continued*

Chapter Assessment

Understanding Main Ideas (Part A)

In the space at the left, write the letter of the word or phrase that best completes the statement or answers the question.

b   **1.** Habitat degradation can be limited by
    a. decreasing the edge effect.   **b.** reducing pollution.
    c. establishing habitat corridors.   **d.** increasing biodiversity.

c   **2.** Which of the following sequences is the most likely to occur?
    a. endangered species → threatened species → extinct species
    b. extinct species → threatened species → endangered species
    c. threatened species → endangered species → extinct species
    d. threatened species → extinct species → endangered species

a   **3.** Which of the following is not caused by air pollution?
    a. algal blooms   **b.** acid precipitation
    c. increased UV radiation   **d.** loss of the ozone layer

b   **4.** Which of the following animals would be least affected by habitat fragmentation?
    a. wolves   **b.** hawks   **c.** zebras   **d.** lions

c   **5.** Reintroduction programs involve the
    a. establishment of protected areas.   **b.** reduction of pollution.
    c. capture of endangered species.   **d.** introduction of exotic species.

c   **6.** The removal of coral reefs by people is an example of habitat
    a. fragmentation.   **b.** degradation.   **c.** loss.   **d.** preservation.

a   **7.** National parks help prevent the extinction of many species by
    a. preserving the species' habitats.   **b.** reducing pollution.
    c. introducing exotic species.   **d.** allowing the sustainable use of resources.

b   **8.** Problems associated with habitat fragmentation can be lessened by
    a. reducing pollution.   **b.** establishing habitat corridors.
    c. introducing exotic species.   **d.** establishing national parks.

b   **9.** DDT had been passed to large birds, such as the bald eagle, through
    a. water.   **b.** food chains.   **c.** air.   **d.** soil.

d   **10.** Acid precipitation is caused by
    a. pesticides.   **b.** CFCs.   **c.** the release of acid fumes.   **d.** burning fossil fuels.

Name _____ Date _____ Class _____

Chapter 5 Biological Diversity and Conservation, *continued*

Understanding Main Ideas (Part B)

Use the map to answer questions 1–3. Explain your answers.

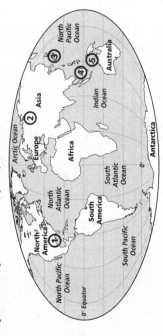

1. In which numbered location on the map would you expect to find the least biodiversity?
   Location 2 would be expected to have the least biodiversity because it is farthest
   from the equator and has a very cold climate.

2. Would you expect to find more biodiversity on island 4 or 5?
   Island 4 would be expected to have more biodiversity because it is larger than
   island 5 and probably has more kinds of ecosystems.

3. Would you expect to find more biodiversity on island 3 or island 5?
   Even though island 5 is smaller than island 3, island 5 would be expected to have
   more biodiversity because it is closer to the equator, where the climate is warmer.

Answer the following questions.

4. How does acid precipitation affect land and water organisms?
   Acid precipitation that falls to the ground leaches mineral nutrients from the soil,
   affecting the growth of plants. Acid precipitation can also damage plant tissues.
   Acid precipitation that falls into bodies of water can kill plants, animals, and other
   organisms living in the water.

5. What are some problems associated with the introduction of an exotic species into an ecosystem?
   The exotic species may lack competitors or predators in the ecosystem, resulting
   in the species's exponential growth and the eventual elimination of native species.

CHAPTER ASSESSMENT   CHAPTER 5   BIOLOGY: The Dynamics of Life   27

Name _____ Date _____ Class _____

Chapter 5 Biological Diversity and Conservation, *continued*

Thinking Critically

Suppose that fertilizers are being used by a farmer to add nutrients to depleted soil. At present, a nearby lake is a healthy ecosystem with floating algae and lake plants growing in balance with the fish and other lake inhabitants. Aerobic (oxygen-using) bacteria in the lake are the major decomposers.

1. Under what conditions could the fertilizer become a pollutant? Which part of the environment would be affected?
   Answers may vary. If it rains very hard soon after the fertilizer is applied, before
   the fertilizer has had a chance to become incorporated into the soil, much of it will
   wash into the lake. An excess of nutrients in the lake would be considered water
   pollution.

2. How might fertilizer pollution affect the organisms in the lake?
   An excess of nutrients in the lake could produce an increase in algae growth, or an
   algal bloom. As the algae die and decompose, much of the oxygen in the water
   would be used by the decomposers. The algal bloom also might cover the lake and
   prevent light and air from reaching the other organisms in the lake. As a result,
   many lake organisms could die.

When a dam is built across a river, the dam creates an artificial lake or reservoir upstream. Dams are useful because they hold river water and collect and store runoff. Dams can also cause problems, however.

3. How could the building of a dam just downstream of a shorebird habitat cause a species of shorebirds to become threatened?
   Answers may vary. The reservoir created by the dam could flood the land around
   the part of the river where the shorebirds make their homes and obtain their food.
   The birds themselves may be killed by the flooding or eventually decline in numbers
   because of these changes to their habitat and the decreased food supply.

4. How could the building of the dam affect farmland located downstream from the dam?
   By disrupting the flow of the river, the dam reduces the amount of water and nutri-
   ent-rich sediments the land receives. The land would probably become less produc-
   tive and support fewer organisms.

28   CHAPTER 5   BIOLOGY: The Dynamics of Life

Biological Diversity and Conservation, *continued*

Applying Scientific Methods

You are an environmental scientist who has been hired by the management of a nuclear power plant to help decide how and where to store the plant's radioactive waste materials. The power plant is located along the ocean coast, close to several large cities and towns. Although some of the radioactive waste is stored on site at the plant, most of it has been sealed in steel storage tanks that have been buried just a few feet under the soil surface of a nearby open field. Some people have suggested that the tanks be taken out to deep sea and lowered to the bottom of the ocean. Another group has suggested building a permanent storage area deep under the soil surface.

1. Why is the disposal of radioactive wastes a problem?
   Answers may vary. Radioactive wastes are very dangerous to humans and other
   organisms.

2. What are some of the limitations of the present method of shallow burial of radioactive wastes?
   Answers may vary. The site is not protected from natural disasters, such as floods
   or earthquakes. Leakage from the tanks could penetrate and pollute the soil, local
   water supplies, and the air. Because the tanks are buried near the surface, they
   could be accidentally dug up and damaged if the field becomes a construction site.

3. What environmental problems could deep-sea burial present?
   Answers may vary. Salt water might eventually corrode the containers, causing
   leakage of radioactive wastes into the ocean. As radioactive water from the ocean
   moves through the water cycle, the radioactivity could affect organisms hundreds
   of miles away. Furthermore, burying the tanks on the ocean bottom does not
   protect them from undersea earthquakes or volcanoes.

4. What abiotic factors would need to be considered in choosing a deep-burial site on land?
   Answers may vary. Rock structure (impermeability and permeability of surrounding
   rock) and the locations of earthquake faults and underground water supplies must
   be considered.

Biological Diversity and Conservation, *continued*

Applying Scientific Methods   *continued*

5. What biotic factors would need to be considered?
   Answers may vary. The types of organisms (species diversity) in the area and the
   number of organisms must be considered. The possibility of relocating organisms
   should also be taken into consideration.

6. In order to determine the possible effects of building a deep-burial land site in a particular area, what preliminary steps would you recommend?
   Answers may vary. Population studies of the organisms in the area should be
   conducted over a period of years to understand the patterns of growth, behaviors,
   and interactions of the organisms that would be affected. Geological histories also
   should be studied.

7. After deciding on deep-sea or underground burial for storing the radioactive wastes, how might scientists monitor the effectiveness of the chosen storage method?
   Answers may vary. Scientists could obtain soil and water samples from around the
   storage area and test them for radioactivity. Organisms living near the storage area
   could be observed for abnormalities resulting from exposure to radioactivity.

Name _____ Date _____ Class _____

Chapter Assessment

Chapter 6 — The Chemistry of Life

Reviewing Vocabulary

Match the definition in Column A with the term in Column B.

Column A

d 1. Center of an atom

h 2. Mixture in which one or more substances are distributed evenly in another substance

c 3. All of the chemical reactions that occur within an organism

e 4. Bond formed between amino acids

b 5. Protein that changes the rate of a chemical reaction

f 6. Molecule with unequal distribution of charge

g 7. Large molecule formed when many smaller molecules bond together

a 8. Net movement of particles from an area of higher concentration to an area of lower concentration

Column B

a. diffusion

b. enzyme

c. metabolism

d. nucleus

e. peptide bond

f. polar molecule

g. polymer

h. solution

In the space at the left, write the term in parentheses that makes each statement correct.

isotopes 9. Atoms of the same element with different numbers of neutrons are (*isotopes, isomers*).

compounds 10. Atoms of two or more elements chemically combined are (*mixtures, compounds*).

covalent 11. Two atoms that share electrons are held together by (*ionic, covalent*) bonds.

acid 12. Any substance that forms hydrogen ions in water is a(n) (*acid, base*).

nucleotides 13. The smaller subunits that make up nucleic acids are (*amino acids, nucleotides*).

diffusion 14. Some substances move into cells by (*hydrogen bonding, diffusion*).

CHAPTER ASSESSMENT

Name _____ Date _____ Class _____

Chapter Assessment

Chapter 6 — The Chemistry of Life, *continued*

Understanding Main Ideas (Part A)

In the space at the left, write the letter of the word or phrase that best completes the statement.

a 1. Unlike carbohydrates and lipids, proteins contain
   a. nitrogen.   b. carbon.   c. hydrogen.   d. oxygen.

b 2. A(n) _____ is formed when two atoms share electrons, such as with hydrogen and oxygen in water.
   a. solution   b. covalent bond
   c. ionic bond   d. isotope

c 3. An atom of fluorine has 9 electrons. Its second energy level has
   a. 2 electrons.   b. 8 electrons.   c. 7 electrons.   d. 9 electrons.

d 4. The total number of atoms in a molecule of sucrose, $C_{12}H_{22}O_{11}$, is
   a. 11.   b. 12.   c. 22.   d. 45.

a 5. Carbon-12, carbon-13, and carbon-14 are
   a. isotopes.   b. polymers.   c. radio-isotopes.   d. macromolecules.

d 6. A very strong base might have a pH of
   a. 3.   b. 5.   c. 9.   d. 13.

b 7. Glucose and fructose, both with the formula $C_6H_{12}O_6$, differ in
   a. numbers of atoms.   b. arrangement of atoms.
   c. kinds of atoms.   d. arrangement of electrons.

d 8. The various enzymes in our bodies are
   a. lipids.   b. carbohydrates.   c. nucleotides.   d. proteins.

a 9. A chlorine atom becomes a chloride ion when it
   a. gains an electron.   b. loses an electron.
   c. gains a neutron.   d. loses a proton.

c 10. When molecules of glucose and fructose combine to form sucrose, they do so by
   a. hydrolysis.   b. electron clouds.   c. condensation.   d. radiation.

b 11. Water dissolves many ionic and molecular compounds because of its
   a. ionic bonding.   b. polarity.
   c. capillary action.   d. size.

b 12. When is there no difference in the concentration of a substance from one area to another,
   a. diffusion occurs.   b. dynamic equilibrium has been reached.
   c. the atoms stop moving.   d. there is a concentration gradient.

CHAPTER ASSESSMENT

Chapter 6 — The Chemistry of Life, *continued*

Understanding Main Ideas (Part B)

Study the diagram, which shows the formation of magnesium chloride and hydrogen fluoride. Then answer the questions.

1. Which compound is formed by ionic bonding? Explain.
Magnesium chloride; it is formed by ionic bonding because two electrons are transferred from the magnesium atom, one to each chlorine atom, to form two chloride ions and one magnesium ion.

2. Which compound is formed by covalent bonding? Explain.
Hydrogen fluoride; it is formed by covalent bonding because two electrons, one from each atom, are shared by the atoms that make up the hydrogen fluoride molecule.

3. How many electrons are in the third energy level of a magnesium atom? **two**

4. Which atom forms an ion by the loss of electrons? **magnesium**

CHAPTER ASSESSMENT

CHAPTER 6   BIOLOGY: The Dynamics of Life   **33**

Chapter 6 — The Chemistry of Life, *continued*

Thinking Critically

To answer questions 1 and 2, use the table of acid–base indicators below.

Indicator	Color at lower pH values	pH range of color transition	Color at higher pH values
Methyl red	Red	4.4–6.0	Yellow
Litmus	Red	5.5–8.0	Blue
Bromothymol blue	Yellow	6.0–7.6	Blue
Phenol red	Yellow	6.8–8.4	Red
Phenolphthalein	Colorless	8.3–10.0	Red

1. A small volume of dilute hydrochloric acid is placed in a beaker and two drops of phenolphthalein are added. The solution remains colorless. A dilute solution of sodium hydroxide is then added drop by drop until a color change occurs. In what pH range does the color change occur? Describe the color change that occurs.
8.3–10.0; colorless to red

2. If you exhale carbon dioxide (CO_2) into a solution of bromothymol blue, the solution turns from blue to yellow. Does CO_2 dissolve in water to form an acid or a base?
an acid

Refer to the figure at the right for questions 3–5.

3. What type of biological compounds are A and B?
fatty acid

4. Classify A and B as either saturated or unsaturated. Explain.
A is saturated because it contains only single carbon–carbon bonds. B is unsaturated because it contains a double carbon–carbon bond.

5. In most lipids, compounds like A and B are attached to a 3-carbon molecule of _____ **glycerol** .

34   CHAPTER 6   BIOLOGY: The Dynamics of Life

CHAPTER ASSESSMENT

Name _____ Date _____ Class _____

Applying Scientific Methods

Two students carry out an investigation to determine the action of the enzyme pepsin on protein digestion in the human stomach. They know that gastric juice in the stomach contains water, pepsin, and hydrochloric acid. They decide to use small, equal-sized pieces of cooked egg white as the protein to be digested.

They set up four test tubes and place equal small amounts of egg white in each test tube. Then they fill each test tube with a different liquid to a height of 3 centimeters. To test tube 1, they add water; to test tube 2, they add hydrochloric acid (HCl diluted in water); to test tube 3, they add pepsin dissolved in water; and to test tube 4, they add pepsin solution and dilute hydrochloric acid. They place the four test tubes in an incubator set at 37°C (body temperature).

After one day, they observe the results. Then they return the test tubes to the incubator and observe them again the next day. The following table is the record of the results.

Test tube	1 day	2 days
1. egg + water	no change	no change
2. egg + hydrochloric acid	no change	no change
3. egg + pepsin solution	liquid slightly cloudy, egg pieces unchanged	liquid cloudy, egg pieces smaller
4. egg + pepsin solution + hydrochloric acid	liquid cloudy, egg pieces smaller	liquid very cloudy, almost no egg remains

1. Which test tube is the control? Explain its purpose.
Tube 1 is the control because it contains the substances, egg white and water,
that are found in all four test tubes. The control is important because it acts as
a standard to which the other test tubes can be compared.

2. What is the independent variable in the experiment? The dependent variable?
The independent variable is the substance that may affect the digestion of
proteins. The dependent variable is the digestion of the egg white.

Name _____ Date _____ Class _____

Applying Scientific Methods   continued

3. What is the hypothesis on which this experiment is based?
Hydrochloric acid helps pepsin digest proteins in the stomach.

4. Was the hypothesis correct? Explain?
Yes; the pepsin digested the egg white more quickly in the presence of
hydrochloric acid.

5. What kind of results would have shown that the hypothesis is not correct?
If test tubes 3 and 4 showed the same results, it could be concluded that
hydrochloric acid does not help pepsin to digest proteins in the stomach.

6. What did the results from test tube 2 tell about protein digestion in the stomach?
The results indicated that the hydrochloric acid itself does not digest proteins in
the stomach.

7. Write a conclusion to the experiment. Base your conclusion on the experimental results.
Pepsin digests proteins slightly at body temperature. In the presence of
hydrochloric acid, the digestion of proteins by pepsin is much more efficient.

Understanding Concepts (Part A)

In the space at the left, write the letter of the word or phrase that best completes the statement.

__a__ 1. Cell walls of multicellular plants are composed mainly of
   a. cellulose.
   b. chitin.
   c. pectin.
   d. vacuoles.

__d__ 2. The term *least* closely related to the others is
   a. cytoskeleton.
   b. microfilament.
   c. microtubule.
   d. cell juncture.

__b__ 3. In a chloroplast, the stacks of membranous sacs are called
   a. stroma.
   b. grana.
   c. plastids.
   d. thylakoid membrane.

__d__ 4. The structure most responsible for maintaining cell homeostasis is the
   a. cytoplasm.
   b. mitochondrion.
   c. cell wall.
   d. plasma membrane.

__b__ 5. If a cell contains a nucleus, it must be a(n)
   a. plant cell.
   b. eukaryotic cell.
   c. animal cell.
   d. prokaryotic cell.

__b__ 6. One advantage of electron microscopes over light microscopes is their
   a. size.
   b. higher magnification.
   c. two-dimensional image.
   d. use of live specimens.

__a__ 7. When a cell is ready to reproduce, its DNA is packed into
   a. chromosomes.
   b. chromatin.
   c. nucleoli.
   d. nucleoids.

__a__ 8. The scientist who first described living cells as seen through a simple microscope was
   a. van Leeuwenhoek.
   b. Schleiden.
   c. Hooke.
   d. Schwann.

__c__ 9. Each of the following is a main idea of the cell theory *except*
   a. all organisms are composed of cells.
   b. the cell is the basic unit of organization of organisms.
   c. all cells are similar in structure and function.
   d. all cells come from preexisting cells.

__c__ 10. A plasma membrane is made up of a(n)
   a. cholesterol layer.
   b. enzyme bilayer.
   c. phospholipid bilayer.
   d. protein layer.

Reviewing Vocabulary

Write the word or phrase that best completes the statement.

1. A structure outside the plasma membrane in some cells is the __cell wall__.

2. The functions of a eukaryotic cell are managed by the __nucleus__.

3. In a cell, the tangles of long strands of DNA form the __chromatin__.

4. The folded system of membranes that forms a network of interconnected compartments inside the cell is called the __endoplasmic reticulum__.

5. The pigment that gives plants their green color is __chlorophyll__.

6. The network of tiny rods and filaments that forms a framework for the cell is called the __cytoskeleton__.

7. In plants, the structures that transform light energy into chemical energy are called __chloroplasts__.

In the space at the left, write the term in parentheses that makes each statement correct.

__Transport proteins__ 8. (*Phospholipids, Transport proteins*) make up the selectively permeable membrane which controls which molecules enter and leave the cell.

__cilia__ 9. Short, hairlike projections used for locomotion are (*cilia, flagella*).

__mitochondria__ 10. In a cell, the breakdown of molecules in order to release energy occurs in the (*mitochondria, Golgi apparatus*).

__prokaryote__ 11. An organism with a cell that lacks a true nucleus is a(n) (*prokaryote, eukaryote*).

__plasma membrane__ 12. The movement of materials into and out of the cells is controlled by the (*cytoplasm, plasma membrane*).

__organelles__ 13. The small, membrane-bound structures inside a cell are (*chromatin, organelles*).

__ribosomes__ 14. In a cell, the sites of protein synthesis are the (*ribosomes, nucleolus*).

__lysosomes__ 15. Cell structures that contain digestive enzymes are (*plastids, lysosomes*).

Chapter Assessment

Chapter 7   A View of the Cell, *continued*

Understanding Concepts (Part B)

The diagram below of a bacterium shows a light area with no surrounding membrane in the center of the cell. This area contains a single large DNA molecule. Use the diagram to answer questions 1 and 2.

1. Identify the structures labeled A, B, and C.
A is the nucleoid; B is the cell wall; C is the plasma membrane.

2. Based on the diagram, would scientists classify this cell as a prokaryote or a eukaryote? Explain.
Scientists would classify this bacterium as a prokaryote because it has no membrane-bound internal structures and it does not have a distinct nucleus, even though it does contain a nucleoid with DNA.

Answer the following questions.

3. In plants, cells that transport water against the force of gravity are found to contain many more mitochondria than do some other plant cells. What is the reason for this? **Mitochondria are organelles that produce energy for cell reactions; active cells usually have more mitochondria than do less active cells. It would be reasonable to conclude that the number of mitochondria is in direct relation to the amount of work done by the cells.**

4. Why did it take almost 200 years after Hooke discovered cells for the cell theory to be developed? **Cells could not be viewed until the technology was available to develop efficient microscopes.**

Chapter Assessment

Chapter 7   A View of the Cell, *continued*

Thinking Critically

Answer the following questions.

1. Many types of animal cells have a thin, flexible cell covering outside the plasma membrane. This cell covering, called a glycocalyx, consists of complex carbohydrates bonded to the proteins and lipids in the plasma membrane. How is the glycocalyx similar to the cell wall of a green plant? How is it different?
Both the glycocalyx and the cell wall surround the plasma membrane. The cell wall is made of cellulose and is fairly thick, stiff, and rigid; the glycocalyx is a complex carbohydrate that is quite thin and flexible. The glycocalyx is bonded to the plasma membrane; the cell wall is not.

2. The stomach lining contains mucus, which helps prevent the digestion of the stomach lining. If this mechanism fails, digestive enzymes in the stomach cause the stomach to digest itself, producing an ulcer. Compare this process with the way lysosomes prevent destruction of the cell's proteins. **Lysosomes also contain digestive enzymes, but the membrane surrounding a lysosome prevents these enzymes from leaving the lysosome and destroying the cell's proteins. If the lysosome membrane should break down, the contents would digest the cell's proteins just as the stomach enzymes may digest the stomach.**

3. Between which cell types is the difference greater—plant and animal cells or prokaryotic and eukaryotic cells? Give reasons for your answer. **The difference between prokaryotic and eukaryotic cells is greater because these two types of cells differ in basic cell organization. Eukaryotic cells are characterized by membrane-bound organelles. Prokaryotic cells do not have membrane-bound organelles and must carry on all essential life processes without them. Plant and animal cells are both eukaryotic and have many organelles in common (for example, nucleus, mitochondria, endoplasmic reticulum, Golgi apparatus, lysosomes). Animal cells lack a cell wall and the plastids found in plant cells.**

Applying Scientific Methods

For many years, scientists thought of the nucleus as "a bag of chromatin floating in a sea of cytoplasm." Using electron microscopes, scientists saw that the nucleus was much more complex. The nuclear envelope was two-layered and covered with pores.

Scientists began further research. Scientist S punched small holes in the nuclear envelope, allowing the contents to pour out. He observed that the nucleus retained its spherical shape. From this, scientist S hypothesized that the nucleus had some other structural framework, beyond the membrane itself. The next experiment performed by scientist S revealed that the nucleus indeed had a fibrous protein framework, now called the nuclear matrix.

Three other scientists repeated this experiment, but each changed one part of it. Scientist X used detergents and salt to remove the nuclear contents. Scientist Y used chemicals, and scientist Z used enzymes. All three observed that a nuclear matrix remained.

Further electron microscopy revealed that the chromatin strands are anchored to a fibrous layer that lines the inner layer of the nuclear envelope.

1. What was the hypothesis of scientist S in his first experiment?
that the nucleus would retain its shape even when its contents was removed

2. What observation from scientist S's second experiment supported the original hypothesis?
A fibrous protein network (nuclear matrix) was observed to be present in the nucleus.

3. Why did scientists X, Y, and Z carry out their experiments?
to verify or disprove the presence of a nuclear matrix reported by scientist S

4. What was the variable in the experiments by scientists X, Y, and Z?
The variable was the method and substance used to remove the contents of the nucleus. Each scientist used a different substance.

5. Why did scientists X, Y, and Z use different substances to remove the nuclear contents?
to demonstrate that the nuclear matrix did not result from any chemical reactions but actually existed as an independent structure

6. Describe a procedure to determine whether the attachment of the chromatin to the nuclear envelope is necessary for the chromatin to become chromosomes.
Answers may vary. A scientist could detach chromatin strands from the fibrous layer and observe whether or not chromosomes form when the cell is ready to reproduce.

Applying Scientific Methods   *continued*

In the 1890s, E. Overton performed experiments to determine the structure of the plasma membrane. After many years and various procedures, he determined that large, uncharged molecules enter a cell at a rate proportional to their solubility in lipids. This observation was the first indication that the plasma membrane is probably made up of lipids. Many scientists began to pursue the question of how the lipids were arranged.

In 1925, two Dutch scientists determined that the area covered by the lipids from a single red blood cell is twice the area of the surface of the cell. From this, they reasoned that the cell is covered by a double layer of lipid molecules. Based on this work, various scientists hypothesized that the membrane was like a "fat sandwich" with two outer layers of protein on the surface of the lipid layer.

None of the ideas seemed a satisfactory explanation until microscopic studies of membranes prepared by a new technique of "freeze-fracture" revealed that the proteins are actually embedded in the lipid layer. In 1972, on the basis of these results and other evidence, two American scientists proposed the fluid-mosaic model.

7. What was the problem that Overton was trying to solve with his experiments?
He was trying to determine the structure of the plasma membrane.

8. Is his hypothesis stated in the discussion above? If so, what was it?
no

9. The result of one experiment often leads to further experiments. How do Overton's experiments illustrate this fact?
Many scientists, including the Dutch, experimented to determine the actual arrangement of the lipids in the plasma membrane.

10. What conclusion did the Dutch scientists reach?
that the membrane consists of a double layer of lipid molecules

11. What inference did the Dutch scientists make to reach their conclusion?
Because the surface area of the red blood cell was only half the surface area of the lipids from that cell, the cell covering must be a double layer of lipids.

12. What model of the plasma membrane was based on their results?
the "fat sandwich" model

13. Why was it almost 50 years between the Dutch scientists' research and the proposal of a fluid mosaic model?
A new procedure, "freeze-fracture," had to be developed before scientists could observe the actual arrangement of lipids and proteins.

Name _____ Date _____ Class _____

Cellular Transport and the Cell Cycle

Reviewing Vocabulary

Write the word or phrase that best completes each statement.

1. The transport of materials against a concentration gradient is called **active transport**.

2. The phase of mitosis in which the sister chromatids separate from each other is **anaphase**.

3. A solution in which the concentration of dissolved substances is lower than the concentration inside a cell is **hypotonic**.

4. The sequence of growth and division of a cell make up the **cell cycle**.

5. The period during which chromosomes duplicate is **interphase**.

6. The segment of DNA that controls the production of a protein is a **gene**.

7. The phase of mitosis in which chromosomes line up on the equator of the spindle is **metaphase**.

8. The two halves of a doubled chromosome structure are called **sister chromatids**.

9. The uncontrolled division of cells may result in **cancer**.

10. Passive transport with the aid of transport proteins is **facilitated diffusion**.

11. The process by which nuclear material is divided equally between two new cells is **mitosis**.

12. Some cells surround and take in materials by the process of **endocytosis**.

13. The structures that hold together sister chromatids are **centromeres**.

Write a sentence that uses each pair of terms.

14. (spindle, centrioles)
During prophase, the spindle forms between the pairs of centrioles.

15. (tissues, organs)
Organs are made of tissues organized in various combinations.

Name _____ Date _____ Class _____

Cellular Transport and the Cell Cycle, continued

Understanding Main Ideas (Part A)

In the space at the left, write the letter of the word or phrase that best completes the statement or answers the question.

c 1. When placed in a hypotonic solution, a cell will
   a. diffuse. b. shrink. c. swell. d. stay the same.

a 2. As the size of a cell increases,
   a. volume increases faster than surface area.
   b. volume increases and surface area decreases.
   c. volume and surface area increase at the same rate.
   d. surface area increases faster than volume.

b 3. The longest phase of the cell cycle is
   a. prophase. b. interphase. c. metaphase. d. mitosis.

b 4. Which of the following does *not* control the cell cycle?
   a. DNA b. mitosis c. enzymes d. genes

d 5. Tangled strands of DNA wrapped around protein molecules make up the
   a. spindle. b. microtubules. c. nuclear envelope. d. chromatin.

d 6. By the end of prophase, each of the following has occurred *except*
   a. chromatin coiling into visible chromosomes.
   b. breaking down of the nuclear envelope.
   c. forming of the spindle.
   d. lining up of chromosomes in the cell.

c 7. Each of the following is an example of passive transport *except*
   a. diffusion. b. osmosis.
   c. exocytosis. d. facilitated diffusion.

c 8. The cells that make up a tissue
   a. are different. b. are the result of interphase.
   c. have the same function. d. no longer undergo mitosis.

b 9. Each of the following is a cause of some cancers *except*
   a. damaged genes. b. bacteria.
   c. ultraviolet radiation. d. viruses.

d 10. Among the following, the term that includes all of the others is
   a. interphase. b. nuclear division. c. mitosis. d. cell cycle.

Cellular Transport and the Cell Cycle, *continued*

Understanding Main Ideas (Part B)

The diagrams below show six cells in various phases of the cell cycle, labeled A through F. Use the diagrams to answer questions 1–7.

Phases of the Cell Cycle

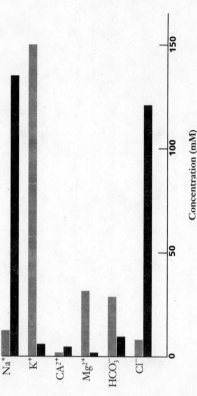

A   B   C   D   E   F

1. Which cell is in metaphase? **C**

2. Cells A and F show an early and a late stage of the same phase of mitosis. What phase is it?
prophase

3. In cell A, what structure is labeled X?
centriole

4. In cell F, what structure is labeled Y?
spindle

5. Which cell is not in a phase of mitosis?
D

6. What two main changes are taking place in cell B?
A separate nuclear envelope is forming around each set of chromosomes.
The spindle is breaking down.

7. Sequence the six diagrams in order from first to last.
D, A, F, C, E, B   or   A, F, C, E, B, D

Answer the following question.

8. What are the main differences between cytokinesis in plant cells and in animal cells?
During cytokinesis in animal cells, the plasma membrane pinches in along the equator to form two new cells. In plant cells, a cell plate forms across the equator; then a plasma membrane forms around each new cell and a new cell wall is secreted on each side of the cell plate.

Cellular Transport and the Cell Cycle, *continued*

Thinking Critically

The graph shows typical concentrations of several ions inside and outside an animal cell. Concentrations of ions inside the cell are shown in gray, outside in black. Use the graph to answer questions 1–5.

1. Compared to its surroundings, does an animal cell contain a higher or lower concentration of potassium (K^+) ions? __**higher**__

2. Which ions are in the greatest concentration outside the animal cell? __**Na^+**__

3. Which ions are in the lowest concentration inside the animal cell? __**Ca^{2+}**__

4. What is the approximate concentration, in mM, of Mg^{2+} ions inside the cell? __**30 mM**__

5. If all available Na^+ and Cl^- ions combine to form NaCl, do any excess Na^+ or Cl^- ions remain?
If so, which? __**yes; Na^+ ions**__

Answer the following question.

6. Describe the process by which a cell maintains differences in concentrations of certain ions on either side of the plasma membrane.
To maintain different concentrations of ions on either side of the plasma membrane, the cell must move the ions against a concentration gradient. To do so, the cell uses active transport, in which carrier proteins bind with the ions and move them across the membrane. This process requires energy.

Name _____ Date _____ Class _____

Chapter 8 · Chapter Assessment

Cellular Transport and the Cell Cycle, *continued*

Applying Scientific Methods

The large size of many fruits and flowers is the result of polyploidy, a condition in which the nuclei of an organism's cells contain extra sets of chromosomes. Polyploidy often occurs naturally, but it can also be artificially induced by plant breeders. How have breeders been able to mimic a naturally occurring phenomenon?

Researchers have determined that the chemical colchicine suppresses cell division by preventing the formation of spindle fibers. Without these fibers, the sister chromatids cannot become properly oriented for separation into individual nuclei. In effect, mitosis is stopped after prophase. However, the cell may continue to make copies of its chromosomes. As a result, the nucleus of the cell contains multiple sets of chromosomes.

Suppose a researcher wished to investigate how extra sets of chromosomes are produced. First, she treated two onion roots with a colchicine solution and left two roots untreated. After a period of several days, she placed thin slices from each root tip on separate microscope slides, stained the specimens, and examined the slides under a microscope at high power.

1. What is the hypothesis the researcher investigated?
Colchicine causes cells to produce multiple sets of chromosomes in their nuclei.

2. Which root tips were the control group? Which root tips were the experimental group?
The untreated root tips were the control group; the root tips treated with colchicine were the experimental group.

3. What was the independent variable in the investigation?
treatment of the onion roots with colchicine

4. What was the dependent variable?
the cell cycle of the onion root cells

5. How do you predict the slides of treated and untreated root tips will differ?
Answers may vary. The slides of untreated root tips will show cells in interphase and in various stages of mitosis. The slides of treated root tips will show cells only in interphase and in prophase. The cells in prophase will have no spindle fibers, and they may show some cells with multiple sets of chromosomes.

6. If the researcher finds only cells in interphase and prophase on the slides of treated root tips but not on the slides of untreated root tips, what might be her interpretation?
The colchicine stopped mitosis after prophase.

Name _____ Date _____ Class _____

Chapter 8 · Chapter Assessment

Cellular Transport and the Cell Cycle, *continued*

Applying Scientific Methods   *continued*

7. What results might lead the researcher to conclude that the colchicine had no effect on the onion cells?
If the cells of the colchicine-treated onion root and the cells of the untreated onion root appeared in the same stages of mitosis under the microscope, the researcher could conclude that the colchicine had no effect.

8. "How does treating cells with colchicine prevent the formation of spindle fibers?" Is this question the statement of the problem or the conclusion of a further investigation? Explain.
It states the problem; a conclusion is never stated as a question.

9. How might the researcher proceed to find out how treating cells with colchicine prevents the formation of spindle fibers?
The researcher might first investigate the structure of spindle fibers and the chemical constituents of colchicine and then design an experiment that specifically tests how colchicine blocks the formation of spindle fibers.

10. Why does polyploidy result in larger fruits and flowers?
When a plant has extra sets of chromosomes, it has extra copies of genes, which produce more of the proteins that the genes code for. Proteins are used in cellular reactions and in cellular structures. Having the additional proteins causes the fruits and flowers to be larger.

Chapter 9 Energy in a Cell

Reviewing Vocabulary

Complete each statement.

1. The reactions in photosynthesis in which light energy from the sun is converted to chemical energy are called **light-dependent reactions**.

2. The process by which plants trap the sun's energy to build carbohydrates is called **photosynthesis**.

3. The transfer of electrons along a series of proteins, releasing energy as they pass, is known as an **electron transport chain**.

4. **Chlorophyll** is a plant pigment that absorbs most wavelengths of light except green.

5. The splitting of water during photosynthesis is **photolysis**.

6. The anaerobic process of breaking down glucose to form pyruvic acid is called **glycolysis**.

7. In photosynthesis, the cycle of reactions that uses carbon dioxide to synthesize glucose is known as the **Calvin cycle**.

8. A cycle of reactions in aerobic respiration that begins and ends with the same 4-carbon compound is the **citric acid cycle**.

Compare and contrast each pair of related terms.

9. aerobic process : anaerobic process
Aerobic processes require oxygen; anaerobic processes do not.

10. photosynthesis : cellular respiration
Both are complex series of reactions that involve energy, require enzymes, occur in specific organelles, and involve movement of electrons. In photosynthesis, CO_2 and H_2O are used to store energy in sugar, and oxygen is given off as a waste. In cellular respiration, energy is released when sugar is broken down in the presence of oxygen; CO_2 and H_2O are given off as wastes.

Chapter 9 Energy in a Cell, *continued*

Understanding Main Ideas (Part A)

In the space at the left, write the letter of the word or phrase that best completes the statement or answers the question.

a **1.** Which of the following is *not* a part of adenosine diphosphate?
  a. glucose   b. adenine
  c. ribose   d. two phosphate groups

b **2.** The light-independent reactions of photosynthesis take place in the
  a. thylakoids.   b. stroma.   c. mitochondria.   d. cytoplasm.

d **3.** The energy in glucose *cannot* be released by
  a. glycolysis.   b. the citric acid cycle.
  c. cellular respiration.   d. photosynthesis.

c **4.** Cells store energy when
  a. the third phosphate group breaks off from an ATP molecule.
  b. they break down sucrose to glucose and fructose.
  c. a third phosphate group is bonded to an ADP molecule.
  d. ions are released into the bloodstream.

d **5.** Leaves appear green because the green portion of the light that strikes them is
  a. changed to heat.   b. absorbed.   c. destroyed.   d. reflected.

b **6.** Which of the following equations best represents photosynthesis?
  a. $C + O_2 + H_2O \rightarrow CO_2 + HOH$
  b. $6CO_2 + 6H_2O \rightarrow C_6H_{12}O_6 + 6O_2$
  c. $6C + 6H_2O \rightarrow C_6H_{12}O_6$
  d. $C_6H_{12}O_6 \rightarrow 6CO_2 + 6H_2O$

d **7.** Kidneys use energy to move molecules and ions in order to keep the blood chemically balanced. This process is an example of cells using energy to
  a. carry on chemosynthesis.   b. control body temperature.
  c. transmit impulses.   d. maintain homeostasis.

a **8.** In respiration, the final electron acceptor in the electron transport chain is
  a. oxygen.   b. ATP.   c. hydrogen ions.   d. water.

b **9.** In glycolysis, _____ molecules of ATP are used in the first step and _____ molecules of ATP are produced in the second step.
  a. four, two   b. two, four   c. two, two   d. four, four

b **10.** In the process of photosynthesis, the
  a. Calvin cycle yields CO_2.   b. light-dependent reactions release oxygen.
  c. Calvin cycle breaks down H_2O.   d. light-dependent reactions produce $NADP^+$.

Name _____ Date _____ Class _____

Chapter Assessment

Chapter 9 Energy in a Cell, *continued*

Understanding Main Ideas (Part B)

Answer the following questions.

1. Synthesis of molecules, transmission of nerve impulses, movement of cilia, and bioluminescence are various activities of organisms.
   a. What requirement do these activities have in common?
   They require energy.
   b. Why is ATP important in each activity?
   The energy required for each activity is obtained by the breakdown of ATP to ADP and inorganic phosphate.

2. Both the wine industry and the bread industry use the process of alcoholic fermentation.
   a. In what way is the use of alcoholic fermentation by these industries similar?
   Both industries use yeast to produce alcohol and carbon dioxide by the process of alcoholic fermentation.
   b. In what way does their use of alcoholic fermentation differ?
   The wine industry uses the alcohol to make the wine; the bread industry uses the carbon dioxide to make the bread dough rise.

3. In cellular respiration, the steps following glycolysis depend on whether oxygen is present. Explain. **If oxygen is present, production of acetyl-CoA, the citric acid cycle, and electron transport chain follow in order. If no oxygen is present, either lactic acid fermentation or alcoholic fermentation follows.**

4. Explain what is meant by carbon fixation. During which stage of photosynthesis does this process take place?
   Carbon fixation occurs during the Calvin cycle, when a carbon atom from atmospheric carbon dioxide is added to a 5-carbon sugar.

5. If you run as fast as you can, your muscles may begin to feel weak and have a burning sensation. Explain what is occurring in your muscle cells that accounts for this muscle fatigue.
   The rate at which oxygen is supplied to the muscle cells limits the level of aerobic respiration that can occur. As a result, anaerobic lactic acid fermentation takes place, changing pyruvic acid to lactic acid. The buildup of lactic acid in the muscle cells causes muscle fatigue.

Name _____ Date _____ Class _____

Chapter Assessment

Chapter 9 Energy in a Cell, *continued*

Thinking Critically

Answer the following questions.

The table below shows the average yield of ATP molecules from the oxidation of glucose in eukaryotic cells.

Reaction	ATP Produced	ATP Used
Glycolysis	2	4
Citric acid cycle	2	
Electron transport chain	32	

1. What is the net production of ATP molecules by *each* of the four reactions?
   glycolysis, 2; citric acid cycle, 2; electron transport chain, 32

2. What is the total net gain of ATP molecules per glucose molecule?
   36 molecules

3. The combination of glycolysis and fermentation yields a net gain of 2 ATP molecules. How many molecules of ATP does fermentation yield? Explain.
   Fermentation yields no molecules of ATP. Since glycolysis yields a net gain of 2 ATP molecules, and glycolysis combined with fermentation also yields 2 molecules of ATP, fermentation must produce zero molecules of ATP.

In an experiment conducted to determine whether green plants take in CO_2, a biologist filled a large beaker with aquarium water to which she added bromothymol blue. She exhaled CO_2 into the solution of bromothymol blue, which made the solution turn yellow. Then she placed a sprig of *Elodea* into two test tubes. She left a third test tube without *Elodea* to serve as a control. She added the yellow bromothymol solution to all three test tubes and placed a stopper in each. Next, she placed all the test tubes in sunlight. After several hours in sunlight, the bromothymol solution in the test tubes with the *Elodea* turned blue. The bromothymol solution in the control remained yellow.

4. What conclusion can be drawn from the experiment? Explain.
   The *Elodea* in the two test tubes must have taken in the CO_2 since the solution in those test tubes changed to blue, but the solution in the control test tube remained yellow.

Chapter Assessment

Chapter 9 Energy in a Cell, *continued*

Applying Scientific Methods

In 1803, Thomas Engelmann of Germany used a combination of aerobic bacteria and a filamentous alga to study the effect of various colors of the visible light spectrum on the rate of photosynthesis. He passed white light through a prism in order to separate the light into the different colors of the spectrum; then he exposed different segments of the alga to the various colors. He observed in which areas of the spectrum the greatest number of bacteria appeared. Refer to the diagram below to answer the questions that follow.

bacteria

filamentous alga

violet | blue | green | yellow | orange | red

1. Using his setup, Engelmann was able to determine in which areas of the visible light spectrum the alga was releasing the most oxygen. Explain his reasoning.
He reasoned that the bacteria would be more numerous where more oxygen was present.

2. Was determining where there was more oxygen the purpose of his experiment? If not, state the purpose.
No; the purpose was to determine the effect of different colors of light on the rate of photosynthesis.

3. How was the observation of the amount of oxygen present related to Engelmann's purpose?
Since oxygen is a product of photosynthesis, he reasoned that more oxygen indicated a greater rate of photosynthesis.

Chapter Assessment

Chapter 9 Energy in a Cell, *continued*

Applying Scientific Methods   *continued*

4. Why did Engelmann select aerobic rather than anaerobic bacteria?
He was using bacteria to determine oxygen levels. Anaerobic bacteria do not require oxygen for their life activities.

5. Based on the diagram, what would Engelmann's conclusion be?
He would conclude that the rate of photosynthesis is greatest in violet light and orange light.

6. What was the independent variable in this experiment?
the different colors of light

7. Describe one control Engelmann might have used. Explain.
Answers will vary. He could have exposed the alga and bacteria to white light and to complete darkness.

8. Did Engelmann's observations verify his hypothesis? Explain.
Yes, his hypothesis was that various colors of light affect the rate of photosynthesis differently, and he observed that they do.

Name _____ Date _____ Class _____

Chapter 10 Mendel and Meiosis

Reviewing Vocabulary

Match the definition in Column A with the term in Column B.

Column A

Column B

h   **1.** The different forms of a gene

b   **2.** The alleles present for a trait are the same.

g   **3.** A cell that contains one member of each chromosome pair

d   **4.** The type of cell division that produces gametes

f   **5.** The cell produced when a male gamete fuses with a female gamete

c   **6.** The uniting of the male and female gametes

a   **7.** The exchange of genetic material between homologous chromosomes

e   **8.** The failure of homologous chromosomes to separate properly during meiosis

a. crossing over

b. homozygous

c. fertilization

d. meiosis

e. nondisjunction

f. zygote

g. haploid

h. alleles

In the space at the left, write the letter of the word or phrase that best completes the statement.

b   **9.** Pollination can best be described as
a. the fusing of the egg nucleus with the pollen nucleus.
b. the transfer of a male pollen grain to the pistil of a flower.
c. the formation of male and female sex cells.
d. the type of cell division that produces diploid gametes.

b   **10.** The gamete that contains genes contributed by the mother is
a. a sperm.   **b.** an egg.   **c.** a zygote.   **d.** dominant.

c   **11.** Cells containing two alleles for each trait are described as
a. haploid.   **b.** gametes.   **c.** diploid.   **d.** homozygous.

c   **12.** The statement: "In meiosis, the way in which a chromosome pair separates does not affect the way other pairs separate," is another way of expressing Mendel's law of
a. dominance.   **b.** heredity.   **c.** independent assortment.   **d.** segregation.

Name _____ Date _____ Class _____

Chapter 10 Mendel and Meiosis, *continued*

Understanding Main Ideas (Part A)

In the space at the left, write the letter of the word or phrase that best completes the statement or answers the question.

a   **1.** A white mouse whose parents are both white produces only brown offspring when mated with a brown mouse. The white mouse is most probably
a. homozygous recessive.   **b.** heterozygous.
c. homozygous dominant.   **d.** haploid.

b   **2.** Polyploid organisms result from
a. crossing over.   **b.** nondisjunction.   **c.** mitosis.   **d.** random assortment.

b   **3.** The numbers in the diagram below represent the number of chromosomes found in each of the dog cells shown.

A

78 → 39
    39
78 → 39

B

39 → 78

The processes that are occurring at A and B are
a. meiosis and fertilization.   **b.** meiosis and fertilization.
c. mitosis and pollination.   **d.** meiosis and pollination.

a   **4.** If a female guinea pig homozygous dominant for black fur color is mated with a male that is homozygous recessive for white fur color, in a litter of eight offspring, you would expect
a. 8 black guinea pigs.
b. 4 black and 4 white guinea pigs.
c. 2 black, 4 gray, and 2 white guinea pigs.
d. 8 white guinea pigs.

d   **5.** A dog's phenotype can be determined by
a. looking at the dog's parents.
b. examining the dog's chromosomes.
c. mating the dog and examining its offspring.
d. looking at the dog.

b   **6.** A couple has two children, both of whom are boys. What is the chance that the parents' next child will be a boy?
a. 0%   **b.** 50%   **c.** 25%   **d.** 75%

Chapter 10 Mendel and Meiosis, *continued*

Chapter Assessment

Understanding Main Ideas (Part B)

In the space at the left, write the letter of the word or phrase that best completes the statement or answers the question.

__b__ 1. The diagram below shows a diploid cell with two homologous pairs of chromosomes.

Due to independent assortment, the possible allelic combinations that could be found in gametes produced by the meiotic division of this cell are
a. Bb, Dd, BB, and DD.
b. BD, bD, Bd, and bd.
c. $BbDd$ and $BDbd$.
d. Bd and bD only.

__b__ 2. When Mendel allowed tall heterozygous plants to self-pollinate, some of their offspring were short because the alleles of the tall plants
a. were dominant.
b. segregated during meiosis.
c. were homozygous.
d. crossed over during meiosis.

__c__ 3. Which process would result in the formation of chromosome C from homologous chromosomes A and B?

A = axial flowers a = terminal flowers
I = inflated pod i = constricted pod
                                   I = inflated pod
A   B   C

a. asexual reproduction
b. independent assortment
c. crossing over
d. segregation

__b__ 4. In chickens, rose comb (R) is dominant to single comb (r). A homozygous rose-combed rooster is mated with a single-combed hen. All of the chicks in the F_1 generation were only allowed to mate within their own group. What is the expected phenotype of the F_2 chicks?
a. 100% rose comb
b. 75% rose comb and 25% single comb
c. 100% single comb
d. 50% rose comb and 50% single comb

Chapter 10 Mendel and Meiosis, *continued*

Chapter Assessment

Thinking Critically

1. Approximately one out of every 20 Caucasian Americans has a recessive allele for a hereditary disorder known as cystic fibrosis (CF), but only one out of every 2000 Caucasian babies born in the United States is afflicted with the disorder. These individuals have two alleles for CF. They produce large amounts of mucus that accumulate in the lungs, liver, and pancreas. The mucus clogs important ducts in these organs and causes extensive damage. Why is there such a difference between the number of individuals who have the allele for CF and the number actually born with the disorder?

In order for an individual to inherit cystic fibrosis, two heterozygous people, each with one recessive allele, must meet and mate. The odds of that occurring are 1/20 x 1/20, or 1/400. Then, using a Punnett square, it can be determined that there is only a 25% chance that a sperm with the recessive allele will fertilize an egg with the recessive allele—hence the relatively low frequency of homozygous recessive children who have cystic fibrosis.

2. How can genetic recombination through segregation and crossing over during meiosis lead to variation in the offspring?

Independent segregation of homologous chromosomes during gamete formation allows for a random assortment of alleles in the sex cells. This allows the members of each pair of alleles to recombine in new ways in the offspring. Crossing over leads to new allele combinations on a chromosome. The resulting gamete may have a combination of alleles that was not possible if crossing over had not occurred.

3. In guinea pigs, the allele for rough coat (R) is dominant to the allele for smooth coat (r), and the allele for black fur (B) is dominant to the allele for white fur (b). If two guinea pigs that are heterozygous for rough, black fur ($RrBb$) are mated, what are the possible phenotypes and what is the frequency of each? Use a Punnett square to find the answers.

The phenotypic ratio is 9 rough, black fur: 3 rough, white fur: 3 smooth, black fur: 1 smooth, white fur

	RB	Rb	rB	rb
RB	RRBB	RRBb	RrBB	RrBb
Rb	RRBb	RRbb	RrBb	Rrbb
rB	RrBB	RrBb	rrBB	rrBb
rb	RrBb	Rrbb	rrBb	rrbb

Name _____ Date _____ Class _____

Applying Scientific Methods

Some biology students wanted to determine whether a pair of brown mice purchased at a pet store was homozygous dominant or heterozygous for fur color. They let the mice mate and examined the offspring. Six mice were born. All six had brown fur.

Some of the students felt that this was enough evidence to prove that the parent mice were homozygous for brown fur color. Other students did not, so another experiment was planned.

1. Do you think the experiment described above was adequate to prove that the parent mice were homozygous brown? Explain your answer, using the principles of genetics you have studied.

No, because the number of offspring produced isn't large enough to make definite

conclusions. Several conclusions are possible. Both mice could be homozygous

brown and that is why the recessive allele does not segregate out and appear in

the offspring, but only one mating and six offspring are not enough to prove this

mathematically. One of the pair of mice could be heterozygous and the other

homozygous brown and again, the recessive trait would not be seen in the off-

spring. Another possibility is that both mice are heterozygous. There would be

only a 25% chance that the recessive alleles would segregate out and combine

during fertilization. Six offspring may not be a large enough sample mathemati-

cally to reasonably expect the 25% chance of white mice to be expressed.

2. Describe the next experiment the students could conduct to determine whether the parent mice are homozygous brown or heterozygous brown.

There are a number of ways students could respond correctly to this problem.

a) The parent mice could be permitted to mate several more times with each other

and produce large numbers of offspring. The larger F₁ population would increase

the likelihood of the recessive allele being expressed if both parents were

heterozygous.

b) The students could allow several of the F₁ mice to interbreed. If one or

both of the parents were heterozygous, about 50% of the F₁ should be

heterozygous. With the larger number of offspring produced by the F₁ matings,

there would be a greater chance of the recessive phenotype showing in the

F₂ population.

Name _____ Date _____ Class _____

Applying Scientific Methods   continued

c) The parent mice each could be mated with a homozygous recessive mouse. In

that way, if a parent were heterozygous, there would be a 50% chance of the off-

spring showing the recessive trait. There are other possible correct responses. All

of the responses should in some way indicate the need for more offspring, since

heredity operates according to the laws of probability.

3. What could you conclude if three of the offspring had white fur?
   Both parents were heterozygous for brown fur.

4. What could you conclude if all six of the offspring had white fur?
   The same thing; both parents were heterozygous for brown fur. The probability
   of all six offspring being white is small but not impossible.

Chapter 11   DNA and Genes

Reviewing Vocabulary

From the words provided in the list, write the one that best completes each of the following statements. Use these choices:

mRNA	point mutation	codon	replication
nitrogen bases	tRNA	double helix	nondisjunction
frameshift mutation	translation	chromosomal mutation	cancer

1. During the process of transcription, DNA serves as the template for making **mRNA**, which leaves the nucleus and travels to the ribosomes.

2. A **frameshift mutation** involves the addition or deletion of a single base in a DNA molecule.

3. Watson and Crick developed the **double helix** model of DNA.

4. Thymine, adenine, guanine, and cytosine are **nitrogen bases**.

5. The process by which DNA makes a copy of itself is called **replication**.

6. Each set of three nitrogen bases representing an amino acid is referred to as a **codon**.

7. **tRNA** brings amino acids to the ribosomes for the assembly of proteins.

8. A change in a single base pair of the DNA molecule is called a **point mutation**.

9. **Nondisjunction** is the failure of a pair of homologous chromosomes to separate properly during meiosis.

10. The process of converting RNA code into an amino acid sequence is called **translation**.

11. When parts of chromosomes are broken off and lost or reattached incorrectly during mitosis or meiosis, the result is a **chromosomal mutation**.

12. Mutations in DNA can result in cells reproducing rapidly, producing the disease called **cancer**.

Chapter 11   DNA and Genes, *continued*

Understanding Main Ideas (Part A)

In the diagram, label the strand of DNA represented.

1. Use the letter **P** to label all of the phosphate groups.

2. Use an **S** to label all the sugar molecules.

3. For labeling the nitrogen bases, use a **T** for thymine and a **C** for cytosine. Guanine and adenine have been filled in for you.

4. Circle and label a codon.

5. Circle and label a nucleotide.

Codons and nucleotides may vary. Students may represent a codon by circling either 3 bases or 3 nucleotides.

In the space at the left, write the letter of the word or phrase that best completes the statement or answers the question.

d   6. X rays, ultraviolet light, and radioactive substances that can change the chemical nature of DNA are classified as
   a. growth regulators.   b. metamorphic molecules.
   c. hydrolytic enzymes.   d. mutagens.

c   7. An RNA molecule is a polymer composed of subunits known as
   a. polysaccharides.   b. ribose molecules.
   c. nucleotides.   d. uracil molecules.

a   8. The hereditary information for a particular trait is generally
   a. controlled by alleles located on chromosomes.
   b. controlled by chromosomes located on an allele.
   c. carried from the nucleus by tRNA to the gamete.
   d. coded for by a ribosome located on the reticulum.

b   9. Which series is arranged in order from largest to smallest in size?
   a. chromosome, nucleus, cell, DNA, nucleotide
   b. cell, nucleus, chromosome, DNA, nucleotide
   c. nucleotide, chromosome, cell, DNA, nucleus
   d. cell, nucleotide, nucleus, DNA, chromosome

c   10. A DNA nucleotide may be made up of a phosphate group, along with
   a. deoxyribose sugar and uracil.   b. ribose sugar and adenine.
   c. deoxyribose sugar and thymine.   d. ribose sugar and cytosine.

Copyright © Glencoe/McGraw-Hill, a division of The McGraw-Hill Companies, Inc.

Chapter 11 DNA and Genes, continued

Chapter Assessment

Understanding Main Ideas (Part B)

In the space at the left, write the letter of the word or phrase that best completes the statement or answers the question.

a ___ 1. The diagram labeled **Insect A** represents the chromosomes taken from the body cell of a normal female insect. The diagram labeled **Insect B** represents those taken from the body cell of a female of the same species but with an abnormal phenotype.

Insect A   Insect B

The chromosomal alteration seen in Insect B could have resulted from

a. nondisjunction   b. crossing over.

c. a frameshift mutation.   d. a point mutation.

Refer to the diagram below to answer questions 2–5.

a ___ 2. The process illustrated is

a. translation.   b. replication.   c. monoploidy.   d. transcription.

b ___ 3. Structure III represents a(n)

a. gene.   b. amino acid.   c. codon.   d. DNA molecule.

a ___ 4. Which of the above structures are composed of RNA?

a. II and IV   b. III and IV   c. I and V   d. III and V

c ___ 5. Where in the cell does this process occur?

a. in the nucleus   b. in food vacuoles

c. at the ribosomes   d. within the plasma membrane

Chapter 11 DNA and Genes, continued

Chapter Assessment

Thinking Critically

For each set of terms in questions 1–3, complete the analogy by writing the appropriate term in the space provided. Then explain why you chose the term.

1. adenine: thymine :: guanine: _____cytosine_____

Cytosine is a nitrogen base and it forms complementary bonds with guanine just as thymine forms complementary bonds with adenine.

2. DNA: RNA :: double-stranded: _____single-stranded_____

RNA is usually made up of a single strand of nucleotides, whereas the DNA molecule is a double-stranded molecule.

3. translation: protein :: transcription: _____messenger RNA_____

Transcription refers to the process of transferring information from the DNA code to a strand of mRNA. Translation refers to the utilization of information in mRNA in the synthesis of proteins.

In the blank at the left, write the letter of the term that best completes the statement.

b ___ 4. Applicants for the first job, "Positions Available," could qualify if they were

a. DNA.   b. mRNA.

c. tRNA.   d. rRNA.

c ___ 5. Applicants for the second job, "Accuracy and Speed," could qualify if they were

a. DNA.   b. mRNA.

c. tRNA.   d. rRNA.

a ___ 6. Applications for the third job, "Executive Position," could qualify if they were

a. DNA.   b. mRNA.

c. tRNA.   d. rRNA.

b ___ 7. Applicants for the fourth job, "Supervisor," could qualify if they were

a. DNA.   b. mRNA.

c. tRNA.   d. rRNA.

Help Wanted

Positions Available in the genetics industry. Hundreds of entry-level openings for tireless workers. No previous experience necessary. Must be able to transcribe code in a nuclear environment. The ability to work in close association with ribosomes is a must.

Accuracy and Speed vital for this job in the field of translation. Applicants must demonstrate skills in transporting and positioning amino acids. Salary commensurate with experience.

Executive Position available. Must be able to maintain genetic continuity through replication and control cellular activity by regulation of enzyme production. Limited number of openings. All benefits.

Supervisor of production of proteins—all shifts. Must be able to follow exact directions from double-stranded template. Travel from nucleus to the cytoplasm is additional job benefit.

Chapter 11 DNA and Genes, *continued*

Applying Scientific Methods

Watson and Crick explained the structure of DNA in 1953. How DNA actually replicated was still a mystery. Matthew Meselson and Frank Stahl set out in 1957 to determine exactly how it was accomplished. There were three different ways of thinking about replication. (See Figure 1.) Some scientists believed that the two strands of the double helix separated during replication but that each strand remained intact. Each strand then served as the template for the assembly of a new DNA strand that it would bond with. This method is called *semiconservative replication*.

According to a second hypothesis, referred to as *conservative replication*, the original double-stranded DNA remains intact while an entirely new double-stranded DNA is formed alongside it. Hence, all of the new molecules lack any of the original DNA.

According to a third hypothesis, the DNA molecule is dismantled piece by piece and replication occurs along the pieces. The new DNA contains some of the original molecule and some new material. This hypothesis is referred to as *dispersive replication*.

Meselson and Stahl used the ultracentrifuge and isotope-labeled biomolecules to answer the replication question. Special techniques were used to isolate DNA from bacteria. The DNA was then centrifuged in a way that allows each type of molecule to settle in distinct bands based on density. Under normal conditions, bacteria are exposed to nutrients that contain the common isotope of nitrogen, N-14. The researchers grew and then isolated DNA from normal bacteria, centrifuged this DNA, and established a reference line for where DNA containing N-14 would settle and form a band when centrifuged. (See Figure 2.) A second reference line was also established by growing many generations of bacteria on a nutrient source that contained nucleotides labeled with N-15. The DNA extracted from these bacteria contained only molecules with the heavier N-15. It formed a band lower in the centrifuge tube than that of the DNA containing N-14. Once these two reference points were established, the experiment to determine how DNA replicates could begin.

First, bacteria were grown for many generations on a food source that contained N-15. This was done to insure that most of the bacteria in these cultures would have N-15 present in their chromosomes. The bacteria from this culture were removed, washed, and re-suspended in a culture that contained food with only N-14 nucleotides. Only one round of replication was permitted. Cells from this culture were removed, and the DNA was extracted and centrifuged.

Chromosomes After Replication

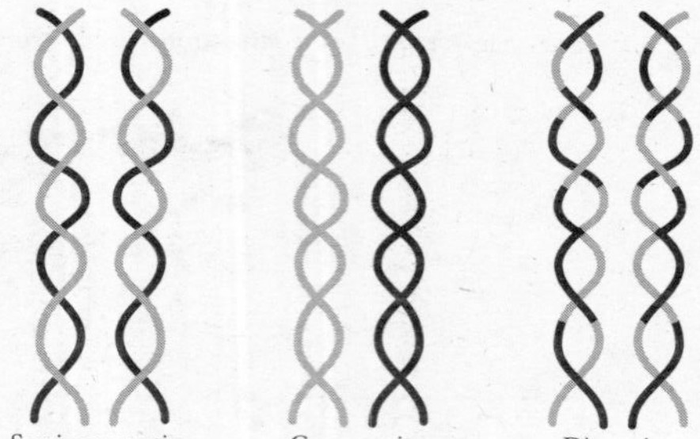

Semiconservative   Conservative   Dispersive

Figure 1

100% nitrogen-15   100% nitrogen-14

Figure 2

Chapter 11 DNA and Genes, *continued*

Applying Scientific Methods *continued*

1. Prediction: In each of the appropriate tubes in Figure 3 below, draw a band or bands where the DNA would settle if replication is (a) semiconservative, (b) conservative, and (c) dispersive. (Hint: Determine how much of each resulting molecules is made with heavy nitrogen bases and how much with lighter ones.)

Figure 3

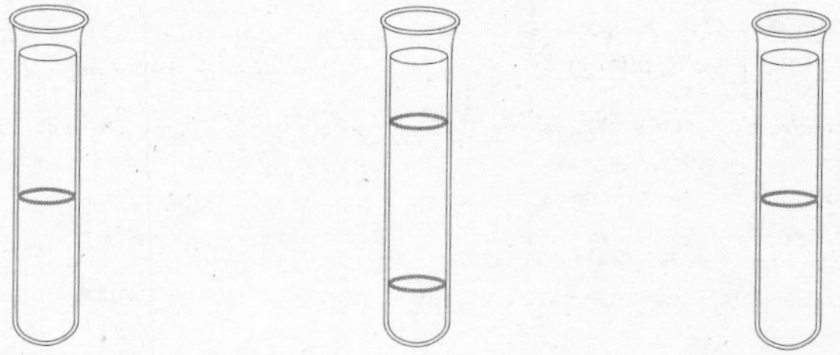

(a) Semiconservative replication   (b) Conservative replication   (c) Dispersive replication

2. Explain why you drew each of the bands where you did.

(a) This band would be in the middle between the original two because each DNA molecule would contain one strand of DNA with N-15 and one strand of DNA with N-14.

(b) There will be two bands because the original DNA with N-15 would remain intact and be denser. The new DNA molecules would contain N-14 and be less dense. They would be located in the same areas as the bands of N-15 and N-14 in the original two trials.

(c) This band would also form in the middle since each DNA molecule would be made of segments of the original DNA with N-15 and an equal number of segments of DNA with N-14.

3. Is one round of testing enough to distinguish among all three possible types of replication? Explain the reasoning behind your answer.

One round of testing is not enough because both the semiconservative and dispersive hypotheses could cause the DNA to band in the middle of the tube. One round would only confirm or eliminate the conservative hypothesis.

Name _____ Date _____ Class _____

Chapter 12 Patterns of Heredity and Human Genetics

Reviewing Vocabulary

In the space at the left, write the term that best fits the definition. Use these choices:

incomplete dominance	carrier	codominant alleles
completely dominant alleles	simple recessive heredity	polygenic inheritance
pedigree	autosomes	sex-linked traits

codominant alleles   1. Phenotypes of both homozygotes are produced in the heterozygote.

completely dominant alleles   2. Phenotypes of both heterozygous and homozygous dominant individuals have the same phenotype.

incomplete dominance   3. The phenotype of the heterozygote is intermediate between those phenotypes expressed by the homozygotes.

carrier   4. Another name for a heterozygous individual

simple recessive heredity   5. Inheritance pattern of phenylketonuria and Tay-Sachs disease

polygenic inheritance   6. Inheritance pattern of a trait controlled by two or more genes

pedigree   7. A graphic representation of an individual's family tree

autosomes   8. Humans have 22 pairs of these types of chromosomes.

sex-linked traits   9. Traits controlled by genes located on the X or Y chromosome

In the space at the left, write the letter of the word or phrase that best completes the statement.

b   10. The 23rd pair of chromosomes that differ in males and females are called
- a. autosomes.
- b. sex chromosomes.
- c. multiple alleles.
- d. polygenes.

d   11. A trait controlled by four alleles is said to have
- a. homologous alleles.
- b. autosomes.
- c. hybridization.
- d. multiple alleles.

Name _____ Date _____ Class _____

Chapter 12 Patterns of Heredity and Human Genetics, continued

Understanding Main Ideas (Part A)

In the space at the left, write the letter of the word or phrase that best completes the statement or answers the question.

b   1. When roan cattle are mated, 25% of the offspring are red, 50% are roan, and 25% are white. Upon examination, it can be seen that the coat of a roan cow consists of both red and white hairs. This trait is one controlled by
- a. multiple alleles.
- b. codominant alleles.
- c. sex-linked genes.
- d. polygenic inheritance.

c   2. If a female fruit fly heterozygous for red eyes (X^RX^r) crossed with a white-eyed male (X^rY), what percent of their offspring will have white eyes?
- a. 0%
- b. 25%
- c. 50%
- d. 75%

Base your answers to questions 3–6 on the pedigree shown at the right, which shows the incidence of hemophilia over three generations of a family.

□ homozygous dominant
■ homozygous recessive
○ homozygous dominant
● homozygous recessive

b   3. What is the relationship between individual I-1 and individual III-2?
- a. grandfather–granddaughter
- b. grandmother–grandson
- c. great aunt–nephew
- d. mother–son

d   4. For the trait being followed in the pedigree, individuals II-1 and II-4 can be classified as
- a. homozygous dominant.
- b. mutants.
- c. homozygous recessive.
- d. carriers.

d   5. What type of inheritance pattern does the trait represented by the shaded symbols illustrate?
- a. incomplete dominance
- b. multiple alleles
- c. codominance
- d. sex-linked

a   6. If individual III-2 marries a person with the same genotype as individual I-1, what is the chance that one of their children will be afflicted with hemophilia?
- a. 0%
- b. 25%
- c. 50%
- d. 75%

Chapter Assessment

Chapter 12 Patterns of Heredity and Human Genetics, *continued*

Understanding Main Ideas (Part B)

In the space at the left, write the letter of the word or phrase that best completes each statement.

__a__ 1. Which of the bar graphs represents what the phenotypic frequencies might be for polygenic inheritance?

a. b. c. d.

__d__ 2. Because the gene for red-green colorblindness is located on the X chromosome, it is normally *not* possible for a

a. carrier mother to pass the gene on to her daughter.
b. carrier mother to pass the gene on to her son.
c. colorblind father to pass the gene on to his daughter.
d. colorblind father to pass the gene on to his son.

__d__ 3. A cross between a white rooster and a black hen results in 100% blue Andalusian offspring. When two of these blue offspring are mated, the probable phenotypic ratio seen in their offspring would be

a. 100% blue.
b. 75% black, 25% white.
c. 75% blue, 25% white.
d. 25% black, 50% blue, 25% white.

__d__ 4. A human genetic disorder caused by a dominant gene is

a. Tay-Sachs disease.
b. cystic fibrosis.
c. PKU.
d. Huntington's disease.

Answer the following questions.

5. How does polygenic inheritance differ from Mendelian inheritance? **In Mendelian inheritance, traits are determined by dominant and recessive paired alleles of single genes. In polygenic inheritance, a trait is controlled by two or more genes.**

6. How does incomplete dominance differ from multiple alleles? **In incomplete dominance, there are only two alleles, neither of which is dominant to the other. In multiple alleles, there are more than two alleles, any one of which may be dominant to any recessive allele.**

Chapter Assessment

Chapter 12 Patterns of Heredity and Human Genetics, *continued*

Thinking Critically

In the space at the left, write the term that does *not* belong in the list. Then explain your choice.

__homozygous__ 1. heterozygous, carrier, homozygous

Explanation: **The other terms involve contrasting alleles for a trait. A homozygous individual possesses two identical alleles for a trait.**

__phenotype__ 2. genotype, phenotype, heterozygous, homozygous

Explanation: **The other terms describe the gene combinations an organism would possess and not the expression of those genes.**

__autosomes__ 3. autosomes, X and Y chromosomes, sex-linked traits, sex chromosomes

Explanation: **It is the only term not related to the sex chromosomes.**

Answer the following questions.

4. Explain how some traits are expressed differently in males and females. Give an example of such a trait. Genetic makeup represents an individual's potential. **Traits are also affected by hormones and structural differences in individuals. Male-pattern baldness in humans is an example of a trait that is expressed differently in males and females.**

5. The gene for nearsightedness in humans is found on the X chromosome. A boy has a nearsighted father. Will the boy be nearsighted? Explain. **No, the boy would have to inherit the nearsighted trait from his mother.**

6. A male is said to be *hemizygous* for genes on the X chromosome. Explain why you think this term was chosen. **The prefix *hemi*-means "half." Since only one of a male's two sex chromosomes is an X chromosome, only half his sex chromosomes can carry the genes.**

Chapter 12 — Patterns of Heredity and Human Genetics, continued

Applying Scientific Methods

Geneticists are constantly on the lookout for organisms with mutations. Such individual organisms provide information about the heredity and development of the entire species. When a mutation is discovered, phenotypic differences are examined. Then unique details of the mutation's genotype and inheritance pattern are carefully analyzed. This was true in the time of Thomas Morgan and is still true today. Historically, much work in the field of genetics has been done with fruit flies, because huge numbers of them can be cultured in a relatively small space, and because large populations of offspring can be obtained in short periods of time.

Forearmed with this knowledge and seeking scientific fame, you search your garden for fruit flies. You trap one male with miniature wings and several normal females. You carefully place the flies in a culture vial and allow them to mate. When you see tiny larvae feeding on the culture medium, you place the adults in another culture vial. All that is left in the original culture vial is the F_1 generation of flies. When these mature, you note that none of the flies has miniature wings.

1. How might the disappearance of the trait of miniature wings be explained?
Answers may vary. It might be that the miniature-wing trait is not inherited but that something happened to the male fly to make its wings deformed. It could also be that miniature wings is a trait that is recessive to normal wings and would not appear in the F_1 generation.

You next place males and females from the F_1 generation in a number of fresh culture vials and allow them to mate. Eventually, you end up with close to 4000 F_2 offspring. Of these, 740 have miniature wings. The remainder of the flies have normal wings.

2. What does this tell you about the trait for miniature wings?
The trait for miniature wings is probably genetically controlled and recessive to the trait for normal wings.

Next, you examine all of the flies with miniature wings. If you are to become famous for your work in genetics, you need to keep very precise records, so you carefully record information about each of the flies in your cultures. When you are finished, you notice something truly unusual. All of the flies with miniature wings are males.

3. How can this odd result be explained? Use Punnett squares illustrating the first (F_1) and second (F_2) generation to confirm your answer.
The trait for miniature wings is on the X chromosome. All of the F_1 females were heterozygous because they inherited the allele for miniature wings from the male parent and the allele for normal wings from the female parent. Because the trait for normal wings is dominant to the trait for miniature wings, the phenotype of all of the F_1 flies is normal wings.

Chapter 12 — Patterns of Heredity and Human Genetics, continued

Applying Scientific Methods   continued

	X^N	Y
X^N	$X^N X^N$	$X^N Y$
X^n	$X^N X^n$	$X^n Y$

In the F_2 generation, the allele for miniature wings shows only in some of the male flies because it is carried on the X chromosome. Half of the male flies inherit this allele from their mothers.

4. Just to be safe, you want to be sure that this isn't a situation where it is lethal for female flies to inherit two alleles for miniature wings. Design an experiment that should result in some female flies with miniature wings. Illustrate the cross with a Punnett square.
A heterozygous F_1 female with normal wings could be testcrossed either with the original miniature-winged male or with an F2 male that has miniature wings.

	X^n	Y
X^N	$X^N X^n$	$X^N Y$
X^n	$X^n X^n$	$X^n Y$

Chapter 13 Genetic Technology
Chapter Assessment

Reviewing Vocabulary

Write the word or phrase that best completes the statement. Use these choices:

human genome	transgenic organisms	linkage map	gene therapy
vectors	restriction enzymes	plasmid	inbreeding	testcross

1. __Restriction enzymes__ are used to cut DNA into fragments.

2. __Gene therapy__ is based on the insertion of normal genes into cells with defective genes in an attempt to correct genetic disorders.

3. The entire collection of genes within human cells is referred to as the __human genome__.

4. A(n) __plasmid__ is a small, circular piece of DNA found in bacterial cells.

5. A(n) __linkage map__ shows the location of genes on a chromosome.

6. __Transgenic organisms__ are produced when DNA from another species is inserted into the genome of an organism, which then begins to use the foreign DNA as its own.

7. A(n) __testcross__ is a cross of an individual of unknown genotype with an individual of known genotype.

8. A gene gun and a virus may both be classified as __vectors__ because they are mechanisms by which foreign DNA may be transferred into a host cell.

9. __Inbreeding__ is mating between closely related individuals.

Explain the following terms. Use complete sentences.

10. genetic engineering
__Genetic engineering is the manipulation of an organism's genetic material (DNA) by either introducing or eliminating specific genes.__

11. gene splicing
__The rejoining of cut DNA fragments is called gene splicing.__

12. recombinant DNA
__Recombinant DNA results from the process of cutting and recombining DNA fragments from different organisms.__

Chapter 13 Genetic Technology, continued
Chapter Assessment

Understanding Main Ideas (Part A)

In the space at the left, write the letter of the word or phase that best completes the statement or answers the question.

__a__ 1. A small amount of DNA obtained from a mummy or from a human long frozen in glacial ice may be cloned through
  a. polymerase chain reaction techniques. **b.** gel electrophoresis.
  c. DNA fingerprinting. **d.** gene splicing.

__c__ 2. Examine the piece of DNA represented in the figure at the right. The nucleotide sequences on both strands, but running in opposite directions, are in an arrangement called a
  a. vector
  b. chromosome mutation.
  c. palindrome.
  d. transgenic codon.

G — C
A — T
A — T
T — A
T — A
C — G

__a__ 3. Transgenic bacteria are currently used to produce
  a. human growth hormone, insulin, and phenylalanine.
  b. human growth hormone, PKU, and interferon.
  c. hexosaminidase A, phenylalanine, and insulin.
  d. PKU, insulin, and interferon.

__c__ 4. Gel electrophoresis is a technique used to
  a. clone chromosomes of various species.
  b. cut DNA into fragments of various sizes.
  c. separate DNA fragments by charge and length.
  d. inject foreign DNA into animal and plant cells.

__b__ 5. A nasal spray containing copies of the normal gene that is defective in persons with cystic fibrosis has been used on a trial basis. It is hoped that the cells in the lungs will take in the healthy gene from the spray and produce normal mucus. This is an attempt at
  a. palindrome formation. **b.** gene therapy.
  c. DNA fingerprinting. **d.** linkage mapping.

__b__ 6. How might a breeder determine if a certain golden retriever is a carrier of an undesirable trait?
  a. prepare a linkage map
  b. perform a testcross
  c. clone the dog
  d. splice the undesirable allele into the dog's genome

Understanding Main Ideas (Part B)

In the space at the left, write the letter of the word or phase that best completes the statement or answers the question.

b 1. A linkage map such as the one illustrated in the figure at the right, for human chromosome number 4, can be produced as a result of
  a. a study of antigen-antibody reactions and PCR.
  b. a determination of the frequency with which the genes occur together.
  c. a process called karyotyping.
  d. both karyotyping and palindrome formation.

Figure labels: Huntington's disease — Atypical PKU — Serum album — Red hair color

c 2. Below follows a list of procedures involved in the production of a transgenic organism. From the choices provided, what is the sequence that represents the proper order of events?
  A. Recombinant DNA is transferred into a suitable host.
  B. A desirable gene is identified in a DNA sequence.
  C. The DNA fragment to be inserted is joined with a vehicle to transport it.
  D. The DNA fragment to be inserted is isolated.
  a. A, B, C, D b. B, C, A, D c. B, D, C, A d. D, A, B, C

In 1973, Stanley Cohen and Herbert Boyer inserted a gene from an African clawed frog into a bacterium. The bacterium produced the protein coded for by the inserted frog gene.

a 3. In their experiment, Cohen and Boyer produced a DNA molecule composed of both frog DNA and bacterial DNA. Because the new genetic material consisted of DNA from two different organisms, it can be referred to as
  a. recombinant DNA. b. a linkage map.
  c. a vector. d. gene therapy.

b 4. This insertion of a small fragment of frog DNA into the DNA of another species can most accurately be called
  a. cloning. b. genetic engineering.
  c. electrophoresis. d. gene therapy.

d 5. At the conclusion of the experiment, a bacterium containing functional frog DNA would be classified as a
  a. clone. b. DNA fingerprint.
  c. plasmid. d. transgenic organism.

Thinking Critically

Read the paragraph below. Then answer the questions that follow.

Agrobacterium tumefaciens is a bacterium that causes crown gall disease, a tumorous growth on the growing tip of certain plants. The bacterium is able to enter a plant through small cuts in the outer cell layer. When *Agrobacterium* enters a plant cell, a DNA sequence from the bacterium integrates into the plant's DNA. This new section of DNA causes the plant's cell to reproduce quickly to form a tumor and to synthesize a food molecule needed by the bacterium. A critical bit of information that scientists have learned about the process is that the tumor-causing information is carried on a large plasmid that is separate from the bacterium's main chromosome. During the infection process, the DNA on the plasmid that codes for food production and rapid reproduction leaves the plasmid, moves into the plant cell nucleus, and integrates with one of the plant cell's chromosomes. Thus, when the plant cell reproduces, it passes along the bacterium's genetic information, which has been incorporated into the plant genome.

1. Why is the above information about how *Agrobacterium* causes crown gall disease important to scientists hoping to produce transgenic plants?
Answers may vary. This knowledge is important because plant cells are surrounded by a thick cell wall that makes the introduction of foreign DNA difficult. *Agrobacterium* offers a way of successfully placing foreign DNA in a plant cell.

2. What could be used to cut open an *Agrobacterium* plasmid and insert a gene that would increase the rate of conversion of atmospheric nitrogen into nitrates?
Restriction enzymes could be used to cut open a plasmid so that the desired gene could be inserted.

3. Illustrate and label what the plasmid might look like with the desired gene inserted.
Illustrations may vary.

plasmid { foreign gene, bacterial DNA

4. What benefits to agriculture could stem from scientists being able to engineer plants genetically?
Answers may vary. They might be able to engineer plants that require less fertilizer, produce more protein, are resistant to disease, grow in less favorable environments, and are a more nutritious food source.

Chapter Assessment

Chapter 13 — Genetic Technology, *continued*

Applying Scientific Methods

At the DNA level, humans are very similar, and the genes that code for their proteins follow fairly standard patterns. However, the segments of noncoding DNA found between the genes—referred to as "junk" DNA—follow patterns that vary from one individual to another. For example, in Individual A the "junk" DNA base sequence represented by CAT (cytosine, adenine, and thymine) could be repeated 3 times (CATCATCAT) in one place in that individual's genome and 6 times in another place. In Individual B, the same noncoding DNA sequence could form a different pattern, with 10 repetitions of CAT in one place and 30 repetitions in another. In a given population, there may be a large number of segments of DNA that differ on the basis of the noncoding DNA pattern. Therefore, if Individuals A and B have a child, the child is likely to be heterozygous for the segments of DNA involving noncoding sequences.

The patterns of noncoding DNA sequences give all individuals (except identical twins) a distinctive "fingerprint." The fingerprint is constructed by isolating DNA from a few cells, cutting it into fragments using restriction enzymes, and sorting the fragments by size using gel electrophoresis. The shorter the DNA fragment, the farther it will migrate through the gel. The result is a visual representation of an individual's DNA, or a DNA fingerprint.

A DNA fingerprint can be used to identify a child's biological father. The basis for such an identification is that a repetitive, noncoding sequence present in the child but not found in the mother must have been inherited from the father. Examine the bands in the diagram of the DNA fingerprints shown below. Each band represents a fragment of DNA. The first vertical lane of bands represents standard markers of known size, which are used as a reference. To the right of the standard markers is the lane of bands representing the child's DNA fingerprint. The next lane is the mother's DNA, followed by the DNA fragments from two men who might be the child's father. Study the pattern of each lane of DNA bands. Then answer the questions.

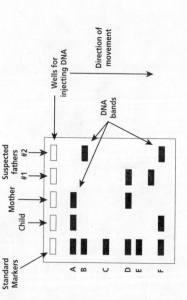

Chapter Assessment

Chapter 13 — Genetic Technology, *continued*

Applying Scientific Methods   *continued*

1. Which location represents the longest DNA fragment? Which location represents the shortest fragment? Explain.
   Location A represents the longest fragment; location F represents the shortest fragment. Because smaller fragments of DNA move more quickly through the gel, the farther the standard marker band is from the well, the smaller is the fragment.

2. Which of the men, Father #1 or Father #2, is probably the biological father of the baby? Explain.
   Father #2 might be the biological father because he matches a band with the child at F. Suspected Father #1 does not match any bands with the child.

3. What would be indicated if you saw only one band in a lane?
   It would mean that the person is homozygous for the segment of DNA containing the repeated sequence. If the person is heterozygous, a separate band will be seen for each of the two alleles. However, if he or she is homozygous, there will be only one band visible.

4. Below is a drawing of a hypothetical gel. Included on the gel is the banding pattern of the mother and father of two children. Draw what the pattern of bands for each of the children might look like. Indicate the possible parental source using ♂ for the male (father) and ♀ for the female (mother).

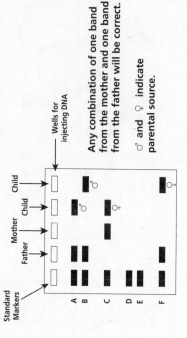

Any combination of one band from the mother and one band from the father will be correct.

♂ and ♀ indicate parental source.

Name _____ Date _____ Class _____

Chapter 14 The History of Life

Reviewing Vocabulary

Complete the paragraph by writing the correct term on the appropriate line. Use these choices:

archaebacteria   fossils   protocells
biogenesis   plate tectonics   spontaneous generation

From ancient times until recently, it was believed that living organisms could arise from nonliving materials. This belief is referred to as **(1) spontaneous generation** . According to the three-century-old writings of Jean Van Helmont, if a dirty shirt and grains of wheat are placed in a container and left for 21 days, mice will form from the fermenting wheat. With the invention of the microscope and careful experimentation, it has been reasonably proven that life arises only from life. This idea is referred to as **(2) biogenesis** . The oldest organisms of which scientists have any record are approximately 3.5 billion years old. **(3) Fossils** provide evidence of such organisms. The question of how the first unicellular organisms were produced from inorganic materials is a problem scientists are still studying. One possible answer is that conditions on the ancient Earth led to the formation of organized structures that carried out some life activities. These structures, called **(4) protocells** , were capable of growth and division. After much time, they evolved into heterotrophic prokaryotes. Over more time, organisms evolved that could synthesize food from inorganic raw materials. These organisms were probably similar to today's prokaryotes that survive in harsh conditions without oxygen. These organisms are known as **(5) archaebacteria** .

The geological activity of Earth has influenced the development of organisms. For example, at the beginning of the Mesozoic era, the modern continents were merged into one large landmass. The landmass broke into individual continents that moved apart. The geological explanation of how the continents moved is called **(6) plate tectonics** . As the continents moved apart, descendants of organisms living on the continents may have experienced different climates because of the new locations of the continents.

Name _____ Date _____ Class _____

Chapter 14 The History of Life, *continued*

Understanding Main Ideas

In the space at the left, write the letter of the word or phrase that best completes the statement or answers the question.

b 1. A clear fish imprint in a rock indicates that the rock is probably
    a. volcanic. **b.** sedimentary. **c.** metamorphic. **d.** igneous.

a 2. Which fact is the basis for using the fossil record as evidence for the order of evolution?
    a. In undisturbed layers of rock strata, the older fossils are found in the deeper layers.
    b. There are fossils of all life forms to be found in rock layers.
    c. All fossils were formed at the same time.
    d. Fossils have been shown to provide a complete record of human evolution.

a 3. A theory concerning the origin of life states that Earth's ancient atmosphere contained
    a. water vapor, methane, and ammonia.
    b. water vapor, oxygen, and hydrogen.
    c. methane, ammonia, and oxygen.
    d. methane, carbon dioxide, and oxygen.

b 4. Which group of organisms is believed to have been the earliest to evolve?
    a. land plants **b.** cyanobacteria **c.** aquatic dinosaurs **d.** mammals

d 5. According to one theory, the first prokaryotes probably obtained their food
    a. through the synthesis of organic molecules from inorganic molecules.
    b. through a combination of photosynthesis and aerobic respiration.
    c. by eating carbohydrates formed by autotrophs.
    d. by consuming organic molecules available in their environment.

c 6. Entire organisms, with even their most delicate parts intact, have been found preserved in
    a. igneous rock formations and ice.
    b. mineral deposits and metamorphic rock.
    c. amber and ice.
    d. amber and mineral deposits.

c 7. While looking for fossils on an eroded hillside, you discover fossil coral and fish in one layer. In a layer just above, you find the fossil imprint of a fern frond and some fossil moss. Assuming the rock has not been disturbed, which of the following is the most probable conclusion?
    a. The area had been a sea until recent times.
    b. A forest had once grown there but had become submerged by water.
    c. A sea had been replaced by land in ancient times.
    d. A saltwater sea had changed to a freshwater lake in ancient times.

Understanding Main Ideas (Part B)

In the space at the left, write the letter of the word or phrase that best completes the statement or answers the question.

c   1. Which event contributed most directly to the evolution of aerobic organisms?
   a. an increase in the concentration of methane in the ancient atmosphere
   b. a decrease in the sun's light intensity
   c. the presence of organisms able to carry on photosynthesis
   d. an increase in the number of organisms carrying on fermentation

b   2. Urey and Miller subjected water, ammonia, methane, and hydrogen to heating and cooling cycles and jolts of electricity in an attempt to
   a. determine how the dinosaurs became extinct.
   b. find out whether the conditions of ancient Earth could have formed complex organic compounds.
   c. determine the age of microfossils.
   d. find out how ozone forms in the atmosphere.

Answer the following questions.

3. Explain the role of plate tectonics in the theory of continental drift.
According to the theory of continental drift, the continents have moved during Earth's history and are still moving. The continents move because they ride on Earth's crust, which consists of several rigid plates that drift on top of molten rock.

4. Explain the relationship between early photosynthetic autotrophs and the eventual rise of aerobic life forms.
The photoautotrophs released oxygen, which was missing from the ancient atmosphere and necessary for aerobic respiration. Thus, the autotrophs produced the O_2 needed for the aerobic organisms to evolve.

Thinking Critically

Read the paragraph below. Then answer the questions that follow.

Radioactive isotopes, atoms with unstable nuclei, decay over time, giving off radiation as they break down. The decay rate of every radioactive element is known; moreover, radioactive decay continues at a steady rate. Scientists compare the amount of the original radioactive element to the amount of the new element present, which has formed as a result of the decay. Suppose that you start with 100 grams of a certain radioisotope that decays to half its original amount in 50 000 years.

1. Complete the following table so that the amount of parent material (original radioisotope) and the amount of daughter material (nonradioactive end product) are correct for the number of years that have passed.

Amount of Parent Material	Amount of Daughter Material	Years That Have Passed
100 grams	0 grams	0
50 grams	50 grams	50 000
25 grams	75 grams	100 000
12.5 grams	87.5 grams	150 000
6.25 grams	93.75 grams	200 000
3.125 grams	96.875 grams	250 000

2. On the following grid, graph the data in your table in order to show the relationship between the passage of time and the amount of original radioisotope. (Consider the time 0 as that point at which the decay of the full amount of the isotope begins. The 250 000-year point is the present time.)

Years Passed vs. Amount of Radioisotope

Name _____ Date _____ Class _____

14 The History of Life, *continued*

Applying Scientific Methods

Examine the illustration of rock strata and fossil remains recorded by a paleobiologist who was studying rock layers located at the base of a mountain. Then answer the questions that follow.

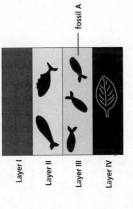

Layer I

Layer II

Layer III

Layer IV

— fossil A

1. Assuming that the oldest of the strata is layer IV and that the youngest is layer I, name and describe two techniques that could be used to determine the age of fossil A.

In order to determine the age of fossil A, scientists could use an absolute dating technique called radiometric dating. It relies on the rate at which unstable radioactive nuclei break down and, over time, give off radiation and eventually become different, stable elements. The ratio of the amount of unstable radioisotope to the amount of the stable end product allows scientists to calculate how much time has passed since the fish was alive. Another method, relative dating, relies on scientists knowing the age of fossils above, below, or within the same layer as the unknown specimen. The age of fossil A can then be estimated.

2. Based on the fossil record, explain what has happened to the type of habitat found in the area as time passed.

The leaf fossils in layer IV would indicate that this area was dry land with plants growing. The fish fossils in layers III and II indicate that the area was later under water and supported aquatic life. Layer I has no visible fossils. This could indicate that the area was a desert with little life and no water present to allow large numbers of fossils to form, or the area could have been covered by ice so that there were no life forms to be preserved.

Name _____ Date _____ Class _____

14 The History of Life, *continued*

Applying Scientific Methods *continued*

Through a chemical analysis of the rock layers represented in the illustration on the previous page and of other, deeper layers, scientists were able to construct a graph of the amount of oxygen present in the atmosphere when the rocks were formed. Examine the graph.

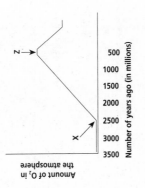

Amount of O_2 in the atmosphere

Number of years ago (in millions)

3500 3000 2500 2000 1500 1000 500

3. Describe what major event occurred in the evolution of life on Earth at point X that is directly related to the change in the graph above.

Photoautotrophs evolved and released O_2 into the atmosphere.

4. How did this event affect the level of oxygen in the atmosphere?

Photoautotrophs released O_2 into the atmosphere. Prior to that, there was no large source of atmospheric oxygen.

5. What major evolutionary event occurred at the point on the graph indicated by Z?

At this stage in Earth's history, aerobic organisms evolved.

6. How did this event affect the oxygen level?

The evolution of aerobes caused a decline in the amount of atmospheric oxygen.

7. What could paleontologists look for to confirm your answers to questions 3 and 6?

They could look for fossils of cyanobacteria (photoautotrophs) and aerobic organisms.

Chapter Assessment

Chapter 15 The Theory of Evolution

Reviewing Vocabulary

Write the word or phrase that best completes the statement. Use these choices:

adaptive radiation	vestigial structure
mimicry	natural selection
polyploid	stabilizing selection
genetic drift	artificial selection
	punctuated equilibrium
	gene pool
	camouflage
	allelic frequency

1. __Artificial selection__ is a technique in which the breeder selects particular traits.

2. A structural adaptation enabling an organism to blend in with its environment is __camouflage__ .

3. Another structural adaptation called __mimicry__ protects an organism by copying the appearance of another species.

4. The total number of genes present in a population is the __gene pool__ .

5. The __allelic frequency__ is the percentage of a particular allele in a population.

6. The alteration of allelic frequencies by chance events is known as __genetic drift__ .

7. __Stabilizing selection__ is the type of selection that favors average individuals in a population.

8. Any species with a multiple set of chromosomes is known as a(n) __polyploid__ .

9. __Natural selection__ is a mechanism for change in a population in which organisms with favorable variations live, reproduce, and pass on their favorable traits.

10. The concept that evolution occurs over long periods of stability that are interrupted by geologically brief periods of change is known as __punctuated equilibrium__ .

11. Any structure that is reduced in function in a living organism but may have been used in an ancestor is known as a(n) __vestigial structure__ .

12. The evolution of an ancestral species into an array of species that occupy different niches is called __adaptive radiation__ .

Chapter Assessment

Chapter 15 The Theory of Evolution, *continued*

Understanding Main Ideas (Part A)

In the space at the left, write the letter of the word or phrase that best completes the statement.

__d__ 1. Natural selection can best be defined as the
   a. survival of the biggest and strongest organisms in a population.
   b. elimination of the smallest organisms by the biggest organisms.
   c. survival and reproduction of the organisms that occupy the largest area.
   d. survival and reproduction of the organisms that are genetically best adapted to the environment.

__c__ 2. Structures that have a similar embryological origin and structure but are adapted for different purposes, such as a bat wing and a human arm, are called
   a. embryological structures.   b. analogous structures.
   c. homologous structures.   d. homozygous structures.

__a__ 3. Mutations such as polyploidy and crossing over provide the genetic basis for
   a. evolution.   b. spontaneous generation.
   c. biogenesis.   d. sexual reproduction.

__d__ 4. Within a decade of the introduction of a new insecticide, nearly all of the descendants of the target pests were immune to the usual-sized dose. The most likely explanation for this immunity to the insecticide is that
   a. eating the insecticide caused the bugs to become resistant to it.
   b. eating the insecticide caused the bugs to become less resistant to it.
   c. it destroyed organisms that cause disease in the insects, thus allowing them to live longer.
   d. it selected random mutations that were present in the insect population and that provided immunity to the insecticide.

__a__ 5. The flying squirrel of North America very closely resembles the flying phalanger of Australia. They are similar in size, have long, bushy tails, and skin folds that allow them to glide through the air. The squirrel is a placental mammal, while the phalanger is a marsupial. These close resemblances, even though genetically and geographically separated by great distances, can best be explained by
   a. convergent evolution.   b. divergent evolution.
   c. spontaneous generation.   d. vestigial structures.

__a__ 6. Hawaiian honeycreepers are a group of birds with similar body shape and size. However, they vary greatly in color and beak shape. Each species occupies its own niche and is adapted to the foods available in its niche. The evolution from a common ancestor to a variety of species is an example of
   a. divergent evolution.   b. cross-pollination.
   c. vegetative propagation.   d. convergent evolution.

Chapter Assessment

Chapter 15 The Theory of Evolution, *continued*

Understanding Main Ideas (Part B)

In the space at the left, write the letter of the word or phrase that best completes the statement or answers the question.

c 1. Which of the following is *not* a factor that causes changes in the frequency of homozygous and heterozygous individuals in a population?
  a. mutations   b. migration   c. random mating   d. genetic drift

d 2. When checking shell color for a species of snail found only in a remote area seldom visited by humans, scientists discovered the distribution of individuals that is shown in the graph.

Number of individuals

light ———→ dark
Coloration

Based on the information shown in the graph, the snail population is undergoing
  a. stabilizing selection.
  b. disruptive selection.
  c. artificial selection.
  d. directional selection.

c 3. The theory of continental drift hypothesizes that Africa and South America slowly drifted apart after once being a single landmass. The monkeys on the two continents, although very similar, show numerous genetic differences. Which factor is probably the most important in maintaining these differences?
  a. comparative anatomy   b. comparative embryology
  c. geographic isolation   d. fossil records

b 4. Which combination of characteristics in a population would provide the *greatest* potential for evolutionary change?
  a. small population, few mutations   b. small population, many mutations
  c. large population, few mutations   d. large population, many mutations

c 5. Upon close examination of the skeleton of an adult python, a pelvic girdle and leg bones can be observed. These features are an example of
  a. artificial selection.   b. homologous structures.
  c. vestigial structures.   d. comparative embryology.

b 6. Mutations occur because of
  a. the introduction of new variations from elsewhere.
  b. the introduction of new variations through mistakes in DNA replication.
  c. the chance survival and reproduction of new variations.
  d. change in allele or genotype frequencies.

Chapter Assessment

Chapter 15 The Theory of Evolution, *continued*

Thinking Critically

Read the information that follows and then answer the questions. A study of the squirrel population in a large northern city revealed that many of the squirrels inhabited large park areas that were also populated by numerous squirrel predators. The graph at the right reflects the data collected in regard to color and number of squirrels.

Number of squirrels

←——— Darkness of fur

1. Explain why the light- and dark-colored squirrels might be selected for and the medium-colored squirrels selected against.

The light-colored squirrels blend in well with the soil found in the area and with the leaves that fall from the trees and cover the ground in the autumn. The darker-colored squirrels blend in well with the paved walkways of the park area and also with the darkened tree trunks. The medium-colored squirrels would be more visible to predators and thus be selected against.

2. Explain how this type of disruptive selection can lead to the separation of this population into two distinct species.

After a long period of time, squirrels with the once most common phenotype, medium fur color, will produce fewer and fewer offspring and will gradually be eradicated. The light- and dark-colored individuals will live and reproduce successfully. After a while, disruptive selection will concentrate the color distribution at the two extremes. Eventually, the two groups may no longer recognize each other for mating purposes. This reproductive isolation could lead to the two types becoming separate species. Another possibility with the same end result is that these squirrels would tend to survive most successfully in areas where either dark or light coat color variation would be most advantageous. This would lead to geographic isolation.

Chapter 15 — The Theory of Evolution, *continued*

Applying Scientific Methods

A biologist studying a variety of fly in the rain forest noticed that the types of foods the fly preferred were located either high in the trees or in the foliage on the ground. There didn't seem to be any of the preferred foods anywhere in between. An experiment was designed that would select for a genetically determined behavior known as *geotaxis*. If a fly shows positive geotaxis, it flies downward. If the fly shows negative geotaxis, it flies upward.

1. In terms of evolution and natural selection, why would the researcher suspect that the flies being studied would show geotaxis?

It would be reasonable to expect that the flies would move either directly upward toward food or directly downward toward food because there wasn't anything for them to eat in-between those areas.

To conduct the experiment, the flies being studied were marked and placed in a maze (illustrated below). Each fly was placed in the "start" chamber. To exit the chamber, the fly had to make a decision about which of the three exits to enter. One exit faced upward, indicating negative geotaxis, and another exit aimed downward, indicating positive geotaxis. A third exit permitted the fly to remain on middle ground. Each fly was placed in the maze 15 times and its choice of direction recorded. Some flies consistently went upward and entered the food vial at the end of the exit tube. Others consistently went downward and entered the food vial at the lower end. Some flies chose the upward and downward exits equal numbers of times; others went for the middle exit.

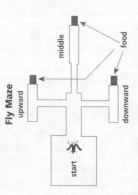

Fly Maze — upward, middle, downward, food, start

2. If the selection of direction is a genetic trait, what should happen when flies consistently selecting the upward exit are mated, those selecting the downward exit are mated, and the "no preference" and middle choice flies discarded?

You should end up with two different types of flies. One type will consistently fly only upward and the other will fly only downward.

Chapter 15 — The Theory of Evolution, *continued*

Applying Scientific Methods   continued

3. What type of selection pressure is operating in this experiment? Explain your answer.
Disruptive selection would be operating. The two extremes are being favored, while the middle choice and "no preference" flies are being selected against. This is true because the middle and "no preference" flies are being discarded in the experiment, while the two extremes are being retained and allowed to mate.

4. Describe what would be happening to the frequency of the allele for negative geotaxis in the above experiment.
The frequency of the allele for negative geotaxis would be increasing.

5. What might be acting in the flies' environment to select for flies that do not exhibit a distinct preference for flying upward at every trial or downward at every trial?
The preferred foods could ripen at different times, so that at one point in the year it would be beneficial to fly upward and at a different time of the year it would be more productive to fly downward. It might be, for example, that they feed on the pollen or other product of a particular species of flower. The flower may open only in the evening. So at that time of the day, the fly would do better to fly upward toward the flower. At other times, the fly may do better moving downward. There could also be a variety of predators that feed on the flies. Perhaps some of these predators also have preferred niches that are related to height levels in the vegetation.

6. What might eventually happen if in the wild the flies developed into two populations, with one showing positive geotaxis and the other showing negative geotaxis?
Eventually the two populations would become reproductively isolated owing to their height preferences. Two distinct species with their separate gene pools would result.

Name _____ Date _____ Class _____

Chapter 16 Primate Evolution

Reviewing Vocabulary

Complete the paragraphs by writing the correct term on the appropriate line. Use these choices:

anthropoids	bipedal	australopithecines	primates
hominids	prehensile tail	opposable thumb	Cro-Magnon
		Neanderthals	

A distinctive characteristic of humans is **(1)** ___bipedal___ locomotion, the ability to walk on two legs in an upright position. Another characteristic that humans share with most

(2) ___primates___ is the ability to touch the thumb to the forefinger. Called the

(3) ___opposable thumb___ , it permits objects to be tightly grasped.

Anthropologists are also concerned with the origin of humans. Primates are classified in two groups, the prosimians and the **(4)** ___anthropoids___ . The prosimians are small-bodied and include the lemurs and tarsiers. The other group can be divided into Old World monkeys, New World monkeys, and hominoids. Hominoids include the humanlike, bipedal primates such as the apes, chimpanzees, and gorillas. New World monkeys are entirely arboreal. Their success in the tree tops can be partially attributed to their **(5)** ___prehensile tail___ , which functions almost like an extra hand, enabling them to tightly grasp branches.

Modern humans and humanlike fossils are classified as **(6)** ___hominids___ . Based on fossil evidence and biochemical evidence, it is believed that apes and humans began to evolve about 30 million years ago, developing along different paths but arising from the same common ancestor. In 1924, Raymond Dart discovered a skull with both apelike and human characteristics. The skull derived from the first of several African primates, now collectively referred to as **(7)** ___australopithecines___ , which show both humanlike and apelike qualities. *Homo sapiens* may have first appeared between 100 000 and 400 000 years ago. The first of the species to have communicated through spoken language appeared around 100 000 years ago. They have been named **(8)** ___Neanderthals___ . About 35 000 years ago, these disappeared from the fossil record as a group called **(9)** ___Cro-Magnons___ evolved.

Name _____ Date _____ Class _____

Chapter 16 Primate Evolution, *continued*

Understanding Main Ideas (Part A)

In the space at the left, write the letter of the word or phrase that best completes the statement or answers the question.

___c___ **1.** Which is the oldest hominid species to be unearthed?
 a. *Homo habilis*   b. *Homo erectus*
 c. *Australopithecus afarensis*   d. *Australopithecus africanus*

___d___ **2.** The skeleton of the hominid nicknamed "Lucy" gave anthropologists evidence that
 a. cavemen coexisted with dinosaurs.
 b. Neanderthals coexisted with *Homo habilis*.
 c. upright walking evolved after large brains.
 d. upright walking evolved before large brains.

___c___ **3.** Most early hominid fossils have been found in
 a. Egypt.   b. France.   c. Africa.   d. North America.

___a___ **4.** The earliest primate identifiable from the fossil record is
 a. *Purgatorius*.   b. *Australopithecus*.   c. *Neanderthalus*.   d. *Afarensis*.

___b___ **5.** The first hominids to make and use simple stone tools were
 a. *Homo sapiens*.   b. *Homo habilis*.
 c. *Australopithecus afarensis*.   d. *Australopithecus africanus*.

___c___ **6.** As primates evolved, they developed
 a. a good sense of smell and large lower vertebrae.
 b. good vision and large teeth.
 c. stereoscopic vision and rotating shoulder joints.
 d. large teeth and a well-developed collar bone.

___a___ **7.** The hominid that had the most advanced tool-making abilities and spoken language was
 a. Cro-Magnon.   b. Neanderthal.   c. *Purgatorius*.   d. *Homo habilis*.

___c___ **8.** Based on the fossil record, it has been determined the earliest primates probably lived in the
 a. grasslands.   b. mountains.   c. forests.   d. deserts.

___d___ **9.** Primates evolved approximately
 a. 200 000 years ago.   b. 2 million years ago.
 c. 8 million years ago.   d. 66 million years ago.

___a___ **10.** The anthropologists who discovered the skull of *Homo habilis* were
 a. the Leakeys.   b. the Darts.   c. the Johansons.   d. the Priestleys.

Understanding Main Ideas (Part B)

In the space at the left, write the letter of the word or phrase that best completes the statement or answers the question.

b 1. Which factor may have played a large role in human evolution?
  a. a geologic event that released much radiation into the environment, which in time resulted in an increased mutation rate
  b. climatic changes that caused existing primates to search for new food sources
  c. flooding due to melting glaciers causing primates to seek refuge in the trees
  d. massive grassland fires that caused existing primates to flee to the mountains

d 2. Evidence that *Homo erectus* was more intelligent than its predecessors would include
  a. a small cranial capacity as indicated by their skeletal remains.
  b. involved messages they wrote on cave walls.
  c. signs of agriculture and tilled fields.
  d. tools, such as hand axes, that have been found near their fire pits.

c 3. Some primate skeletons were located in a cave in association with these things: a variety of tools, the charred bones of some animals they had cooked and eaten, and numerous paintings on the walls. Carbon-14 dating techniques determined that the bones and other artifacts were about 35 000 years old. The skeletal remains probably belonged to
  a. *A. afarensis.*   b. *Homo habilis.*   c. Cro-Magnons.   d. *Homo erectus.*

b 4. The jaw from the skull of the genus *Homo* and one from the genus *Australopithecus* are different in that the jaw from the genus *Homo* would
  a. be much heavier with large teeth and well-defined canines.
  b. be smaller with smaller teeth and not so much definition of tooth type.
  c. be larger with a multitude of small teeth with well-defined canines.
  d. be smaller with larger teeth that were all about the same.

c 5. The nucleotide sequence of human and chimpanzee genes differs by about only 1.6%. This fact, along with the fossil record, reveals that
  a. humans descended from chimpanzees.
  b. chimpanzees descended from humans.
  c. humans and chimpanzees evolved from a common ancestor.
  d. convergent evolution has resulted in chimpanzees and humans becoming more alike.

a 6. Evidence for the determination of bipedal locomotion in an animal could be found by an examination of the
  a. skull.   b. upper arm (humerous).
  c. finger (carpal).   d. jaw.

Thinking Critically

Answer the following questions.

1. Early primates spent most, if not all of their time in trees. How did their successful adaptations there eventually lead to important hominid adaptations?
Successful primate adaptations for arboreal life include binocular vision, an opposable thumb, the rotating ball-and-socket shoulder joint, and in some cases, the prehensile tail. All but the last adaptation have been significant in the evolution of hominids. Binocular vision permits depth perception, which is critical for tree life, allows for better judgment of predator and prey distances, and also makes the fashioning of tools possible. The opposable thumb makes grasping and crafting tools possible. The flexible shoulder joint made movement through the trees easier for primates and, for hominids, was a necessary step in the evolution of efficient arm movements.

2. Why is bipedal locomotion an important hominid trait?
Being bipedal allowed hominids to use their hands for tasks other than locomotion, such as tool-making and food-gathering.

3. You are on an expedition searching for early hominid fossils. You unearth a jaw bone. What traits would indicate to you that you have discovered an ape jaw and not a hominid jaw?
Ape jaws are larger and heavier than hominid jaws. Apes have large teeth with big canines. The basic shape of the ape jaw is not as rounded as that of a hominid.

4. Why is it that we are still piecing together a picture of how human evolution occurred and how is it possible that our understanding of it might be flawed?
The fossil record is not complete. Many of our interpretations of which primate or hominid preceded the other is based on fragments of skeletons. In addition, ancient human fossils are rare due to poor conditions for fossilization at most of the sites.

Name _____ Date _____ Class _____

Applying Scientific Methods

It is speculated that environmental changes in the African habitat from warm, moist forest to cool, dry grassland exerted selection pressures on all native species, including prehumans. Of all the theories attempting to explain hominid evolution, the one presently receiving much attention links the emergence of humankind to wide-scale climatic change. Two such major events in human evolution occurred, the first 2.8 million years ago and the second, 1 million years ago.

Ocean-bottom core samples taken from the west coast of Africa, the Arabian Sea, and the Gulf of Aden off the east coast of Africa lend credibility to this theory. A thick layer of dust and silicate particles has been found in the cores at levels determined to have been deposited 2.8 million and 1 million years before the present. Scientists attribute the deposits to the fact that grasses draw large quantities of silicates from the soil and concentrate them in their tissues for structural use. In a grassland environment, as grasses live, die, and decompose over many years, quantities of silicates accumulate in the surface soil.

Deposits of dust and silicates also coincide with ice sheet formation and the onset of two ice ages in the Northern Hemisphere. Computer models show that the cooling and ice sheet formation influenced weather in both hemispheres. The models illustrate how cool, dry winds would have been diverted toward Africa as the ice sheets grew.

Another important piece of information has been obtained from the Gulf of Aden core. It contains volcanic ash, along with dust and silicates blown by monsoon winds from the Rift Valley. This type of ash is also found in association with some hominid fossils discovered in the Rift Valley.

1. What does the above information tell us about the African environment that existed approximately 2.8 million and 1 million years ago? Explain.
The silicate deposits indicate a relatively dry grassland environment. This hypothesis is reinforced by the computer models predicting cool, dry air being diverted toward Africa as ice sheets grew in the Northern Hemisphere.

2. Describe what the African environment might have been like 2 million years ago.
The African habitat had changed from grassland back to large expanses of forest. This change would have been due to the recession of the ice sheets in the Northern Hemisphere, which resulted in a climate change from cool and dry to warm and moist. The warmer air could hold more moisture. Also, core samples did not contain silicates and dust deposits 2 million years ago, indicating that large expanses of grassland were no longer present.

Name _____ Date _____ Class _____

Applying Scientific Methods   continued

3. In what way does the presence of volcanic ash in the Gulf of Aden cores and in the Rift Valley help in tracing human evolution?
The presence of volcanic ash in the cores and in the Rift valley allows for a more precise time correlation between hominid fossils found on land and the climatic record provided by the ocean cores.

When African forests declined and were replaced with vast areas of grassland, competition for food among animal species intensified. In an attempt to survive, hominids radiated outward from small forested areas. A vegetarian group, the australopithecines, emerged a few thousand years after the cooling period 2.8 million years ago. These hominids had to rely on seeds and tubers during the harsher seasons and on dense vegetation along river banks during the remainder of the year. Exploiting a variety of habitats at about the same time as the australopithecines was the first representative of the genus *Homo*. Members of this group consumed many kinds of food, including meat.

4. How would a diet of meat improve the chances of this group's survival, compared to australopithecines?
By eating meat, the chances of survival were greatly increased since meat is available year-round. Thus, eating a variety of foods, including meat, enhanced the quality of their diet.

5. How would a diet of meat select for a different jaw and tooth structure than is seen in earlier primates?
The jaw of a vegetarian animal is necessarily heavy with broad, flat teeth. This allows for the chewing and grinding necessary to prepare the food for further digestion. The tooth and jaw structure of an omnivore or a carnivore does not require the same massive structure. Meat does not require the same amount and kind of mechanical processing. A meat-eater would also need teeth modified for tearing the flesh of the animals consumed.

Reviewing Vocabulary

Match the definition in Column A with the term in Column B.

Column A

d 1. Group of related phyla
e 2. Classification system based on phylogeny
a 3. Group of related orders
h 4. Evolutionary history of a species
b 5. Group of related genera
c 6. Group of related species
g 7. Group of related classes
f 8. Group of related families

Column B

a. class
b. family
c. genus
d. kingdom
e. cladistics
f. order
g. phylum
h. phylogeny

In the space at the left, write the letter of the word or phrase that best completes the statement.

d 9. The branch of biology that groups and names organisms is
 a. classification.   b. phylogeny.   c. nomenclature.   d. taxonomy.

c 10. A group of related classes of plants is a(n)
 a. order.   b. kingdom.   c. division.   d. phylum.

c 11. A heterotrophic eukaryote that absorbs nutrients from organic materials in the environment is a(n)
 a. bacterium.   b. herbivore.   c. fungus.   d. animal.

b 12. The placing of information or objects into groups based on similarities is
 a. biochemical analysis.   b. classification.
 c. phylogeny.   d. speciation.

a 13. The system for identifying organisms that uses two words to name the species is
 a. binomial nomenclature.   b. dichotomous keying.
 c. cladistics.   d. fan diagramming.

b 14. Prokaryotes that live in most habitats are
 a. protists.   b. eubacteria.   c. archaebacteria.   d. fungi.

Understanding Main Ideas (Part A)

In the space at the left, write **true** if the statement is true. If the statement is false, change the italicized word or phrase to make the statement true.

environment 1. In Aristotle's system of classification, animals were classified on the basis of their *size and structure*.

true 2. The greater the number of taxa two organisms have in common, the *more closely* related they are.

species 3. Organisms that are similar in structure and form and successfully interbreed belong to the same *family*.

a genus 4. A phylum is related to a class as a family is related to *an order*.

genus 5. In the scientific name of the white oak, *Quercus alba, Quercus* is the *species* name.

fewer 6. Two groups of organisms that are farther from each other on a cladogram share *more* derived traits than groups that are closer to each other.

true 7. In a fanlike diagram, groups represented by rays that begin *closer to the edge* of the fan evolved more recently.

true 8. When organisms are classified within the same group, it can be assumed that they have a common *phylogeny*.

Eubacteria 9. *Escherichia coli*, a type of bacterium that lives in the small intestine, is classified in the Kingdom *Protista*.

true 10. Linnaeus used similarities in *structure* to determine relationships among organisms.

Classify each of the following as a bacterium, protist, or fungus.

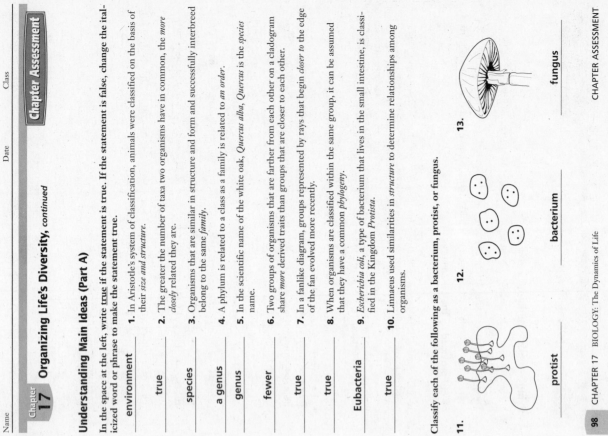

11. _____ protist

12. _____ bacterium

13. _____ fungus

Name _____ Date _____ Class _____

Chapter 17 Organizing Life's Diversity, *continued*

Understanding Main Ideas (Part B)

Answer the following questions.

1. What was one shortcoming of Aristotle's classification system?

Answers may state that Aristotle's system didn't account for animals that live in more than one kind of environment, nor did it show evolutionary relationships among organisms.

2. What are two advantages of using scientific names for organisms?

Answers may vary. Scientific names use Latin words, which do not change and are recognized by scientists all over the world. The use of scientific names avoids confusion where there is more than one common name for an organism. Common names can be misleading in terms of what an organism actually is. Scientific names reflect how organisms are related to each other.

3. On what basis are members of one kingdom distinguished from those of another kingdom?

Differences in cellular characteristics and methods of obtaining food are used to distinguish kingdoms.

Complete the following table of the characteristics of the six kingdoms.

Characteristic	Eubacteria and Archaebacteria	Protista	Fungi	Plantae	Animalia
4. Cell type	prokaryotic	eukaryotic	eukaryotic	eukaryotic	eukaryotic
5. Body form	unicellular	unicellular or multicellular	unicellular or multicellular	multicellular	multicellular
6. Method of obtaining food	heterotrophic or autotrophic	heterotrophic or autotrophic	heterotrophic	autotrophic	heterotrophic
7. Presence of complex organ systems	no	no	no	yes	yes

Name _____ Date _____ Class _____

Chapter 17 Organizing Life's Diversity, *continued*

Thinking Critically

The table below shows the complete classification of several species of animals. Use the table to answer the questions that follow.

Organism	House cat	Red Fox	Dog	Wolf	Gopher	Fly
Kingdom	Animalia	Animalia	Animalia	Animalia	Animalia	Animalia
Phylum	Chordata	Chordata	Chordata	Chordata	Chordata	Arthropoda
Class	Mammalia	Mammalia	Mammalia	Mammalia	Mammalia	Insecta
Order	Carnivora	Carnivora	Carnivora	Carnivora	Rodentia	Diptera
Family	Felidae	Canidae	Canidae	Canidae	Geomyidae	Muscidae
Genus	*Felis*	*Vulpes*	*Canis*	*Canis*	*Thomomys*	*Musca*
Species	*F. domesticus*	*V. fulva*	*C. familiaris*	*C. lupus*	*T. bottae*	*M. domestica*

1. What kind of animal is *Vulpes velox*? How do you know?

Vulpes velox is a species of fox because it is of the same genus as the red fox, *Vulpes fulva*.

2. What is the complete classification of *Vulpes velox*?

kingdom: Animalia; phylum: Chordata; class: Mammalia; order: Carnivora; family: Canidae; genus: *Vulpes*; species: *V. velox*

3. From the table, which two animals are most closely related? Explain.

The dog and the wolf are most closely related because they have the greatest number of levels of classification in common, differing only at the species level.

4. At what classification level does the evolutionary relationship between gophers and house cats diverge?

Gophers and house cats share the same kingdom, phylum, and class; they diverge at the order level.

5. How does the table indicate that a dog is more closely related to a red fox than to a house cat?

A dog, a red fox, and a house cat share the same kingdom, phylum, class, and order. However, dogs and foxes are in the same family, whereas dogs and cats are not.

CHAPTER ASSESSMENT

ANSWER KEY   BIOLOGY: The Dynamics of Life   **T285**

Name _____ Date _____ Class _____

Chapter 17 Organizing Life's Diversity, *continued*

Chapter Assessment

Applying Scientific Methods

When a sample solution of DNA is heated to about 80°C, the DNA "melts," separating into single strands of nucleotides. If the sample is then cooled slightly and incubated, matching nucleotide sequences begin to reassociate. The solution can then be filtered to allow the single strands to pass through.

One technique for comparing DNA of different species involves the labeling of single strands of DNA with radioactive iodine and using the labeled DNA to form hybrid DNA. In this procedure, a small amount of labeled, single-stranded DNA from one species is mixed with a large amount of unlabeled, single-stranded DNA from another species and the mixture is incubated over time. A percentage of the strands form hybrid DNA consisting of one labeled and one unlabeled strand. (See Figure 1.)

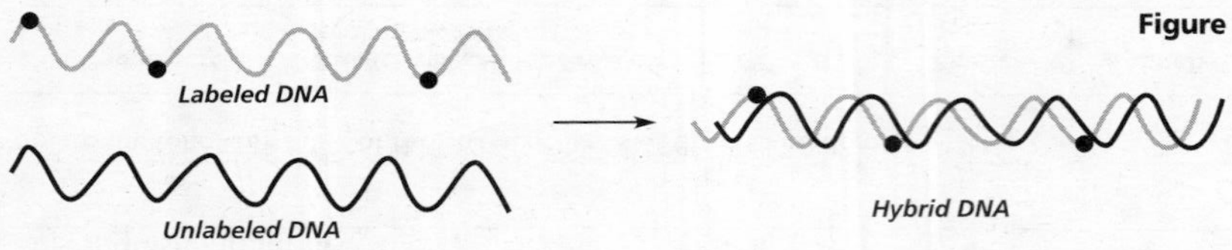

Figure 1

Labeled DNA

Unlabeled DNA

Hybrid DNA

The more closely related the two species are, the greater the number of matched sequences there will be in the hybrid DNA. (See Figure 2.) Hybrid DNA with a high proportion of matched sequences melts at higher temperatures than that with a low proportion of matched sequences.

Regions of matched sequences

Figure 2

Hybrid A

Figure 3

Hybrid B

Use Figure 3 below to answer the questions that follow.

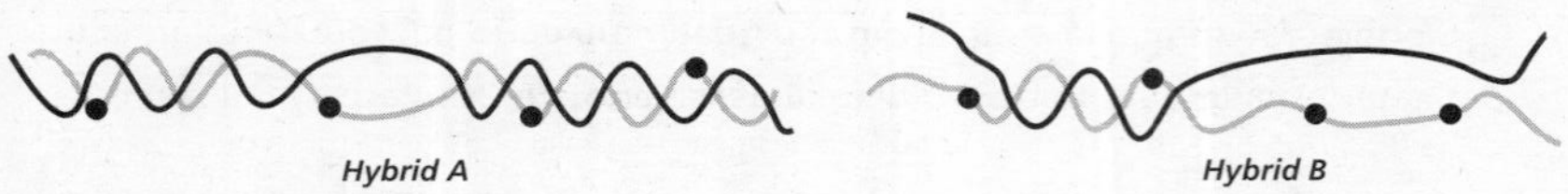

1. Which hybrid DNA was formed by DNA from two closely related species?
Hybrid A

2. Which hybrid DNA would melt at a lower temperature when heated?
Hybrid B

Name _____ Date _____ Class _____

Chapter 17 Organizing Life's Diversity, *continued*

Chapter Assessment

Applying Scientific Methods   *continued*

3. A solution containing Hybrid A is heated in stages, in 2.5-degree increments, from 55°C to 95°C and filtered at each stage to let single strands of DNA pass through. The radioactivity of the filtered material is measured at each stage. Would you expect to find a higher radioactivity level at 60°C or 85°C? Why?
The radioactivity level would be higher at 85°C. Because Hybrid A has a high proportion of matched sequences, it has a higher melting temperature; thus, single strands containing radioactive iodine would not be present at lower temperature.

A, B, and C are three groups of birds belonging to the same order. Birds in groups A and B show some structural similarities. Initially the two groups were classified together. However, recent microscopic comparisons of the vocal apparatus of birds in groups A and C show similarities in anatomy. Moreover, some birds in group A also exhibit many of the same behavioral patterns as birds in group C.

4. What is one hypothesis you could form about the relationships among bird groups A, B, and C, based on the given information?
Answers may vary. The birds in group A are more closely related to the birds in group C and should be classified together.

5. How could you use the hybrid DNA technique to test your hypothesis?
Mix radioactively labeled, singled-stranded DNA from birds in group A with unlabeled, single-stranded DNA from birds in group C to form hybrid DNA. Then determine the proportion of matched sequences by measuring levels of radioactivity in the filtrate as the hybrid DNA is heated in stages. Then repeat the experiment using DNA from groups A and B and compare the results.

6. What would be the independent and dependent variables in your experiment?
The independent variable is the two types of bird DNA (group A, B, or C) that are mixed. The dependent variable is the proportion of matched sequences in the hybrid DNA.

7. What control could you devise?
The control would be mixing labeled DNA from birds in group A with unlabeled DNA from birds in the same group.

Name _____ Date _____ Class _____

Chapter 18 Viruses and Bacteria

Reviewing Vocabulary

Match the definition in Column A with the term in Column B.

Column A

i	**1.** Poison produced by some bacteria
j	**2.** Nonliving particle that replicates inside a living cell
f	**3.** Process by which some bacteria convert nitrogen gas into ammonia
a	**4.** Virus that infects only bacteria
c	**5.** Process by which bacteria reproduce sexually
b	**6.** Requires oxygen for respiration
h	**7.** Process by which bacteria reproduce asexually
d	**8.** Bacterial form produced under unfavorable environmental conditions
e	**9.** Cell in which a virus reproduces
g	**10.** Enzyme injected into a host cell, which copies viral RNA into DNA

Column B

a. bacteriophage
b. obligate aerobe
c. conjugation
d. endospore
e. host cell
f. nitrogen fixation
g. reverse transcriptase
h. binary fission
i. toxin
j. virus

Compare and contrast each pair of related terms.

11. archaebacteria, eubacteria

Archaebacteria and eubacteria are both prokaryotes. Archaebacteria live in

extreme environments, whereas eubacteria line in many environments. They also

differ in their cell structure and genetic makeup.

12. provirus, retrovirus

A provirus is a DNA virus that has been inserted into a host cell's chromosome.

A retrovirus is an RNA virus that contains the enzyme reverse transcriptase,

which copies viral RNA into DNA.

Name _____ Date _____ Class _____

Chapter 18 Viruses and Bacteria, continued

Understanding Main Ideas (Part A)

Study the diagram. Then in the space at the left, write the letter of the stage of the lytic cycle
depicted that is described in each statement that follows.

Lytic Cycle

C	**1.** Viral nucleic acid and proteins are made.
E	**2.** The host cell breaks open, and the new virus particles are released.
B	**3.** The virus injects its nucleic acid into the host cell.
D	**4.** New virus particles are assembled.
A	**5.** The virus attaches to a host cell.

In the space at the left, write the letter of the word or phrase that best completes each statement.

d	**6.** Bacteria that live in the roots of legumes
	a. change ammonia into nitrogen gas. **b.** provide ATP for the plants.
	c. are autotrophic. **d.** provide usable nitrogen for the plants.
b	**7.** A bacterium's circular chromosome is copied during
	a. conjugation. **b.** binary fission. **c.** mitosis. **d.** lysis.
b	**8.** Penicillin kills bacteria by
	a. consuming them. **b.** causing holes to develop in their cell walls.
	c. staining them. **d.** depriving them of nutrients.

Chapter 18 Viruses and Bacteria, *continued*

Understanding Main Ideas (Part B)

Explain what happens in stages 1, 2, and 3 of the lysogenic cycle shown in the diagram.

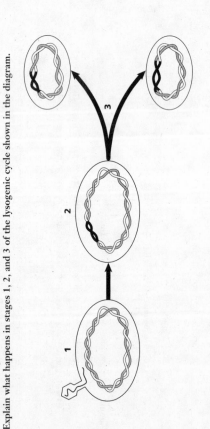

1. A virus injects its DNA into a bacterium.

2. The viral DNA becomes part of the host chromosome as a provirus.

3. The provirus is inactive but is replicated when the host cell's chromosome
   replicates.

Answer the following questions.

4. Why are viruses not considered to be living things?
   **Viruses do not carry out respiration, grow, or develop. They can replicate, but only
   when they are inside a living cell.**

5. How does a virus recognize its host?
   **A protein on the surface of a virus has a shape that matches a molecule in the
   plasma membrane of its host, allowing the virus to lock onto the host cell.**

6. Why is penicillin ineffective in destroying viruses or animal cells?
   **Penicillin causes bacteria to develop holes in their cell walls. Since neither viruses
   nor animal cells have cell walls, penicillin has no effect on them.**

Chapter 18 Viruses and Bacteria, *continued*

Thinking Critically

Study the table showing the percentages of deaths in developed and developing countries due to various causes. Then answer the questions.

Causes of death	Developed countries		Developing countries			
	Americas	Europe	Americas	Southeast Asia	Africa	Eastern Mediterranean
Infectious diseases	3.6	8.6	31.1	43.9	49.8	44.5
Cancer	21.5	18.1	9.0	4.4	2.9	4.2
Circulatory diseases	54.5	53.8	24.5	15.6	11.7	14.1
Accidents	8.4	5.6	6.3	4.3	3.8	4.1

1. What is the chief cause of death in developing countries? In developed countries? How does the table
   reflect the fact that the availability of antibiotics affects the number of deaths due to infectious diseases?
   **In developing countries, the chief cause of death is infectious diseases; in devel-
   oped countries, it is circulatory diseases. Developed countries have better access to
   doctors and antibiotics for curing infectious diseases than do developing countries.
   That's why fewer deaths from infectious diseases occur in developed countries.**

2. What conditions in developed countries may check the spread of bacteria that cause disease?
   **Water purification and sanitary waste disposal help prevent the spread of disease-
   causing bacteria in developed countries.**

3. Why do doctors sometimes advise patients who are taking antibiotics to eat yogurt?
   **The antibiotics kill beneficial, as well as harmful, bacteria in the body. Because
   yogurt contains some of these beneficial bacteria, eating yogurt can help to
   replace them in the patient's body.**

4. At one time, bacteria were classified as plants. Why do you think bacteria were classified this way?
   Give at least two reasons why bacteria should not be classified as plants.
   **Like plants, bacteria have cell walls and lack typical animal characteristics. Unlike
   plants, bacteria are prokaryotic, their cell walls lack cellulose, and only some are
   autotrophs.**

Name _____ Date _____ Class _____

Chapter Assessment

Chapter 18 Viruses and Bacteria, *continued*

Applying Scientific Methods

In 1957, Heinz Fraenkel-Conrat and his coworkers were studying two viruses that infect tobacco plants. One of the disease-causing viruses was called TMV and the other, HRV. Both viruses were similar in structure. (See the diagrams below.) It was easy to tell which virus had infected a tobacco plant because each virus caused different lesions on the leaves. Fraenkel-Conrat knew that TMV and HRV are RNA viruses. He wanted to find out which part of the virus—the protein coat or the RNA—was carrying the genetic information needed to specify the reproduction of these viruses. He decided that he would find the answer by producing hybrids of the viruses. A hybrid has the RNA of one virus and the protein coat of another virus. In this case, the two hybrids are denoted H-T and T-H, where the first letter indicates the virus from which the RNA was obtained.

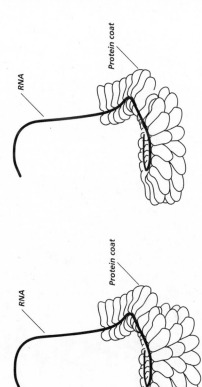

RNA

Protein coat

HRV

RNA

Protein coat

TMV

1. Suggest how Fraenkel-Conrat might produce the two hybrids.

Answers may vary but may include that he would have to separate the RNA from the protein coat of each virus. Then he would mix the RNA of the HRV with the protein coat of the TMV to produce the H-T hybrid. He would mix the TMV RNA with the HRV protein coat to produce the T-H hybrid.

Name _____ Date _____ Class _____

Chapter Assessment

Chapter 18 Viruses and Bacteria, *continued*

Applying Scientific Methods   *continued*

2. How might he determine whether the RNA or the protein coat of the H-T hybrid carried the genetic information of the virus?

Answers will vary but may include that he could inject the H-T hybrid into a healthy tobacco plant. If the hybrid causes the same kind of lesion that HRV typically causes, he would know that the RNA of the H-T hybrid provides the genetic information, since the hybrid has the RNA of HRV.

3. In lesions caused by the H-T hybrid on tobacco leaves, the new viruses produced were not hybrids. They were all HRV. Why would this be so?

Since HRV RNA was providing the genetic message, only HRV protein coats would be made.

4. Hypothesize what kind of lesion the T-H hybrid will cause. Explain.

The T-H hybrid will cause the same kind of lesion caused by TMV because the hybrid has the RNA of the TMV.

5. What controls were used in this experiment?

tobacco plants infected with TMV and tobacco plants infected with HRV

6. What were the variables in the experiment?

The two kinds of hybrids were the variables.

7. What was the most convincing evidence in this experiment that showed which part of the virus carried the genetic information?

The fact that the H-T virus produced only HRV viruses showed that the RNA of the HRV was controlling the reproduction of the viruses.

CHAPTER ASSESSMENT   ANSWER KEY   BIOLOGY: The Dynamics of Life   **T289**

Chapter 19 Protists

Reviewing Vocabulary

Match the definition in Column A with the term in Column B.

Column A

- i 1. An animal-like protist

- d 2. A protozoan that moves by beating hairlike parts that cover its cell

- k 3. A reproductive cell that can produce a new organism without fertilization

- a 4. Multicellular and unicellular photosynthetic protists

- f 5. A kind of reproduction that occurs when an individual breaks up into pieces, each of which grows into a new individual

- g 6. The haploid form of an alga that produces sex cells

- h 7. In slime molds, the mass of cytoplasm that contains many diploid nuclei but no cell walls or membranes

- e 8. A group of cells that live together in close association

- l 9. The diploid form of an alga that develops from a zygote and produces spores

- j 10. Extensions of an amoeba's plasma membrane, which function in locomotion

- c 11. Kind of reproduction in which a single parent produces offspring identical to itself

- b 12. Life cycle of organisms that have a haploid stage followed by a diploid stage

Column B

- a. algae
- b. alternation of generations
- c. asexual reproduction
- d. ciliate
- e. colony
- f. fragmentation
- g. gametophyte
- h. plasmodium
- i. protozoan
- j. pseudopodia
- k. spore
- l. sporophyte

Chapter 19 Protists, *continued*

Understanding Main Ideas (Part A)

In the space at the left, write the letter of the word or phrase that best completes the statement or answers the question.

- b 1. Many protozoans are classified according to
  - a. their method of getting food.
  - b. the way that they move.
  - c. their method of reproduction.
  - d. their habitats.

- c 2. An amoeba engulfs food by
  - a. using its oral groove and the action of cilia.
  - b. osmosis.
  - c. surrounding the food with pseudopodia.
  - d. forming cysts.

- d 3. Excess water is pumped out of a paramecium by means of
  - a. its pellicle.
  - b. a micronucleus and macronucleus.
  - c. its gullet.
  - d. a pair of contractile vacuoles.

- d 4. Which of the following forms a mass of amoeboid cells?
  - a. amoeba
  - b. plasmodial slime mold
  - c. water mold
  - d. cellular slime mold

- a 5. During the gametophyte generation, a green alga
  - a. has the haploid number of chromosomes.
  - b. has the diploid number of chromosomes.
  - c. reproduces asexually.
  - d. develops from a zygote.

- b 6. Dinoflagellates are able to spin by means of
  - a. the cilia that emerge through their pellicle.
  - b. two flagella at right angles to each other.
  - c. a pillbox shell that opens and closes.
  - d. a holdfast that attaches them to a rock.

- c 7. Slime molds are said to be like animals during much of their life cycle because they
  - a. look like animals.
  - b. reproduce by making spores.
  - c. move about and engulf food.
  - d. grow on rotting leaves or tree stumps.

- b 8. Which ancient protist group was probably the ancestor of plants?
  - a. diatoms
  - b. green algae
  - c. red algae
  - d. slime molds

- d 9. A protozoan that moves by lashing one or more of its whiplike parts is a
  - a. thallus.
  - b. sporozoan.
  - c. water mold.
  - d. flagellate.

Name _____ Date _____ Class _____

Understanding Main Ideas (Part B)

Answer the following questions.

1. How do protists differ from bacteria?
   Bacteria are prokaryotes; protists are are eukaryotes with a variety of membrane-bound organelles, including a nucleus.

2. Euglenoids have characteristics of both autotrophs and heterotrophs. Explain.
   Most euglenoids have chlorophyll and carry out photosynthesis, as autotrophs do; however, when light is not available, euglenoids can ingest food from the surrounding water, as heterotrophs would do.

3. What is the relationship between the sporophyte and gametophyte stages of some algae?
   Each stage produces the other. The diploid sporophyte stage forms haploid spores that develop into gametophytes. The gametophytes produce gametes, which fuse and form the sporophyte.

4. What triggers sexual reproduction in diatoms?
   When diatoms reproduce asexually, the two halves of the diatom's shell separate, and each half produces a new half to fit inside itself. Thus, half the offspring are smaller than the parent. When the new diatoms are one-fourth the full size, they reproduce sexually to form a full-size diatom.

5. What causes the dangerous red tides in the ocean?
   Population explosions occur among dinoflagellates that produce a strong nerve toxin.

6. What adaptation helps red algae to live in deep water?
   Red algae contain pigments called phycobilins. These pigments absorb green, violet, and blue light waves, which are the only part of the light spectrum that penetrates water below a depth of 100 m. The phycobilins enable red algae to photosynthesize in deep water.

Name _____ Date _____ Class _____

Thinking Critically

Answer the following questions.

1. Ciliates have specialized cilia whose motion sweeps particles and/or bacteria into the ciliates' oral groove. In an experiment, inert latex beads and bacteria of the same size were placed in water with ciliated protozoans. Equal numbers of latex beads and bacteria were ingested by the ciliates. Form a hypothesis to explain these results.
   Answers will vary but may include that these ciliated protozoans have no chemoreceptors to aid them in selecting food.

2. A study of the protozoan populations per gram of leaf litter in a deciduous forest provided the data in the table. Interpret the data.

Season	Ciliates	Testate Amoebas
Winter	1500/gm	7000/gm
Summer	400/gm	700/gm

   One possible interpretation: In summer, before the leaves fall, there is less leaf litter than in winter, after the leaves fall. The number of protozoans increases with increasing leaf litter because the amount of available nutrients increases.

3. Anemia is a condition in which the blood is deficient in red blood cells and in hemoglobin. Why does a person with malaria develop anemia?
   A person with malaria develops anemia because after the *Plasmodium* spores reproduce asexually in the person's liver, they move into the blood and destroy red blood cells.

4. In the 1840s, a famine killed hundreds of thousands of people in Ireland. The famine was caused by a downy mildew that destroyed the entire potato crop. Hypothesize why the downy mildew was able to do such damage.
   The climate in Ireland is cool and damp. This provided an excellent environment for the downy mildew to spread.

5. Why is the relationship between some termites and the flagellates that live in their intestines said to be mutualistic?
   Some termites feed on wood but cannot digest the cellulose. The flagellate in such a termite's intestine converts cellulose into a carbohydrate that both the termite and the flagellate can use. The flagellates are also provided with protection.

Applying Scientific Methods

It has been well-documented that populations of protozoans increase when water is polluted. The increase of protozoans may simply indicate that these organisms feed on the bacteria, the active decomposers of organic matter in the polluted water. Imagine that you are working with a team of scientists to determine if protozoans, like bacteria, would have any beneficial effects on a water purification system in which organic wastes are decomposed. The line at the top of the grid below shows the rate of decomposition of the hay in water when bacteria are present alone. The lower line shows the rate of decomposition when both bacteria and protozoans are present.

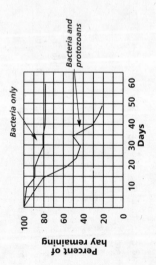

1. What does the graph show about the amount of decomposition that occurs when only bacteria are present?
In 60 days, only about 21 percent of the hay has been decomposed by the bacteria.

2. What happens to the same amount of hay when protozoans also are present?
When protozoans are present with the bacteria, the hay decomposes at a much faster rate.

3. One member of the team hypothesizes that the protozoans are the decomposers in this case. Plan an experiment to prove whether this hypothesis is true or not.
Answers will vary. In one experiment, you might add penicillin to the water to kill the bacteria. Then you could record the rate at which the hay decomposes when only protozoans are present.

Applying Scientific Methods continued

4. Suppose that very little of the hay decomposed in 50 days when protozoans were present alone. What might you hypothesize then about the role of protozoans in decomposition?
Answers will vary but might include that the bacteria and protozoans have some type of mutual feeding relationship. One possibility is that the bacteria alter the physical environment (pH, temperature, oxygen content) so that the protozoans become more efficient in decomposing organic matter themselves or cause the bacteria to become more efficient decomposers.

5. Suppose you have a vial of *Carchesium polypinum*, a species of ciliates found in waste water. You have just read that these protozoans produce a kind of mucus, which they secrete into the water. You want to develop a laboratory model of waste-water treatment. As your model, you drop some India ink into a beaker of tap water and add a vial of *Carchesium*. What effect might the mucus produced by the ciliates have on the India ink? How might you apply your results to the effect of the mucus on waste matter in water?
The mucus might cause the particles of ink to stick together, making it easier to filter the ink out. The same technique might work with any kind of waste matter in water.

Name _____ Date _____ Class _____

Chapter Assessment

Chapter 20 Fungi

Reviewing Vocabulary

Match the definition in Column A with the term in Column B.

Column A	Column B
e	**1.** In parasitic fungi, specialized hyphae that penetrate cells and absorb nutrients	**a.** ascospore
h	**2.** Case in which asexual spores are produced	**b.** ascus
j	**3.** Thick-walled spore adapted to withstand unfavorable conditions	**c.** chitin
i	**4.** Hyphae that grow horizontally along the surface of a food source	**d.** gametangia
c	**5.** Complex carbohydrate in the cell walls of fungi	**e.** haustoria
f	**6.** Mutualistic association between a fungus and a green alga or cyanobacterium	**f.** lichen
b	**7.** Saclike structure in which sexual spores develop in some fungi	**g.** mycorrhiza
a	**8.** Spore produced by sac fungi	**h.** sporangium
g	**9.** Mutualistic association in which a fungus lives in close contact with the roots of a plant partner	**i.** stolons
d	**10.** In zygomycotes, the haploid structures that fuse to form a diploid zygote	**j.** zygospore

Compare and contrast the following pairs of related terms.

11. hypha, mycelium

In a multicellular fungus, a hypha is a basic structural unit in the form of a thread-like filament. A network of branched hyphae forms a mycelium.

12. basidium, basidiospore

A basidium is a club-shaped hypha that produces spores. A spore produced in a basidium is called a basidiospore.

CHAPTER 20   BIOLOGY: The Dynamics of Life   115

Name _____ Date _____ Class _____

Chapter Assessment

Chapter 20 Fungi, *continued*

Understanding Main Ideas (Part A)

In the space at the left, write the letter of the word or phrase that best completes each statement.

b   **1.** Fungi are classified into groups by their
　　a. symbiotic relationships.　　**b.** spore-producing structures.
　　c. nutrition.　　**d.** recycling ability.

c   **2.** Fungi that break down complex organic substances into raw materials that other organisms can use are
　　a. parasites.　　**b.** mutualists.　　**c.** decomposers.　　**d.** autotrophs.

d   **3.** In hyphae divided by septa, cytoplasm flows from one cell to the next through
　　a. haustoria.　　**b.** chitin.　　**c.** spores.　　**d.** pores.

a   **4.** Yeasts usually reproduce asexually by
　　a. budding.　　**b.** meiosis.　　**c.** fission.　　**d.** fragmentation.

a   **5.** The bread mold *Rhizopus* produces sexual zygospores when
　　a. environmental conditions are unfavorable.
　　b. environmental conditions are favorable.
　　c. there is moist food.
　　d. rhizoids are present.

c   **6.** Fossils of fungi are rare due to fungi's
　　a. late appearance on the Geologic Time Scale.
　　b. lack of species diversity.
　　c. composition of soft materials.
　　d. ability to form protective zygospores.

In the space at the left, write **true** if the statement is true. If the statement is false, change the italicized word to make it true.

conidia　　**7.** During asexual reproduction, ascomycotes produce *ascospores*.

absorptive　　**8.** Mycorrhizae increase the *reproductive* surface of plant roots.

true　　**9.** The four major divisions of fungi are Zygomycota, Ascomycota, *Basidiomycota*, and Deuteromycota.

deuteromycote　　**10.** The fungus that produces penicillin is an example of a *basidiomycote*.

rhizoids　　**11.** Bread mold is able to penetrate bread by means of *zygospores*.

CHAPTER ASSESSMENT

Understanding Main Ideas (Part B)

Answer the following questions.

1. How do fungi obtain nutrients? What is this process called? **Hyphae grow into cells and release digestive enzymes, which break down large organic molecules into small molecules that diffuse into the hyphae. Because food is digested outside the cells of the fungus, the process is called extracellular digestion.**

2. What is the role of saprophytic fungi in food chains? **Saprophytic fungi decompose the remains of dead organisms at each level of a food chain, producing inorganic nutrients that can be used by plants to make food, which is passed on to other organisms in the food chain.**

3. How does the symbiotic relationship of a lichen benefit both organisms? **The alga or cyanobacterium provides food for itself and the fungus. The fungus helps retain moisture, provides the alga or cyanobacterium with water and minerals, and protects it from environmental changes.**

4. How is reproduction in deuteromycetes different from that in other fungi? **Deuteromycetes have no known sexual phase, whereas all other fungi have both an asexual and a sexual phase.**

5. How is a zygospore formed? **The hyphae of two different mycelia, each with a haploid nucleus, come together and fuse, forming two gametangia. When the nuclei of the two gametangia fuse, a diploid zygote forms and develops into a thick-walled zygospore.**

6. Why are mycorrhizae economically important? **They help plants grow larger and be more productive.**

Thinking Critically

Answer the following questions.

1. A soil fungus is one of the sources of cyclosporine. This drug is given to patients who are about to receive an organ transplant. Cyclosporine suppresses the body's natural response to reject the organ transplant as a foreign substance. Hypothesize about how cyclosporine may be useful to the fungus that produces it. **Cyclosporine suppresses a reaction against the fungus by the cells that are penetrated by the fungus's hyphae.**

2. Wheat rust is a fungus that causes enormous damage to wheat crops. The life cycle of wheat rust alternates between two different hosts: wheat plants and barberry bushes. The wheat rust needs both hosts to complete its sexual cycle. What could farmers do to protect their wheat crops? **They could eliminate any barberry bushes in the vicinity of their wheat fields.**

3. Hypothesize about how mycorrhizal associations may have evolved. **Answers will vary. Some plants living in unfavorable conditions may have become infected with a fungus. If the hyphae of the fungus grew out into the soil where minerals were more plentiful, the beginning of a beneficial relationship would have begun. The fungus would provide the plant with minerals and water, which would make the plant grow larger and healthier than it would without the fungus. In turn, the plant would provide food for the fungus.**

4. Fossil plants often had mycorrhizal roots. How might the mycorrhizal association have played a role in the invasion of plants onto land? **Answers may vary, but may include that the soil in which early plants grew lacked sufficient minerals for growth. If it hadn't been for mycorrhizal roots, the early plants would have had difficulty in obtaining the minerals they needed. Also, the fungus helped maintain water around the plant, an advantage in dry soils.**

5. A biologist proposes classifying fungi together with protists, rather than in a separate kingdom. Why might this suggestion be accepted? Why might the suggestion be rejected? **Answers may vary. Fungi, like protists, are eukaryotic and have both plant and animal characteristics. However, most fungi are multicellular and have more complex life cycles than do most protists.**

Copyright © Glencoe/McGraw-Hill, a division of The McGraw-Hill Companies, Inc.

Chapter Assessment

Chapter 20 Fungi, continued

Applying Scientific Methods

At first, it may seem that the fungus in a mycorrhizal association receives the greatest benefit. After all, the fungus uses the organic nutrients produced by the plant. However, the fungus is also useful to the plant. For example, the fungal hyphae increase the absorptive surface of the plant's roots. The table below records the inflow of phosphate in two kinds of onion plants—mycorrhizal and non-mycorrhizal.

Inflow of Phosphate in Onion Plants

Trials	Interval Duration (days)	Inflow (pmol/cm/s)	
		Mycorrhizal	Non-mycorrhizal
1	14	0.17	0.050
2	7	0.22	0.016
3	10	0.13	0.042
	Averages:	0.17	0.036

1. In each of the trials recorded, contrast the amount of phosphate that moved into an onion plant that is mycorrhizal with the amount that moved into a non-mycorrhizal onion plant. What conclusion do you reach?
   In the first trial, the mycorrhizal onion plant took in more than 3 times as much phosphate as the non-mycorrhizal plant. In the second trial, the mycorrhizal plant absorbed more than 13 times as much phosphate. In the third trial, the mycorrhizal plant took in more than 3 times as much phosphate as the non-mycorrhizal plant. The conclusion is that the mycorrhizal association greatly increases phosphate inflow.

2. Explain why mycorrhizal and non-mycorrhizal plants take in different amounts of phosphate.
   Mycorrhizal mycelium greatly increases the absorptive surface of the plant roots. Also, since the mycelium grows farther out into the soil, it obtains phosphates that are otherwise inaccessible to the plant.

Chapter Assessment

Chapter 20 Fungi, continued

Applying Scientific Methods continued

To study the effect of mycorrhizal associations on plant growth, an investigator grew six seedlings in nutrient solution. The seedlings illustrated in the drawing on the left were then planted in soil that contained no mycorrhizal fungi. The seedlings illustrated on the right were grown first in forest soil rich in mycorrhizal fungi and then transferred to the soil without mycorrhizal fungi. All the plants grew for the same amount of time.

3. What was the variable in this investigation?
   The variable was the kind of soil in which the plants were grown first.

4. What was the control in the investigation?
   The control was the group of plants grown only in the soil without mycorrhizal fungi.

5. You have been given six healthy plants that were grown in soil with mycorrhizal fungi. Hypothesize what might happen to the mycorrhizae if you transplant the plants to soil that is phosphate-rich.
   Answers will vary but may include that the mycorrhizae may proliferate, producing much larger plants and larger fungal mass.

6. Plan an experiment to test your hypothesis.
   Answers will vary, but approaches should be based on using the six plants with mycorrhizae from question 5. Transplant three plants to phosphate-rich soil; after a period of time, compare the masses of these plants and their fungal masses with the plant and fungal masses of the three control plants.

Chapter 21 What Is a Plant?

Reviewing Vocabulary

Match the definition in Column A with the term in Column B.

Column A

Column B

e 1. A plant organ that absorbs water and minerals from the soil

f 2. Contains tissues of tubelike, elongated cells through which water and food are transported

g 3. Provides structural support for upright growth and contains tissues for transporting materials from one part of the plant to another

a 4. Structures that support male and female reproductive structures

h 5. Structure that contains an embryo along with a food supply and is covered by a protective coat

c 6. Protective, waxy layer covering most fruit, leaves, and stems

b 7. Leaves found on ferns that vary in length from 1 cm to 500 cm

d 8. Broad, flat structure of a plant that traps light energy for photosynthesis

a. cone

b. frond

c. cuticle

d. leaf

e. root

f. vascular plant

g. stem

h. seed

Write a definition for each term listed below.

9. nonvascular plant

A nonvascular plant is a plant that lacks the vascular tissues made up of tubelike, elongated cells through which water and food are transported

10. vascular tissues

Vascular tissues are the tissues made up of tubelike, elongated cells through which water, food, and other materials are transported.

Chapter 21 What Is a Plant?, *continued*

Understanding Concepts (Part A)

Complete the three tables by using the following list of words and phrases:

club mosses
ferns
flowering plants
hornworts
horsetails
liverworts

mosses
needlelike or scaly leaves
only one living species
palmlike trees with cones as long as 1 m
three distinct genera
whisk ferns

Phylogeny of Plants (based on division)

Non-seed nonvascular plant divisions

Division	Common Name
Hepatophyta	a. liverworts
Anthocerophyta	b. hornworts
Bryophytes	c. mosses

Non-seed, vascular plant division

Division	Common Name
Psilophyta	d. whisk ferns
Lycophyta	e. club mosses
Spenophyta	f. horsetails
Pterophyta	g. ferns

Seed Plants

Division	Common characteristics
Cycadophyta	h. palmlike trees with cones as long as 1 m
Gnetophyta	i. three distinct genera
Ginkgophyta	j. only one living species
Coniferophyta	k. needlelike or scaly leaves
Anthophyta	l. flowering plants

Name _____ Date _____ Class _____

Chapter 21 What Is a Plant?, *continued*

Understanding Concepts (Part B)

Answer the following questions.

1. Why do scientists think that plants probably evolved from green algae?

Both plants and green algae have cell walls that contain cellulose. Both groups have the same types of chlorophyll used in photosynthesis. Algae and plants store food in the form of starch; other organisms store food as glycogen and other sugars.

2. In what ways does vascular tissue provide an adaptive advantage for plants?

The evolution of vascular tissue enabled plants to survive in many more habitats. Vascular plants can live farther from water than nonvascular plants. Vascular tissue also helps support upright growth and allows vascular plants to grow larger than nonvascular plants.

3. How does the cuticle prevent water loss?

The waxy cuticle is composed of lipids, and water does not dissolve in lipids, so the cuticle helps prevent the water in plant tissues from evaporating into the atmosphere.

4. What major events highlight the evolution of plants?

Major events that highlight the evolution of plants from green algae, the development of vascular tissue, the production of seeds, and the formation of flowers.

5. Compare the seeds of cycads, conifers, and flowering plants.

Both cycads and conifers produce seeds in cones. Cones are scaly structures that support male or female reproductive structures. Flowering plants, in contrast, produce seeds enclosed in a fruit.

CHAPTER ASSESSMENT

Name _____ Date _____ Class _____

Chapter 21 What Is a Plant?, *continued*

Thinking Critically

Use the graph to answer questions 1–3.

1. Investigators study the influence of light on spore germination in bryophytes. A spore has germinated when a small, green filament of cells is just protruding through the ruptured spore coat. Based on the graph, what wavelength of light appears to initiate spore germination?

Light at a wavelength of 550nm initiates germination.

Wavelength of light (nm)

2. What is the optimum wavelength for spore germination?

At 700 nm, 100 percent of the spores germinate.

3. What colors of light favor spore germination?

orange and red

Answer the following questions.

4. Aquatic bryophytes have been invaluable in monitoring pollution by heavy metals in contaminated water. However, the highest concentrations in the water do not always correspond to the highest values in the plants. Why might this be?

Accept any reasonable answer. Many chemical processes occur in a plant. The processes may cause a metal to combine with other substances to form a harmless compound. A test would not reveal the presence of a metal in a compound.

5. Some mosses that live in deserts dry out, and all their metabolic activities cease during a dry spell. At the next rainfall, however, they revive, grow, and reproduce. Why is this behavior adaptive?

This behavior helps the moss survive during the dry period by making it inactive. It makes the moss active only at a time when conditions are right for it to grow.

CHAPTER ASSESSMENT

CHAPTER ASSESSMENT   ANSWER KEY   BIOLOGY: The Dynamics of Life   **T297**

Chapter Assessment

Chapter 21 What Is a Plant?, *continued*

Applying Scientific Methods

In an effort to understand alternation of generations in bryophytes, scientists have tried in the laboratory to develop moss sporophytes from gametophytes *without fertilization*. When filaments of cells that develop into haploid gametophytes were cultivated in a sugar-free medium, only gametophytes were produced. However, when botanists transferred these cell filaments to a medium supplemented with 2 percent sucrose, the filaments produced a large number of sporophyte sporangia.

1. Formulate a hypothesis to explain why a medium with 2 percent sucrose causes this change in the reproductive cycle. (Be creative in your thinking.)
Answers will vary. Students may suggest that the sucrose somehow causes a normal haploid cell to undergo changes that double its chromosome number and make it ready to produce sporophytes.

2. Plan an experiment to prove your hypothesis.
Plans will vary, depending on the hypothesis. Students may vary the amount of sucrose in the medium to observe the effect on the reproductive cycle.

3. What will be your variable in this experiment?
The variable may be differing amounts of sucrose in the medium.

4. What will be your control?
The medium with no sucrose will be the control.

5. Some experimenters showed that the effect of sucrose is enhanced when lower light intensities are also present. How might less light affect the experiment?
Less light will reduce the rate of photosynthesis.

Chapter Assessment

Chapter 21 What Is a Plant?, *continued*

Applying Scientific Methods   continued

6. Scientists also discovered that after about 12 weeks of producing sporophytes, the plants stopped reproducing. However, if the gametophytes were transferred to a new sucrose medium, they began the formation of sporophytes again. In a medium lacking sucrose, the plants produced only gametophytes. How might these results be explained?
Answers will vary but may include that gametophytes require additional nutrients in order to produce a totally different generation—the sporophyte generation. Perhaps the plants need less energy to produce another similar generation—the gametophyte generation.

7. Why would botanists perform an experiment like this, which seems to involve events that do not usually occur in nature?
Answers will vary but may explain how and why alternation of generation occurs and may have applications in plant technology.

Name _____ Date _____ Class _____

Chapter 22 The Diversity of Plants

Reviewing Vocabulary

Match the definition in Column A with the term in Column B.

	Column A	Column B
j	**1.** Cluster of sporangia	**a.** cotyledon
d	**2.** Leaf of a fern	**b.** embryo
c	**3.** Plants that lose all their leaves at one time	**c.** deciduous plant
h	**4.** Early gametophyte in lycophytes, sphenophytes, and pterophytes	**d.** frond
		e. fruit
b	**5.** Organism at an early stage of development	**f.** ovule
i	**6.** Thick, underground stem	**g.** pollen grain
a	**7.** Food-storage organ of some plant embryos	**h.** prothallus
e	**8.** The ripened ovary of a flower	**i.** rhizome
f	**9.** Structure in which the female gametophyte develops	**j.** sorus
g	**10.** Structure that includes sperm cells, nutrients, and a protective outer covering	

Compare and contrast each pair of terms.

11. antheridium, archegonium

Gametophytes produce two kinds of sexual reproductive structures. The antheridium is the male reproductive structure in which sperm are produced. The archegonium is the female reproductive structure in which eggs are produced.

12. annuals, perennials

These terms refer to the life spans of anthophytes. Annuals live for only a year or less. Perennials live for several years, producing flowers and seed periodically—usually once each year.

Name _____ Date _____ Class _____

Chapter 22 The Diversity of Plants, *continued*

Understanding Main Ideas (Part A)

In the space at the left, write the letter of the word or phrase that best completes the statement or answers the question.

b **1.** Horsetails are
    a. bryophytes.   **b.** sphenophytes.   **c.** lycophytes.   **d.** pterophytes.

b **2.** You can recognize that a plant is a dicotyledon if it has
    a. parallel veins.   **c.** one seed leaf within the seed.
    b. branched veins.   **d.** flower parts in multiples of three.

a **3.** Sphagnum, or peat moss, which is used in the horticultural industry, is a(n)
    a. bryophyte.   **b.** hepatophyte.   **c.** anthocerophyte.   **d.** lycophyte.

c **4.** In the fern life cycle, a spore germinates to form a(n)
    a. thallus.   **b.** antheridium.   **c.** prothallus.   **d.** archegonium.

d **5.** Which of the following divisions do *not* include nonvascular plants?
    a. Bryophyta   **b.** Hepatophyta   **c.** Anthocerophyta   **d.** Anthophyta

a **6.** In most seed plants, fertilization does *not* require
    a. a film of water to carry the sperm to the egg.
    b. alternation of generations.
    c. the production of eggs.
    d. a gametophyte generation.

d **7.** Which of these are vascular plants?
    a. club mosses   **b.** spike mosses   **c.** ferns   **d.** all of these

b **8.** The fronds of ferns are divided into
    a. rhizomes.   **b.** pinnae.   **c.** cycads.   **d.** sori.

b **9.** Which of the following is *not* a characteristic of a non-seed vascular plant?
    a. These plants exhibit alternation of generations.
    b. The gametophyte generation is dominant.
    c. They have vascular tissues through which water and sugars are transported.
    d. Plants are found in a variety of habitats.

d **10.** Most conifers
    a. lose all their leaves when water is unavailable.
    b. lose most of their water through the leaves.
    c. are deciduous trees.
    d. never lose all their leaves at one time.

Understanding Main Ideas (Part B)

Answer the following questions.

1. Describe the major characteristics of nonvascular plants.
   Nonvascular plants lack vascular tissue and reproduce by producing spores. They usually live in moist, cool environments. The gametophyte generation is dominant.

2. What advantages does a seed plant have over a non-seed plant?
   A seed contains a supply of food to nourish the young plant during the early stages of growth until its leaves develop. The embryo is protected during harsh conditions by a tough seed coat. The seed of many species are also adapted for easy dispersal to new areas, so the young plant does not have to compete with its parents for sunlight, water, soil nutrients, and living space.

3. What are the advantages of fruit-enclosed seeds?
   Fruit provides additional protection for young embryos. Fruit also aids in seed dispersal. Animals may eat seeds or carry them off to store for food. Seeds that are eaten may pass through the animal's digestive system unharmed and are distributed as the animal wanders. Some fruits have structural adaptations that help disperse the seed by wind or water.

4. What advantages does an evergreen tree have?
   Because an evergreen tree never loses its leaves, it can begin photosynthesis in the early spring, as soon as the temperature warms. This gives the tree a head start on growth. Also, an evergreen can grow where nutrients are scarce. Furthermore, its branches and needles are extremely flexible and allow snow and ice to slide off, instead of building up and breaking the branches.

CHAPTER ASSESSMENT

Thinking Critically

Refer to the graph to answer questions 1 and 2.

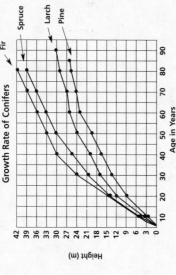

Growth Rate of Conifers

1. In the table, write the correct information about the patterns of growth of certain conifers.

	Age at maximum growth		Maximum height		Height at 45 years
Fir	**80**	Fir	**42 m**	Fir	**32 m**
Spruce	**80**	Spruce	**39 m**	Spruce	**27 m**
Larch	**90**	Larch	**30 m**	Larch	**22 m**
Pine	**85**	Pine	**26 m**	Pine	**18 m**

2. How does the graph show that these conifers grow according to their own growth pattern?
   Each conifer reached its maximum height at a different age. Each reached a different maximum height. Each line displays a different pattern of growth.

3. The ginkgo, with its broad leaves that turn yellow in autumn, looks more like a flowering plant than a gymnosperm. Why is the ginkgo classified as a gymnosperm?
   The ginkgo is classified as a gymnosperm because it produces seeds that are not protected by a fruit.

Name _____ Date _____ Class _____

Chapter Assessment

Chapter 22 The Diversity of Plants, *continued*

Applying Scientific Methods

Bracken ferns are one of the most widely distributed species of ferns. Brackens occur in all but hot and cold desert regions of the world. In many regions, this species invades the grasslands, where it becomes a troublesome weed that is difficult to eradicate because of its persistent underground rhizome. The problem is worsened because bracken is a poisonous plant. It causes thiamine deficiency, which results in the death of certain animals.

1. What circumstances might arise in your community such that you might need to find out how to control the growth of brackens?

Answers may vary. The growth of brackens may stifle the growth of crops in the grasslands, or the brackens might cause a problem by killing animals.

2. Bracken spores will germinate in lava, mortar of brickwork, abandoned building sites, bomb sites, and fire-damaged natural habitats. However, they will not germinate within a bracken colony. Hypothesize as to what the limiting factor in the germination of bracken spores might be.

Hypotheses will vary but may include that the limiting factor in the growth of bracken is biotic, or something chemically produced by living organisms, rather than an environmental factor, because bracken seem able to grow under the worst physical conditions.

3. Plan an experiment to test your hypothesis. Decide the conditions under which you will grow the bracken fern.

The plan for the experiment will vary, but if students decide that the limiting factor is biotic, they will most likely try to grow bracken ferns from spores in the presence of other plants, including another bracken colony.

4. What will be the variable in this experiment?

The variable will be the factor students are testing for. For example, if they were testing to see which plants will allow the growth of bracken spores, they would plant the spores in the same pot with one other plant. They would also most likely choose to grow bracken spores in the same pot with a bracken colony.

Name _____ Date _____ Class _____

Chapter Assessment

Chapter 22 The Diversity of Plants, *continued*

Applying Scientific Methods   continued

5. What will be the control?

The control will be growing the spores in a pot with no other plants.

6. If you found that when bracken spores grew into ferns, the other plant in the pot flourished, what might you conclude?

You might think that the fern had a beneficial effect on the growth of the plant.

7. How could you prove that the conclusion you came to in question 6 was correct?

You would have to find out how the other plant grows without the bracken spores. You might also try growing that same kind of plant with plants other than bracken to see how it grows with other plants.

8. If you found that the plant did not flourish or even died when it was grown with bracken spores, what would you conclude?

You might conclude that the bracken produces a chemical that inhibits the growth of the other plant.

9. How could you prove that the conclusion you came to in question 8 was correct?

You could repeat your trial or try to grow the bracken plant with still more varieties of plants to confirm your conclusion that bracken produces a chemical that inhibits the growth of other plants.

Chapter 23 — Plant Structure and Function

Reviewing Vocabulary

Match the definition in Column A with the term in Column B.

Column A

o   1. Plant tissue that transports water and minerals from the roots to the rest of the plant

m   2. Tubular cell that is tapered at each end and that transports water throughout a plant

i   3. Tissue that gives rise to lateral roots

g   4. A responsive movement of a plant that is not dependent on the direction of the stimulus

j   5. Stalk that joins the leaf blade to the stem

l   6. Any portion of the plant that uses or stores sugars

c   7. Flattened parenchyma cells that cover all parts of the plant

k   8. Tissue composed of living cells that transport sugars from the leaves to all parts of the plant

a   9. Growth tissue that remains just behind the root tip

b   10. Contains a nucleus and helps control movement through the sieve cell

n   11. A plant's response to an external stimulus that comes from a particular direction

e   12. A chemical that is produced in one part of an organism and transported to another part, where it causes a physiological change.

d   13. Cell that surrounds and controls the opening of the stomata

f   14. Photosynthetic tissue of a leaf

h   15. Tissue in the root that can act as a storage area for food and water

Column B

a. apical meristem
b. companion cell
c. epidermis
d. guard cell
e. hormone
f. mesophyll
g. nastic movement
h. cortex
i. pericycle
j. petiole
k. phloem
l. sink
m. tracheid
n. tropism
o. xylem

Chapter 23 — Plant Structure and Function, *continued*

Understanding Main Ideas (Part A)

In the space at the left, write the letter of the word or phrase that best completes the statement or answers the question.

d   1. To control water loss, the size of the stomata is reduced by the
   a. xylem.   b. phloem.   c. cambium.   d. guard cells.

c   2. Xylem is vascular tissue that
   a. is alive.
   b. transports sugar from the leaves to all parts of the plant.
   c. transports water and dissolved minerals from the roots to the leaves.
   d. transports sperm to the eggs.

a   3. Cells in the apical meristem that cause a root to grow longer are found
   a. just behind the root tip.   b. along the sides of the root.
   c. at the top of the root.   d. in the center of the root.

a   4. What area is responsible for producing the cells that allow the roots and stems to increase in length?
   a. apical meristem   b. vascular meristem   c. pericycle   d. endodermis

d   5. What is the primary function of plant leaves?
   a. to support the plant   b. to produce flowers
   c. to take in water   d. to trap sunlight for photosynthesis

c   6. Where does most photosynthesis take place?
   a. in the cells of the cortex   b. in the spongy mesophyll
   c. in the palisade mesophyll   d. in the stomata

d   7. The petiole and veins of a leaf contain the
   a. apical meristem.   b. epidermis.   c. endodermis.   d. vascular tissue.

In the space at the left, write **true** if the statement is true. If the statement is false, change the italicized word or phrase to make it true.

root hair   8. A *root cap* is a tiny extension of a single epidermal cell that increases the surface area of the root and absorbs water, oxygen, and dissolved minerals.

transpiration   9. The loss of water from the stomata of the leaves is called *perspiration*.

true   10. A *vessel element* is a tubular cell that transports water throughout the plant.

Name _____ Date _____ Class _____

Chapter 23 Plant Structure and Function, *continued*

Understanding Main Ideas (Part B)

Answer the following questions.

1. What causes tree rings to form?

The xylem cells produced in the spring tend to be larger than those formed later in the growing season because there is more water available in spring. This alternation in the size of xylem cells produces a pattern of annual growth rings.

2. How do auxins promote cell elogation?

Stems bend toward light because the auxins collect in the cells on the shaded side of the stem. The cells on the auxin-rich side grow longer than the cells on the other side. Auxin causes an increase in stem length by increasing the rate of cell division and promoting cell elongation. This causes the stem to bend toward the light.

3. Explain why fruit kept in a closed container ripens more quickly than fruit left out in an open bowl.

When fruit is kept in a closed container, ethylene gas builds up in the container. Ethylene gas promotes ripening.

4. How do guard cells prevent a plant from drying out?

Guard cells regulate the size of the openings of the stomata according to the amount of water in the plant. When there is less water in tissues surrounding the guard cells, water leaves the guard cells. This lowers the turgor pressure. The guard cells become shorter and thicker, reducing the size of the pore. The smaller the pores, the less water will leave the plant.

5. What are the functions of a root?

The functions of a root are to anchor the plant in the ground, absorb water and minerals, and transport these materials to the base of the stem.

Name _____ Date _____ Class _____

Chapter 23 Plant Structure and Function, *continued*

Thinking Critically

Answer the following questions.

1. A researcher performed an experiment to determine the function of xylem and phloem. He removed the bark, including the phloem, in a complete ring around a tree. The xylem was left intact. After doing this, the researcher noticed a swelling just above the stripped ring; a sweet fluid leaked from this swollen area. The leaves of the tree remained green for several weeks. Eventually, however, they died; the entire tree died soon after. What could the researcher conclude from this experiment? Explain.

The phloem tissue was still intact above the ring. The liquid leaking out contained sugar, indicating that food made in the leaves was being carried down as far as the ring. The researcher concluded that the phloem transports food downward. Because the leaves remained healthy for a time, the researcher also concluded that xylem transports water to the leaves. Without water, the leaves would have wilted and died in only a few hours. The death of the leaves signaled that the roots, which absorb water, had died because of lack of nourishment.

2. The table at the right shows the transpiration rate of some plants measured in liters per day. Why would the transpiration rate of the cactus be so much lower than that of the other plants?

Plant	Liters/Day
Cactus	0.02
Tomato	1.00
Apple	19.00

The cactus grows in dry places. It is adapted to dry conditions and tran-spires much less than the other plants.

3. When he was 12 years old, Joe carved his initials into the bark of a tree in the forest behind his house. The tree was 7 m tall and 20 cm in diameter, and the initials were 1.5 m above the ground. When Joe was 22 years old, he went back to see the tree; it had grown to a height of 10 m and was now 27 cm in diameter. How far above the ground were Joe's initials? Explain.

The initials will still be 1.5 meters above the ground. Growth in length of a plant stem occurs just below the apical meristem of the tip of the stem.

Applying Scientific Methods

Students often perform a simple experiment to verify the fact that water is transported upward from the roots of a plant to its leaves. You may remember that, when you place a celery stalk in colored water, after a few hours, the color reaches the leaves at the top of the celery stalk.

1. Why might you infer that water also reaches the leaves?

Since the color is dissolved in the water, you would infer that the color was carried

in the water upward through the stem to the leaves.

This experiment may lead you to formulate a question about water transport in plants. What causes the water to rise from the roots to the leaves against the force of gravity? The answer is that some other force, greater than the gravitational pull on the water, must pull the water upward. In the tallest sequoias, for example, water must rise about 107 m from roots to top leaves. Quite a pull is needed to get the water up to that height.

The answer lies in transpiration. Transpiration occurs as water evaporates from the stomata in the leaves. Scientists think that it is transpiration that provides the force that pulls the water upward against the force of gravity. As water at the stomata evaporates, the water in the leaf just below the stomata is drawn up to replace the vaporized water. Through this process, water slowly and continuously rises to the leaves.

2. Formulate a hypothesis about how temperature could affect the flow of water upward.

Answers may vary. Students may hypothesize that as temperature increases, tran-

spiration will increase; this in turn will increase the rate of water flow upward.

3. Plan an experiment to prove your hypothesis.

Plans will vary. Students may set up three leafy celery stalks in colored water and

place them in beakers with water at different temperatures—in ice water, in water

at room temperature, and in warm water. All three beakers would be placed in

sunlight.

4. What will be your control in this experiment?

Answers will vary. Students may use the celery stalk at room temperature as the

control.

5. What is the variable in this experiment?

The temperature of water is the variable.

Applying Scientific Methods   continued

6. Transpiration occurs only during the day. Hypothesize why this might be.

Hypotheses may vary. Students may hypothesize that light is needed for

transpiration to take place.

7. How would you verify your hypothesis?

Answers may vary. Students may place one celery stalk in the dark and another in

the light to compare how fast the color rises in each stalk.

8. What will be your control in this experiment?

Answers may vary. Students may leave one celery stick in a window, allowing it to

receive both light and dark as nature provides.

9. What is the variable in this experiment?

The amount of light received by the plant is the variable.

Name _____ Date _____ Class _____

Chapter 24 Reproduction in Plants

Reviewing Vocabulary

Write the word or phrase that best completes each statement. Use these choices:

anther	pistil	stamen	germination
day-neutral plant	megaspores	ovary	petals
endosperm	microspores	micropyle	photoperiodism
protonema			

1. The response of flowering plants to the difference in the duration of light and dark periods in a day is called **photoperiodism** .

2. The **endosperm** is food-storage tissue that supports development of the embryo.

3. The **ovary** is the part of the flower in which ovules containing eggs are formed.

4. The **protonema** is a small green filament of cells that develops into either a male or a female gametophyte.

5. Leaflike, usually colorful, structures arranged in a circle around the tip of a flower stem are called **petals** .

6. The beginning of the development of the embryo into a new plant is called **germination** .

7. The **pistil** is the female structure of the flower.

8. **Megaspores** are female spores that eventually become female gametophytes.

9. The male cones have sporangia that undergo meiosis to produce males spores called **microspores** .

10. The **anther** , at the tip of the stamen, produces pollen that contains sperm.

11. The flowering time of a **day-neutral plant** is controlled by temperature, moisture, or other environmental factors, rather than by day length.

12. The **stamen** is the male reproductive structure of a flower.

13. The **micropyle** is a tiny opening in the ovule through which a sperm cell moves through the pollen tube into the ovule.

Name _____ Date _____ Class _____

Chapter 24 Reproduction in Plants, continued

Understanding Main Ideas (Part A)

Label the parts of a flower in the diagram below.

1. **pistil**

2. **petal**

3. **sepal**

4. **stigma**

5. **anther**

6. **filament**

7. **stamen**

8. **style**

9. **ovary**

10. **ovule**

In the space at the left, write the letter of the word or phrase that best completes the statement or answers the question.

d 11. Where does the process of double fertilization occur?
  a. in the pollen tube b. in the stigma
  c. in the central nucleus d. in the ovule

a 12. The fertilization of the central cell produces a
  a. triploid nucleus. b. zygote.
  c. diploid nucleus. d. haploid egg.

b 13. After fertilization, the central cell develops into the
  a. zygote. b. endosperm. c. pollen tube. d. fruit.

b 14. Which of the following plants has a prothallus that forms archegonia and antheridia and has a dominant sporophyte?
  a. mosses b. ferns c. conifers d. flowering plants

c 15. Which of the following plants produce separate male and female cones that produce microspores and megaspores that develop into male and female gametophytes?
  a. mosses b. ferns c. conifers d. flowering plants

Chapter Assessment

Chapter 24   Reproduction in Plants, *continued*

Understanding Main Ideas (Part B)

Answer the following questions.

1. What is the dominant generation?
Botanists usually refer to the bigger, more obvious plant—either the sporophyte or gametophyte—as the dominant generation. The dominant generation lives longer and can survive independently of the other generation. In most plant species, the sporophyte is the dominant plant.

2. Give at least three of the special requirements that some seeds may have before they germinate.
Answers may vary. Possible answers: Some seeds germinate more readily after passing through the acid environment of an animal's digestive system. Others require a period of freezing temperatures, of extensive soaking in saltwater, or of being exposed to fire before germinating.

3. What steps are involved in fruit and seed formation?
After the eggs in the ovule have been fertilized, the walls of the ovary enlarge and become fruit, and the seeds develop inside each ovule. After fertilization occurs, most of the flower parts die and the seeds begin to develop. The wall of the ovule becomes the hard seed coat. Inside the ovule, the zygote divides and grows into the plant embryo. The triploid central cell divides and develops into the endosperm.

4. What is a photoperiodism? Differentiate between short-day plants and long-day plants.
Photoperiodism refers to the response of flowering plants to the difference in the duration of light and dark periods. Short-day plants are induced to flower by exposure to a long night. These are plants that usually form flower buds in the fall when the days are getting shorter and the nights are longer. Long-day plants flower when the nights are short. Some of the plants that flower during the summer, when days are longer than nights, are long-day plants.

Chapter Assessment

Chapter 24   Reproduction in Plants, *continued*

Thinking Critically

Answer the following questions.

1. Hypothesize why vegetative reproduction is an adaptive advantage for most plants.
Answers may vary. Vegetative reproduction is asexual reproduction in plants where a new plant is produced from an existing vegetative structure. Such reproduction is advantageous because only one parent is needed. Sexual reproduction may not always be possible if two parents are not available. Also, pollination in sexual reproduction often requires the presence of another organism or weather factors such as wind, whereas plants only need roots, stems, or leaves to produce offspring by vegetative reproduction.

2. Flower production uses up large quantities of sugar in a plant. Sugarcane growers try to delay flowering as long as possible in order to allow time for the sugar content of the cane to increase. If sugarcane is a short-day plant, hypothesize as to how they might achieve their goal.
Answers will vary. Growers might shine bright lights on the sugarcane fields for a few minutes each night. This would send the signal to the plant that the days are longer and the nights shorter and would cause the plant to put off flowering until later.

3. Investigators tried an experiment with short-day plants in the laboratory to find out how the day/night stimulus is carried throughout the plant. Immediately after exposing the plants to light during what was normally a dark period, investigators removed all the leaves from the plant.
Flowering did not occur on the plants. However, if they waited and removed the leaves several hours after the light stimulus was given, flowering did occur. Hypothesize as to the function of the leaves in the flowering process. Why did flowering occur when there was a delay before removing the leaves?
Hypotheses may vary. The leaves may produce a specific substance in response to the appropriate day/night stimulus. When the leaves are removed, the stimulus fails to reach the structure where the flowers are formed. When there is a delay before removing the leaves, the substance is produced in the leaves and reaches the structure where the flowers form in time to cause flowering.

Name _____ Date _____ Class _____

Chapter Assessment

Chapter 24 Reproduction in Plants, *continued*

Applying Scientific Methods

Plant physiologists have for a number of years been investigating the stimuli that initiate flowering in plants. They have concluded that some plants are short-day plants. These plants produce flowers in early spring or late summer when days are shorter than nights. Other plants are long-day plants that bloom in summer when days are longer than nights. In still other plants, flowering is controlled by temperature, moisture, or other environmental factors.

1. How does each of these adaptations benefit the plant?

Each adaptation helps the plant to produce flowers when the chances of being

pollinated and of producing numerous seeds that will survive are optimal.

Investigators have known about the day/night length effect on flowering for many years. However, some investigators were unsure as to whether it is the day length or the night length that actually causes flowers of a certain species to bloom.

2. Hypothesize about which of these is the stimulus that causes blooming. You must support your hypothesis with valid reasons for your choice.

Students may choose either hypothesis. Reasons for their selection will vary.

Those who choose day length may hypothesize that since other activities of a

plant are solar-energy dependent, flowering may also depend on a certain number

of hours of sunlight. Those who choose night length over day length may decide

that flowering is a different process from photosynthesis and may require a cer-

tain number of hours a day when the plant is not engaged in photosynthesis in

order to produce its flowers.

3. In planning an experiment to investigate the effect of day/night length on flowering, it is best to use plants whose flowering pattern you know. Why?

Knowing how many hours of daylight and darkness there are at the time when

these flowers usually bloom will help you to narrow the investigation to control-

ling for those day/night lengths only.

Name _____ Date _____ Class _____

Chapter Assessment

Chapter 24 Reproduction in Plants, *continued*

Applying Scientific Methods *continued*

4. Use either short-day or long-day plants. Plan an experiment to support your hypothesis.

Plans will vary but should regulate light and dark periods for growing only short-

day or long-day plants. Students may change the hours of daylight and darkness

by covering plants for a time to shorten the day or by providing intense light dur-

ing brief periods at night.

5. What will be your control during your experiment?

plants of the same species in which the day/night length is not regulated

6. What is the variable in this experiment?

The variable is the amount of light or darkness available to the plant.

7. If the results of your experiment do *not* support your hypothesis, what would you do next?

Answers may vary. The procedure could be checked for possible errors, resulting in

incorrect results. The procedure could be repeated to support the original data. If

the data remains consistent, then a new hypothesis could be developed and a new

experimental procedure designed.

Chapter Assessment

Chapter 25 What Is an Animal?

Reviewing Vocabulary

Match the definition in Column A with the term in Column B.

Column A

i ___ 1. Third cell layer formed in the developing embryo

l ___ 2. Body plan of an organism that can be divided along any plane, through a central axis, into roughly equal halves

a ___ 3. Animal that has three cell layers, with a digestive tract but no body cavities

c ___ 4. Single layer of cells surrounding a fluid-filled space that forms during early development

e ___ 5. Animal in which the mouth does not develop from the opening in the gastrula

f ___ 6. Layer of cells on the outer surface of the gastrula

b ___ 7. Body plan of an organism that can be divided down its length into right and left halves that form mirror images

d ___ 8. Body cavity completely surrounded by mesoderm

g ___ 9. Layer of cells lining the inner surface of the gastrula

j ___ 10. Body cavity partly lined with mesoderm, such as found in roundworms

m ___ 11. Describes organisms that don't move from place to place

h ___ 12. Embryonic structure in animals that consists of two cell layers

k ___ 13. Animal with a mouth that develops from the opening in the gastrula

Column B

a. acoelomate

b. bilateral symmetry

c. blastula

d. coelom

e. deuterostome

f. ectoderm

g. endoderm

h. gastrula

i. mesoderm

j. pseudocoelom

k. protostome

l. radial symmetry

m. sessile

Chapter Assessment

Chapter 25 What Is an Animal?, *continued*

Understanding Main Ideas (Part A)

Match the number of each location on the drawing of the flatworm with the correct descriptive term for the location. Use these choices: ventral, posterior, dorsal, anterior.

1. anterior ___

2. dorsal ___

3. ventral ___

4. posterior ___

In the space at the left, write the letter of the word or phrase that best completes each statement or answers the question.

c ___ 5. The embryonic layer that forms the skin and nervous tissue is the
   a. endoderm.   b. mesoderm.   c. ectoderm.   d. protostome.

a ___ 6. The animal's digestive tract forms from the
   a. endoderm.   b. mesoderm.   c. ectoderm.   d. protostome.

a ___ 7. Which of the following applies to a sponge?
   a. adult is sessile   b. has a gastrula stage
   c. bilateral symmetry   d. develops three embryonic layers

b ___ 8. What type of symmetry does a penny have?
   a. bilateral symmetry   b. radial symmetry
   c. no symmetry   d. biaxial symmetry

d ___ 9. Which of these animals has bilateral symmetry?
   a. sponge   b. hydra   c. jellyfish   d. flatworm

b ___ 10. Animals with bilateral symmetry find food and mates and avoid predators more efficiently because they have
   a. body cavities.   b. more muscular control.
   c. tails.   d. the ability to see in all directions.

Name _____ Date _____ Class _____

Chapter Assessment

Chapter 25 | **What Is an Animal?**, *continued*

Understanding Main Ideas (Part B)

Answer the following questions.

1. What are the main characteristics of an animal?
An animal is an eukaryotic heterotroph that moves, reproduces, obtains food, and protects itself. Animals are multicellular, and their cells have no cell walls.

2. In what way does a sponge qualify as a heterotroph?
A heterotroph obtains energy and nutrients from outside sources. A sponge filters food out of the water surrounding it.

3. How do the structures of the digestive tracts of a flatworm and an earthworm differ?
The digestive tract of a flatworm has only one opening for ingesting food and getting rid of wastes. An earthworm's digestive tract has two openings, one for ingesting food and the other for eliminating digestive wastes.

4. What are the early stages of development from zygote to gastrula?
After the zygote completes a series of continuous cell divisions, the result is a single layer of cells that forms a hollow ball called the blastula. The blastula folds inward to form the gastrula, a hollow area surrounded by two cell layers.

5. In flatworms, different types of tissues are organized into organs, but unlike earthworms, flatworms lack a coelom in which their internal organs are suspended. Where are the internal organs of the flatworms located?
The organs of the flatworms are embedded in the solid tissues of their bodies.

6. Briefly identify the three cell layers formed during embryonic development and give examples of the body organs and tissues that each layer gives rise to.
The ectoderm is the outer layer, which eventually develops into the skin and the nervous tissue of the animal. The mesoderm is the middle layer, which develops between the ectoderm and the inner layer, or endoderm. The mesoderm gives rise to muscles, reproductive organs, and circulatory vessels, while the endoderm cells develop into the lining of the digestive tract.

Name _____ Date _____ Class _____

Chapter Assessment

Chapter 25 | **What Is an Animal?**, *continued*

Thinking Critically

Answer the following questions.

Answer questions 1–4, using the table below, which shows the amount of oxygen required for animals of different body mass to move a given distance.

Animal	Body Mass Moved	mL O$_2$ Required per 1 g of Body Mass
Mouse	10 g	4.00 mL
Kangaroo rat	45 g	2.00 mL
Ground squirrel	140 g	0.80 mL
Dog	13 kg	0.40 mL
Horse	500 kg	0.04 mL

1. How many mL of O$_2$ does a kangaroo rat require per 1 g of body mass? __**2 mL**__

2. How many mL of O$_2$ would a mouse require in all? __**40 mL**__

3. After studying the table, what generalization can you make about the amount of oxygen used by animals of different body mass?
As body mass increases, the amount of oxygen needed to move 1 g of body mass over a given distance decreases. So, to move 1 g of its body mass a given distance, much less oxygen is used by a larger animal than by a smaller animal.

4. Where in the table do you think a 90 kg human adult would fall? Estimate about how many mL of O$_2$ the human would require per 1 g of body mass.
The human would fall between the dog and the horse. Estimates will vary; 0.1–0.2 mL is reasonable.

5. Simpler animals are small in size. As animals evolved, they tended to become more complex. Hypothesize as to why this was necessary.
As animals grew larger, supplying nutrients and oxygen to all their cells became more difficult. Larger animals needed a transport system to carry oxygen and nutrients throughout the body, as well as muscles and a skeletal system to support their body and move it around. They required still another system to excrete wastes produced by cell metabolism, and a nervous system to coordinate all their body processes.

Chapter 25   What Is an Animal?, *continued*

Applying Scientific Methods

The scientific team you are working with wishes to demonstrate that animals become more efficient in interacting with their external environment when the body plan that evolved included bilateral symmetry. You have chosen to work with mealworms, the larvae of grain beetles (Tenebrio molitor).

1. You watch the mealworms moving along the sides of the box in which they are housed. State which factors other than the body plan of the mealworms might affect their behavior.
Light, warmth, humidity, and presence of food would all affect the behavior of the mealworms and should be controlled in all the experiments you carry out.

2. Hypothesize how a mealworm's moving along the sides of a box is related to its bilateral body plan.
Answers will vary. In an effort to protect themselves from predators, mealworms may use the sides of their body to remain in contact with a safe place; in this case, that safe place seems to be the sides of the box.

3. Plan an experiment to prove your hypothesis.
Answers will vary. Students may plan different kinds of walls or even provide a vertical pane of glass or hard, clear plastic along which a mealworm can move. They may note that the mealworm always touches the plate with one side of its body. They may observe what happens when the mealworm reaches the end of the glass plate. (It will turn toward the plate.) They may move the mealworm away from the plate and observe if it tries to return to touching the plate with its side. (If it is not moved too far from the plate, it will return to the plate.) They should include numerous trials and recording of data.

4. What will be your control in this experiment?
The mealworms that are placed far from the pane or the wall tend to be disoriented until they find a surface they can touch with at least one side of their body.

Chapter 25   What Is an Animal?, *continued*

Applying Scientific Methods   continued

5. How could you prove that mealworms are equally sensitive on both the right and left sides of their body?
You could turn them around, but placing them so that they are still touching the wall surface with a side of their body to see if they will continue in the new direction or if they will turn around to go in their original direction.

6. Hypothesize what would happen if you were to provide the mealworm with a vertical pane or wall on both its left and right sides.
Answers will vary, but if the mealworm receives the touch stimuli from both sides, it would probably keep going forward between the plates, rather than crawling up over the plates.

7. Is this behavior seen in other animals? Explain your answer.
Many species will move along the perimeter of their environment instead of through the center. Rodents, rabbits, cats, and deer are examples. The purpose is adaptive as it provides a safer route for the animal. Humans exhibit this behavior, too.

Name _____ Date _____ Class _____

Sponges, Cnidarians, Flatworms, and Roundworms

Reviewing Vocabulary

Write the word or phrase that best completes each statement. Use these choices:

external fertilization	internal fertilization	pharynx
filter feeding	medusa	polyp
gastrovascular cavity	nematocysts	proglottids
hermaphrodites	nerve net	scolex

1. Sponges get their food by __filter feeding__ , in which small particles of food are removed from the water during passage through a part of their body.

2. Cnidarians capture prey by means of __nematocysts__ which are coiled, threadlike tubes that are sticky or barbed or that contain toxins.

3. Digestion in cnidarians takes place in the __gastrovascular cavity__ .

4. During feeding, planarians extend a tubelike, muscular organ, called the __pharynx__ , out of their mouths.

5. A parasitic tapeworm has a knob-shaped head, called a __scolex__ , by which the worm attaches itself to the host's intestinal wall.

6. In __external fertilization__ , fertilization occurs outside the animal's body after eggs and sperm are released.

7. In __internal fertilization__ , eggs remain inside the animal's body and sperm are carried to the eggs.

8. Sponges are considered __hermaphrodites__ because an individual sponge can produce both eggs and sperm.

9. A __polyp__ is the tube-shaped body form with a mouth surrounded by tentacles, which serves as the asexual stage in some cnidarians.

10. A __medusa__ is the sexual form of a cnidarian that has a body form like an umbrella with tentacles hanging down.

11. A tapeworm has reproductive organs in segments called __proglottids__ .

Name _____ Date _____ Class _____

Sponges, Cnidarians, Flatworms, and Roundworms, *continued*

Understanding Main Ideas (Part A)

In the space at the left, write the letter of the word or phrase that best completes each statement or answers the question.

__a__ 1. The collar cells of sponges are similar to
- a. flagellated protists.
- b. amoebas.
- c. ciliated paramecia.
- d. sessile sporozoans.

__b__ 2. Because sponges are sessile, they get their food through
- a. scavenging the sea floor.
- b. filter feeding.
- c. the spicules.
- d. tentacles.

__d__ 3. A group of cnidarians that provide food and shelter for many kinds of animals are the
- a. jellyfish.
- b. hydras.
- c. sea anemones.
- d. corals.

__c__ 4. A _____ has a muscular tube called the pharynx, which can be extended outside its body to suck in food.
- a. jellyfish
- b. sponge
- c. planarian
- d. tapeworm

__b__ 5. In a cnidarian, digestion occurs in the
- a. proglottids.
- b. gastrovascular cavity.
- c. digestive tract.
- d. tentacles.

__a__ 6. Uncooked or undercooked pork may contain
- a. trichina worms.
- b. hookworms.
- c. pinworms.
- d. free-living roundworms.

__c__ 7. Which is an acoelomate animal?
- a. sponge
- b. cnidarian
- c. flatworm
- d. roundworm

__c__ 8. A Portugese man-of-war is an example of
- a. an anthozoan.
- b. a large scyphozoan.
- c. a hydrozoan colony.
- d. a sea anemone.

__b__ 9. Nematocysts discharge when
- a. salt concentration in the ocean drops.
- b. tentacles touch a source of food.
- c. a cnidarian regenerates.
- d. cnidarians reproduce.

Write the numbers 1 to 3 to show the structures through which water passes through a sponge, in order.

__2__ **10.** collar cells   __3__ **11.** osculum   __1__ **12.** pore cells

---

Chapter Assessment

Chapter 26 — Sponges, Cnidarians, Flatworms, and Roundworms, *continued*

Understanding Main Ideas (Part B)

Answer the following questions.

1. How is a sponge's food-gathering technique adapted to its sessile lifestyle?
   A sponge is a filter feeder, which is ideal for a sessile animal because it simply filters its food from the water that passes by or through its body.

2. Describe the process by which sponges reproduce sexually by internal fertilization.
   Sexual reproduction begins with the formation of eggs and sperm. In internal fertilization, eggs remain inside the sponge; sperm are released from one sponge and carried to another by water currents. The collar cells collect the sperm, transfer them to amoebocytes, which then transfer the sperm to eggs. The resulting zygote develops into a flagellated larva that leaves the parent sponge and swims to a new surface to grow into an adult.

3. Compare and contrast the sexual and asexual phases of jellyfish reproduction.
   The sexual phase consists of the external union of sperm released by a male medusa with an egg released by a female medusa. In the asexual phase, polyps develop from the zygote produced in the sexual phase. Polyps form buds that become tiny medusa.

4. The body of the planarian is an advance over the cnidarian body. Explain.
   Planarians have a clearly defined head that senses and responds to changes in the environment. They have eyespots that respond to light. They also have sensory pits on their heads that are able to detect food, chemicals, and movements in the environment. They have a digestive system, two nerve cords, and a brainlike structure. All of these structures are an advance over those of the simpler cnidarians.

5. How do parasitic roundworms keep from being digested by their host organisms?
   They have a thick outer covering that is not digestible.

Chapter Assessment

Chapter 26 — Sponges, Cnidarians, Flatworms, and Roundworms, *continued*

Thinking Critically

Answer the following questions.

1. A biologist places a single, live sponge in a saltwater tank. After several weeks, the biologist observes other, smaller sponges living in the tank. Since the biologist is certain that no other sponge had been introduced into the tank, what other explanation could you provide to explain the observation?
   The additional sponges could be the result of asexual reproduction by budding or by hermaphroditic sexual reproduction.

2. When you see a sponge passed through a sieve and separated into cells, you may think a sponge is simply a colony of individual cells. What makes you realize that it is more than this?
   The cells seem to recognize that they belong together, since they reunite after being separated.

3. When it brushes the tentacles of a sea anemone, a clownfish is recognized by the anemone, which does not trigger the release of nematocysts. One experiment has shown that the slime on the scales of the clownfish inhibits the release of stinging cells. Hypothesize how the slime might work.
   Answers will vary. The slime may contain a chemical that tranquilizes the anemone, or the slime may be so viscous that it interferes with the release of the nematocysts.

4. What advantage is there to the extracellular digestion of cnidarians over the digestion of sponges?
   Being able to digest food in the gastrovascular cavity instead of inside its cells allows the cnidarian to digest organisms larger than its individual cells.

5. Hypothesize why medusae that live in the midwaters where bioluminescent prey are abundant have dark pigmentation.
   Dark pigmentation could be a selection factor, since bioluminescent prey in their stomach would make the medusae visible to their predators. The dark pigmentation would hide the bioluminescent prey.

Name _____ Date _____ Class _____

Chapter 26 — Sponges, Cnidarians, Flatworms, and Roundworms, continued

Applying Scientific Methods   continued

1. What was the control in the experiment?

the larvae that were allowed to develop in untreated water

2. After 48 hours, hydras from the control group looked like polyp A in the figure; most hydras from the 15-drop solution looked like polyp B. How does polyp A differ from polyp B?

Polyp A has an extended base. Its tentacles are close to its mouth. In Polyp B, the base has almost disappeared, and the tentacles are growing lower on the body, away from the mouth. This position will have an effect on its feeding, since tentacles are used to take food to the mouth.

3. After 48 hours, most of the hydras treated with 30 drops of PAF/10 mL of water looked like polyp B, but some looked like polyp C. Describe the hydras that looked like polyp C. **These hydras have no tentacles at the mouth.**

4. What conclusions can you draw from the results shown in the table? **As the hydras received more PAF, the number of tentacles near the mouth decreased and the number near the base increased. PAF disrupts the development of tentacles in hydras and as a result, may interfere with success in feeding.**

Name _____ Date _____ Class _____

Chapter 26 — Sponges, Cnidarians, Flatworms, and Roundworms, continued

Applying Scientific Methods

In an experiment about possible factors that cause the differentiation and growth of cells in hydra larvae, a proportion-altering factor (PAF) was discovered and isolated in a specific colonial cnidarian known as Eudendrium sp. In the experiment, hydra larvae were placed in solutions, one with 10 drops of PAF/mL of water, one with 15 drops, one with 20 drops, one with 30 drops, and a control solution. The experiment showed that PAF factor caused parts of the hydra to grow out of normal proportions. The following table and illustration show the differences in tentacle development that result from varying concentrations of PAF. Study the illustration and the table and answer the questions that follow.

Amount of PAF (drops/10 mL of water)	Number of Hydras		
	tentacles near mouth	tentacles near base	no tentacles formed
0	197	0	0
10	90	119	0
15	74	130	5
20	30	145	26
30	0	160	44

Chapter 27 Mollusks and Segmented Worms

Reviewing Vocabulary

Write the word or phrase that best completes the statement. Use these choices:

closed circulatory system   open circulatory system
gizzard   radula
mantle   setae
nephridia

1. Annelids have a digestive organ called a(n) **gizzard** that grinds organic matter, or food, into small pieces so that it can be absorbed as it passes through the animal's intestine.

2. In bivalves, the **mantle** is a thin membrane that sticks to both shells and forms siphons that are used for drawing in and expelling water.

3. The excretory structures that remove metabolic wastes from the bodies of animals such as mollusks and annelids are called **nephridia**.

4. You dissect an animal and observe pools of blood surrounding its internal organs. This animal has a(n) **open circulatory system**.

5. The **radula** is a tongue-like organ with rows of teeth that is used by gastropods to scrape, grate, or cut food.

6. An animal whose blood moves throughout its body within blood vessels has a(n) **closed circulatory system**.

7. Tiny bristles protruding from each segment of a segmented worm are called **setae**.

Chapter 27 Mollusks and Segmented Worms, *continued*

Understanding Main Ideas (Part A)

Identify each numbered part of the burrowing earthworm shown in the diagram, using the letter of each appropriate term.

A. ventral nerve cord   C. simple brain   E. blood vessels
B. setae   D. hearts   F. gizzard

1. C   2. E   3. D   4. A   5. F   6. B

In the space at the left, write *true* if the statement is true. If the statement is false, change the italicized word or phrase to make it true.

mantle	7. In shelled mollusks, the *radula* secretes the shell.
filter feeding	8. Bivalves obtain food by *predation*.
true	9. The excretory structures in mollusks are called *nephridia*.
Bivalves	10. *Gastropods* have two shells.
gills	11. The respiratory organs in aquatic gastropods are *primitive lungs*.
true	12. Earthworms are *hermaphrodites* because each worm produces both eggs and sperm.
mollusks	13. Based on their pattern of early development and other evidence, earthworms and *cnidarians* are thought to be closely related.
true	14. The first animals to have evolved respiratory organs are the *mollusks*.
cephalopods	15. The most complex and most recently evolved mollusks are *gastropods*.

Name _____ Date _____ Class _____

Chapter 27 | Mollusks and Segmented Worms, *continued*

Understanding Main Ideas (Part B)

Answer the following questions.

1. What adaptations help the octopus and the squid escape their predators?
Both of these mollusks can move by jet propulsion in any direction by ejecting water through their siphons. They have complex nervous systems, acute eyesight, and the ability to learn.

2. What are some of the functions of the mantle in mollusks?
Snails and slugs use the mantle and mantle cavity as a primitive lung. The mantle, which sticks to both shells of a bivalve, forms siphons that are used to move water over the gills, where respiration takes place, and then out of the body. The mantle also secretes the shell of a shelled mollusk.

3. What is the role of the radula?
The radula is used to scrape, grate, or cut food.

4. Compare the circulatory system of gastropods, bivalves, and cephalopods.
Gastropods and bivalves have an open circulatory system. Cephalopods have a closed circulatory system.

5. How do sea slugs improve their survival opportunities by feeding on jellyfishes?
When sea slugs feed on jellyfishes, they incorporate the jellyfish nematocysts into their own tissues. Any fish that tries to eat the slugs is bombarded by a rapid discharge of the transplanted nematocysts.

6. List and give examples of the three major types of segmented worms.
bristleworms and their relatives, leeches, earthworms

Name _____ Date _____ Class _____

Chapter 27 | Mollusks and Segmented Worms, *continued*

Thinking Critically

Answer the following questions.

1. Most cephalopods lack an external shell. What is the adaptive advantage of this feature?
An animal without a shell is freer to move about. Cephalopods can move rapidly, an advantage in their predatory lives. They have a complex brain and nervous system, which is also a decided advantage.

2. Most cephalopods have eyes that are remarkably like vertebrate eyes and fully capable of forming a good image. However, the cephalopod eye develops wholly from the surface ectoderm, whereas the vertebrate eye develops from the neural tube. What does this information indicate about whether or not the vertebrate eye evolved from the cephalopod eye?
It shows that the vertebrate eye did not evolve from the cephalopod eye because the embryonic development of cephalopods and vertebrates is not similar. Students may explain that this is a case of convergent evolution.

3. An oyster produces a natural pearl when a parasite or a bit of sand lodges between the shell and the mantle. The oyster then grows layers of pearl around the foreign body. What is the advantage of pearl-making to the oyster?
The layers of pearl around the particle lodged inside the shell seal the particle off and protect the soft body of the oyster from damage.

4. The Greek philosopher Aristotle called worms "the intestines of the soil." What did he mean?
Usually when an animal eats, its intestines absorb digested food, and wastes are passed out of the body through the intestines. Worms take in soil and use any nutrients in soil as food. They pass undigested matter back into the soil.

5. Suppose you are given an unknown mollusk to identify. The specimen does not have a shell. How could you decide whether the mollusk is an unshelled gastropod or a cephalopod?
Students should suggest using other distinguishing features. For example, if the specimen has a single muscular foot, it is probably a gastropod; if it has tentacles with suckers, it is probably a cephalopod. If the specimen is dissected, an open circulatory system would indicate a gastropod, whereas a closed circulatory system would indicate a cephalopod.

Chapter Assessment

Chapter 27 Mollusks and Segmented Worms, *continued*

Applying Scientific Methods

Alvin, and other submersible vehicles used by oceanographers to study the ocean floor, have also proved invaluable in studying populations of deep-sea mollusks and segmented tube worms. The invertebrates in question live where hot seawater circulates through cracks in the ocean floor called deep-sea vents.

Suppose that you are an invertebrate biologist studying these animals. Your studies show that clams that live near the vents may grow as much as 3.8 cm per year, far more rapidly than other deep-water clams.

1. Form a hypothesis to explain why vent clams grow more rapidly than other clams at the same depth.
   Answers will vary. Students may hypothesize that the water temperature is higher near the vents and stimulates growth or that there is more food available near the vents.

2. Plan an experiment to prove your hypothesis.
   Students will select one factor as an independent variable in their experiment. They may use temperature or food supply. If they study the effect of temperature, they would have to take temperature readings at different locations and relate these readings to clam size at these same locations.

3. Why wouldn't you choose water depth as an independent variable?
   In question 1, the study was limited to clams living at the same depth.

4. Suppose your data show that the temperature is the same in samples taken close to the vents or some distance away from the vents. However, the size of the clams is smaller the farther they are from the vents. What would this indicate?
   It would indicate that a factor other than temperature is affecting the size of the clams. It may have to do with food supply.

Chapter Assessment

Chapter 27 Mollusks and Segmented Worms, *continued*

Applying Scientific Methods   continued

5. Segmented tube worms that live near the vents grow to lengths of 1.5 m in contrast to the growth of related tube worms living in other environments, whose growth is measured only in centimeters at most. You hypothesize that the food that the worms eat is more abundant at the vents. When you collect samples of the worms, you discover that they have no mouth or other means of taking in food. Hypothesize how the tube worms are obtaining nutrients.
   Answers will vary. Students may suspect that a symbiont supplies the worms with food. For example, bacteria in the worm's body may use the gases and nutrients that the worm absorbs from the water to produce carbohydrates and proteins, which the worm uses for growth.

6. Some researchers have hypothesized that life may have begun at deep-sea vents. Why might this be?
   The warmth of the vents, anaerobic conditions and high pressure, the gases, minerals, and water might have led to organic matter forming.

Chapter 28 Arthropods

Reviewing Vocabulary

Match the definition in Column A with the term in Column B.

Column A

k   1. Branching networks of hollow passages that carry air throughout the body

h   2. Chemical odor signal given off by an animal

g   3. Form of asexual reproduction in which an organism develops from an unfertilized egg

j   4. Openings through which air enters and leaves the tracheal tubes

a   5. Any structure, such as a leg, that grows out of the body of an animal

c   6. Fused head and thorax region in some arthropods

d   7. Excretory organ of terrestrial arthropods

b   8. Air-filled chamber containing leaflike plates that serve for gas exchange

f   9. Shedding of the old exoskeleton

e   10. Jaw of an arthropod

i   11. Movable structure used by a spider to turn silk into thread

Column B

a. appendage
b. book lung
c. cephalothorax
d. Malpighian tubule
e. mandible
f. molting
g. parthenogenesis
h. pheromone
i. spinneret
j. spiracles
k. tracheal tubes

Compare or contrast each pair of related terms.

12. simple eye, compound eye
A simple eye is a visual structure with only one lens; a compound eye is a visual structure with many lenses.

13. chelicerae, pedipalps
Chelicerae are the first pair of holding or biting appendages of arachnids; pedipalps are the second pair of appendages and are used for handling food and for sensing.

Chapter 28 Arthropods, continued

Understanding Main Ideas (Part A)

In the space at the left, write the letter of the word or phrase that best completes the statement or answers the question.

c   1. The characteristic that most distinguishes arthropods from other invertebrates is
   a. the coelom.
   b. the endoskeleton.
   c. jointed appendages.
   d. bilateral symmetry.

d   2. Before an arthropod molts, a new exoskeleton
   a. grows on top of its old one.
   b. must be found.
   c. cannot grow.
   d. grows beneath its old one.

b   3. Aquatic arthropods exchange gases through
   a. tracheal tubes.
   b. gills.
   c. their exoskeleton.
   d. book lungs.

d   4. How many pairs of jointed appendages do arachnids have?
   a. two
   b. four
   c. three
   d. six

a   5. When a spider bites, it uses its
   a. chelicerae.
   b. mandibles.
   c. pedipalps.
   d. silk glands.

a   6. In spiders, the exchange of gases takes place in
   a. book lungs.
   b. lungs.
   c. gills.
   d. spiracles.

c   7. Most insects have one pair of _____ that are used to sense vibrations, food, and pheromones in the environment.
   a. pedipalps
   b. wings
   c. antennae
   d. eyes

a   8. The typical tick body consists of _____ segment(s).
   a. one
   b. two
   c. three
   d. four

c   9. Crabs, lobsters, shrimps, and pill bugs are members of the class
   a. Insecta.
   b. Chilopoda.
   c. Crustacea.
   d. Arachnida.

d   10. The stages of incomplete metamorphosis are
   a. egg, larva, pupa, adult.
   b. larva, pupa, nymph.
   c. egg, larva, adult.
   d. egg, nymph, adult.

a   11. Grasshoppers have
   a. two compound eyes and three simple eyes.
   b. three compound eyes and two simple eyes.
   c. two compound eyes and two simple eyes.
   d. none of these.

Chapter Assessment

28 Arthropods, *continued*

Understanding Main Ideas (Part B)

Answer the following questions.

1. How are insects adapted to living on land?

Their thinner exoskeleton allows more freedom to fly and jump; the exoskeleton is covered by a waxy layer that protects against water loss. Most insects breathe through tracheal tubes. The flight and landing mechanisms are also adaptive advantages for land.

2. What are four uses of the jointed appendages of arthropods? Give examples.

Jointed appendages are adapted for sensing, walking, feeding, and mating. Male spiders use the second pair of appendages—the pedipalps—for sensing and mating. Many arthropods use their jointed appendages for walking.

3. How do compound eyes aid arthropods?

The image formed from compound eyes is a composite of many partial images, one for each lens. This type of image is good for detecting motion. Even the slightest movement of prey, mates, or predators can be detected.

4. How do web-spinning spiders create their webs?

Spider silk is secreted by silk glands in the abdomen. The silk passes through many small tubes before being spun into thread by the spinnerets, structures at the rear of the spider.

5. It is believed that arthropods evolved from the annelids. What differences, present in the arthropod structure, make arthropods better adapted to their environment?

Arthropod segments are fewer and are adapted for functions such as locomotion, feeding, and sensing. Arthropod segments show more complex organization. The arthropod shows greater development of nerve tissue and sensory organs, such as well-developed eyes. The exoskeleton of arthropods is harder and provides more protection than the cuticle of annelids.

Chapter Assessment

28 Arthropods, *continued*

Thinking Critically

Answer the following questions.

1. Fossils reveal that the horseshoe crab has remained almost unchanged for 500 million years. Why would an arthropod such as the horseshoe crab fail to evolve? What can you infer about the rate of change of its seaside environment?

The horseshoe crab might be well-adapted for movement, protection, and feeding in its environment. You can infer that its seaside environment must have changed very little.

2. How are insects' different modes of feeding reflected in their mouthparts?

Insects that draw blood have needlelike mouth parts. Those that suck nectar have a rolled-up sucking tube. Those that lap up food have a spongelike tongue. Insects that chew have mouthparts for handling and chewing food.

3. Why do arthropods lack muscle strength after molting?

After molting, the new exoskeleton is soft and does not provide the resistance needed to pull the body when the muscles contract.

4. Barnacles are primarily sessile, filter-feeding crustaceans that live on rocks in the ocean. Many barnacles, however, live on the backs of gray whales. Compare and contrast these two environments with regard to barnacle survival.

Barnacles living on rocks rely on the tides and currents for a food supply. Barnacles living on gray whales are exposed to a richer food supply as the whale moves through the water. Barnacles on rocks are able to reproduce easily, whereas barnacles on whales will have a harder time reproducing.

5. Suppose a new species of insect is introduced into an area as a natural control to rid the area of other insect pests. What are some possible advantages and disadvantages of doing this?

An advantage of introducing insect predators is that they will control pests without polluting soil and water with harmful chemicals. A possible disadvantage is that they might not have natural enemies in the area, leading to a population explosion of the new insect that could upset the ecological balance and food chain.

Name _____ Date _____ Class _____

Applying Scientific Methods

Many invertebrates, from hydrozoans to mollusks and arthropods, have specialized sense organs for monitoring gravity. This sensitivity is related to their sense of equilibrium. Arthropods can sense when they are upright and when they are turned over. The organ that senses changes with respect to gravity is the statocyst, located at the base of each antennule of the crayfish. A statocyst is a chamber that contains sensory neurons with hairlike fibers and a solid mass of sand grains or hardened calcium salts. These grains push against the hair cells, which then trigger signals in associated sensory neurons.

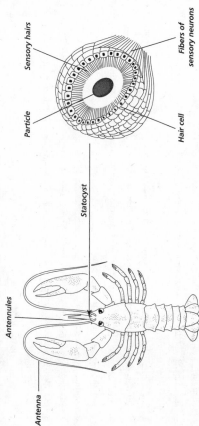

Antenna

Antennules

Statocyst

Particle

Sensory hairs

Hair cell

Fibers of
sensory neurons

1. Hypothesize how the statocyst functions to keep a crayfish upright.
   **Answers will vary but should include that, when a crayfish is on its back, the mass
   of sand grains falls away from its accustomed place on the hairs. This would signal
   the crayfish to turn upright again.**

2. Suppose that scientists on board a space shuttle wanted to investigate the effects of microgravity on
   the uprighting reflex of crayfish. What experiment might they propose?
   **Answers will vary. They might include placing crayfish in several positions to
   observe their ability to turn themselves upright again. Scientists may try to find
   out whether the effects of microgravity are felt more by larger crayfish than by
   smaller crayfish. They may also investigate whether microgravity affects crayfish
   that are in a dry environment more than those that are in water.**

Name _____ Date _____ Class _____

Applying Scientific Methods *continued*

3. Which variable would be tested?
   **Answers will depend on the experiment but will most likely relate to the position
   of the crayfish.**

4. What would be the control?
   **Answers will vary but may include a control group of similar crayfish kept on the
   ground at normal gravity conditions.**

5. What could scientists do if their hypothesis was not supported by the data?
   **They could check the experimental procedure, check the data, or change the
   hypothesis.**

6. Noting that hydrozoans and mollusks also have specialized sense organs for monitoring gravity, what
   experiment might be proposed to compare this mechanism among species?
   **Answers will vary but should include testing one species from each of the three
   phyla mentioned. The same variable, such as position, would be tested on each
   individual. In this case, three controls (one from each phylum) would have to be
   included.**

Chapter 29 Echinoderms and Invertebrate Chordates

Reviewing Vocabulary

Write the word or phrase that best completes each statement. Use these choices:

ampulla	madreporite	regeneration
notochord	tube feet	dorsal hollow nerve cord
pedicellariae	gill slits	water vascular system
rays	sea squirt	

1. Echinoderms have __tube feet__, which are hollow, thin-walled structures that each have a suction cup on the end.

2. The sievelike, disc-shaped opening in an echinoderm's body through which water enters and leaves is called the __madreporite__.

3. __Regeneration__, the replacement or regrowth of missing body parts, is a common feature in echinoderms.

4. The __gill slits__, paired openings located in the pharynx behind the mouth, are present only during embryonic development in some chordates.

5. The __ampulla__ is a round, muscular structure that is located on the opposite end from the suction cup on the tube feet.

6. Another name for a tunicate is a(n) __sea squirt__.

7. The long, spine-covered, tapered arms of sea stars are called __rays__.

8. The __water vascular system__ regulates locomotion, gas exchange, food capture, and excretion in an echinoderm.

9. The __notochord__ is a semirigid, rodlike structure in chordates that is replaced by the backbone in vertebrates.

10. In chordates, the __dorsal hollow nerve cord__ is a hollow tube of cells surrounding a fluid-filled canal that lies above the notochord.

11. Pincerlike appendages called __pedicellariae__ are modified spines found on sea stars.

Chapter 29 Echinoderms and Invertebrate Chordates, continued

Understanding Main Ideas (Part A)

Match each letter on the drawing of the sea star with the appropriate term that follows.

__B__   1. ampulla

__A__   2. madreporite

__D__   3. spine

__C__   4. tube foot

5. Write the names of the structures listed above that are part of the water vascular system.

__madreporite, tube foot, ampulla__

In the space at the left, write the letter of the word or phrase that best completes the statement.

__c__   6. A sea star can hold tightly to the surface it is touching because of the
    a. sieve in the madreporite.   b. endoskeleton.
    c. suction in the tube feet.   d. eyespots.

__c__   7. You could recognize an adult sea squirt as a chordate by its
    a. notochord.   b. dorsal hollow nerve cord.
    c. gill slits.   d. spines.

__d__   8. An animal that retains its chordate features throughout life is the
    a. sea star.   b. sand dollar.   c. sea squirt.   d. lancelet.

__b__   9. The type of symmetry found in adult echinoderms is
    a. horizontal.   b. radial.   c. bilateral.   d. regional.

Name _____ Date _____ Class _____

Chapter 29 **Echinoderms and Invertebrate Chordates,** *continued*

Understanding Main Ideas (Part B)

1. Describe two characteristics that set echinoderms apart from other organisms in the animal kingdom.
Their method of locomotion is unique, as they move by means of hundreds of hydraulic, suction cup-tipped tube feet. Also they have spiny skin.

2. What are the functions of the water vascular system?
The water vascular system regulates locomotion, gas exchange, food capture, and excretion.

3. What three methods do echinoderms use to get food?
Some echinoderms, such as the sea stars, are carnivores that prey on worms or mollusks. Others, such as the sea urchins, are herbivores and graze on algae. Still others feed on dead and decaying matter on the ocean floor.

4. Describe the nervous system of echinoderms.
Echinoderms have a nerve net and nerve ring but no head or brain. Most have no sensory organs, although they do have cells that detect light and touch. Sea stars, however, have a sensory organ called an eyespot at the tip of each ray.

5. Why are echinoderms thought to be related to chordates?
Like chordates, echinoderms have deuterostome development. They are the only major group of deuterostome invertebrates. Echinoderm larvae exhibit bilateral symmetry, as do chordates.

6. Describe how a sea star feeds on a clam.
The sea star uses its tube feet to force open the clam shell. Then it pushes its stomach out of its mouth and spreads the stomach over the soft parts of the clam. Digestive enzymes break down the clam until it is a soupy liquid that the sea star can absorb. When it is finished eating, the sea star retracts its stomach.

Name _____ Date _____ Class _____

Chapter 29 **Echinoderms and Invertebrate Chordates,** *continued*

Thinking Critically

Answer the following questions.

1. When a fossil sea urchin is found with a large number of tube feet specialized for gas exchange, a paleoecologist infers that the sea urchin once lived in warm, tropical water. What would be the reasoning behind such an inference?
Answers will vary. An invertebrate's metabolic rate generally increases with temperature. Therefore, if gas exchange can provide the oxygen needed for metabolism, the environment must be warm. Thus, sea urchins with a large number of tube feet that are specialized for gas exchange show an adaptation for survival in a warm environment.

2. Fertilization in echinoderms may occur in areas where ocean currents are strong or in calm tide pools. Which of these areas would result in a higher rate of fertilization? Explain.
Answers will vary. Students may suggest that a higher rate of fertilization would occur in the tide pool, where there is a better chance that sperm and eggs would meet.

3. Researchers induced male sea urchins to spawn out of season by placing them in an isotonic solution of potassium chloride. They recorded the number of males induced to spawn at different lunar phases: half moon (H), full moon (F), and new moon (N). From the table shown at the right, what can you conclude about the influence of the lunar cycle on spawning?
Answers may vary, but students should conclude that lunar phase did not affect spawning because there were high and low percentages during each lunar phase.

Lunar phase	Total No.	No. induced to spawn	% induced to spawn
H	15	12	80
H	8	8	100
H	7	4	57
H	15	14	93
F	12	10	83
F	22	15	68
F	25	16	64
F	18	16	88
N	12	12	100
N	22	10	45
N	16	7	44

Chapter Assessment

Chapter 29 — Echinoderms and Invertebrate Chordates, *continued*

Applying Scientific Methods

Sand dollars have a system of food grooves on their underside. When food-containing sediment passes over their upper surface, fine particles of food in the sediment drop between the spines on that surface and are carried to the underside. There the fine matter passes to the food grooves. Food particles are captured by the tube feet that border the grooves and are helped along to the mouth.

Suppose that you are a taxonomist confronted with the task of determining the relationship among several families of the order Clypeasteroida, to which the sand dollars belong. You have many fossil sand dollars and are studying the differences in the arrangement of their food grooves. Refer to the diagrams.

1. Plan a way to show the relationships among the six families of sand dollars shown below, all of which belong to the order Clypeasteroida illustrated in the phylogenetic diagram to the right. Base your relationships on the arrangement of the food grooves. Show where each family belongs in the phylogenetic tree. Write the letter of the correct position of each family in the blank below each diagram. (Hint: Consider the number of grooves and the number and position of branches in relation to the mouth or the outer edge of the organism.)

Answers will vary. A possible arrangement is given below.

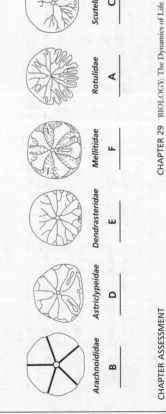

Arachnoididae	Astriclypeidae	Dendrasteridae	Mellitidae	Rotulidae	Scutellaster
B	D	E	F	A	C

Chapter Assessment

Chapter 29 — Echinoderms and Invertebrate Chordates, *continued*

Applying Scientific Methods *continued*

2. Which families were most difficult to place? Explain.
Answers will vary but may include the Mellitidae, the Astriclypeidae, and the Rotulidae because of their complexity.

3. What characteristic did you use to establish where to place the Mellitidae?
Answers will vary, but students may use the Y-shaped branches at the ends of the radial branches to show that the Mellitidae branched from the Scutellidae.

4. Which families were easiest to place in side branches that did not further evolve? Explain.
The Arachnoididae, the Rotulidae, and the Astriclypeidae all were end-of-the-line side branches because their food grooves were so intricate that further variations were more difficult to improve on.

5. Hypothesize about the advantage of food grooves on the underside of sand dollars.
Food grooves on the underside are advantageous to the sand dollar because its mouth is on that side. Food can thus be passed by the tube feet in assembly-line fashion to the mouth.

6. Why would taxonomists use food grooves to trace the evolution of sand dollars?
Food grooves are etched into the endoskeleton and thus can be observed in fossils. Also, food grooves would likely reflect the sand dollar's lifestyle, diet, and environment.

7. Which characteristic of the food grooves seems to have survived variations in the sand dollars' environment?
All sand dollars have five main food grooves radiating from the center.

Chapter 30 Fishes and Amphibians

Reviewing Vocabulary

Write the word or phrase that best completes the statement. Use these choices:

cartilage	scales	ectotherms
spawning	fins	swim bladder
lateral line system	vocal cords	

1. All classes of fishes possess a(n) **lateral line system** , composed of fluid-filled canals arranged along the sides of the body, which permit fishes to detect movement and vibrations in the water.

2. Many bony fishes possess a(n) **swim bladder** , which is a thin-walled, internal sac found just below the backbone. By altering the amount of gas in this structure, a fish can control its depth in the water.

3. The skeletons of lampreys, hagfishes, and sharks are made of a tough, flexible material called **cartilage** .

4. Amphibians are **ectotherms** because their body temperature changes with the temperature of the surroundings.

5. Frogs and toads have bands of tissue in their throats called **vocal cords** , which are capable of producing a wide range of sounds.

6. The **scales** of a fish can be toothlike, diamond-shaped, cone-shaped, or round. These structures are thin bony plates formed from the skin.

7. Breeding in fishes is called **spawning** .

8. Fishes depend on their **fins** for balance, steering, and swimming. These structures are fan-shaped membranes supported by the endoskeleton.

Chapter 30 Fishes and Amphibians, *continued*

Understanding Main Ideas (Part A)

In the space at the left, write the letter of the word or phrase that best completes the statement.

c 1. Lampreys are parasites that attach themselves to other fishes by suckerlike mouths because they lack
  a. teeth.   b. fins.   c. jaws.   d. a skeleton.

d 2. A fish can detect movement and vibrations in the water by means of its
  a. keen sense of smell.   b. scales.
  c. excellent vision.   d. lateral line system.

a 3. Fishes have great flexibility when they swim because they have
  a. separate vertebrae.   b. no limbs.
  c. scales.   d. no skin.

b 4. Frogs have a tympanic membrane that
  a. allows water to pass into cells.
  b. picks up vibrations from water or air and transmits them to the inner ear.
  c. protects cells from harmful chemicals.
  d. allows nutrients to enter the body.

b 5. Scientists believe that amphibians evolved from
  a. sharks.   b. aquatic tetrapods.
  c. lampreys.   d. salmon.

b 6. Bony fishes belong to the class
  a. Agnatha.   b. Osteichthyes.   c. Amphibia.   d. Chondrichthyes.

Write the word or phrase that best completes the statement.

7. Fish have a **two** -chambered heart.

8. Blood flow in fishes is slow because most of the pumping action is used to **push blood through the gills** .

9. Sharks have **internal** fertilization.

10. Amphibians live mostly in warm environments because they are ectotherms whose body temperature changes with the **temperature of the surroundings** .

11. In amphibians, the **skin** is the most important organ for gas exchange.

Chapter Assessment

Chapter 30   Fishes and Amphibians, *continued*

Understanding Main Ideas (Part B)

Answer the following questions.

1. Why was the evolution of jaws an important event in vertebrate history?
Jaws enable an animal to grasp and crush its prey with great force, increasing the possibilities of obtaining food.

2. How do members of class Osteichthyes differ from members of class Chondrichthyes and class Agnatha?
Members of class Osteichthyes have bony skeletons; members of classes Chondrichthyes and Agnatha have cartilaginous skeletons.

3. How does blood circulate in a fish?
A fish has a two-chambered heart. One chamber receives deoxygenated blood from the body tissues, whereas the second chamber pumps blood directly to the capillaries of the gills. There oxygen is picked up and carbon dioxide is released. Oxygenated blood is carried from the gills to the body tissues.

4. What is the function of the swim bladder in bony fishes?
The swim bladder can be filled with gases that diffuse out of a fish's blood. Fish can control their depth by regulating the amount of gas in the swim bladder.

5. What were the advantages of life on land for early amphibians? What were the disadvantages of living on land?
Advantages: life on land provided a large food supply, shelter, and no predators. There was also more oxygen in air than in water. Disadvantages: temperatures varied much more on land than in water. Also, without the support of water, bodies were clumsy and heavy.

6. How does the three-chambered heart equip amphibians for life on land?
Moving about on land requires a great deal of energy and large amounts of oxygen. The three-chambered heart provides more oxygen to cells by having separate chambers to receive oxygen-rich and oxygen-poor blood.

Chapter Assessment

Chapter 30   Fishes and Amphibians, *continued*

Thinking Critically

Answer the following questions.

1. What may have been the selective pressures that favored the evolution of amphibians?
Environmental conditions such as drying out of habitats may have selected for amphibian ancestors that possessed lungs and limbs that helped them survive on land. Another pressure may have been competition for food. More food was available on land.

2. How might being able to jump have been a factor in the success of frogs on land?
The early amphibians moved like modern-day salamanders. The ability to jump was an advantage in escaping predation and in capturing food.

3. In what way does metamorphosis in frogs represent a shortened version of evolution that took place over countless generations?
Evolution from fish to amphibian required the development of limbs for walking on land and lungs for breathing in air. This same process occurs during metamorphosis, when the fishlike tadpole develops lungs, loses its gills, and develops a three-chambered heart from a two-chambered heart. At the same time, the tadpole absorbs its tail and develops limbs for locomotion on land.

4. In what way is hearing in humans similar to lateral-line reception in fish?
The lateral line of a fish detects vibrations in the water. Hearing in humans begins with the ear's detection of vibrations in air.

5. Removing the thyroid gland from a tadpole will prevent it from undergoing metamorphosis. If the gland is reimplanted, the tadpole will then undergo metamorphosis. Make a hypothesis to explain this observation.
The thyroid gland secretes a chemical (hormone) that must be present for metamorphosis to occur.

Chapter 30 — Fishes and Amphibians, *continued*

Applying Scientific Methods

Many investigators would like to know whether sleep has an adaptive function. Some of the studies of sleep focus on fishes. Do fishes sleep? Although fishes cannot close their eyes because they lack eyelids, the fishes do remain immobile for a period of time. At these times, the fishes are less sensitive to disturbances. To an investigator, this means they are asleep. Fish exhibit other signs that are indicative of sleep, such as a decreased rate of respiration, a decreased reaction to sound, and a lessened response to the approach of foreign objects.

1. Propose a hypothesis explaining the adaptive value of sleep for fish.
   Answers will vary. Students may hypothesize that sleep forces fish to become less sensitive to external stimuli and thus conserve energy. They may also suggest that sleep forces fish to find a safe shelter during the time of day when they are most vulnerable to predators.

2. Plan an experiment to test whether fishes sleep. Because 24-hour observations are not feasible, you may want your plan to include recordings by infrared videos, electromechanical sensors, ultrasound telemetry, or infrared photo cells. Another approach might be to change the fishes' sleep patterns by reversing the patterns of light and darkness during a 24-hour period. You could then monitor oxygen consumption as an indicator of the level of the fishes' activity. Make sure that there is a shelter for the fish to go to during the rest phase. Not all fish use a shelter, but many do. Plan a chart or graph to show your findings.
   Plans will vary according to the method of observation.

3. What will be the variable in this investigation?
   Answers will depend on the indicators of sleep that are monitored in the investigation.

4. What will be the control?
   Answers may vary. The control most likely will be the normal patterns of rest.

5. What kind of correlation would you expect to find between any of the variables that you test and the depth of sleep or degree of insensitivity to disturbances?
   Answers will vary, but students may expect that a fish that is in deep sleep will not respond if touched or lifted by hand.

Chapter 30 — Fishes and Amphibians, *continued*

Applying Scientific Methods   continued

6. One nocturnal fish, *Tinca tinca*, has been observed to lie at the bottom of a tank for periods of 15–20 minutes during the day without moving. Its respiratory rate at that time is 65 percent of its nocturnal respiratory rate. What would you expect to happen to the respiratory rate of *Tinca tinca* if lights were left on at night and the tank was darkened during the day?
   The respiratory rate would rise during the day and be lowered at night.

Left page

Chapter Assessment

Chapter 31 Reptiles and Birds

Reviewing Vocabulary

Complete the paragraphs by writing the correct term on the appropriate line. A term may be used more than once. Use these choices.

amniotic egg	feathers	sternum
endotherms	incubate	Jacobson's organ

Although amphibians preceded reptiles in living on land, amphibians retained their dependence on water for reproduction and the early part of their life cycle. Reptiles completely broke their ties to water. For example, the **(1)** __amniotic egg__ was an adaptation that liberated reptiles from their reliance on water for reproduction. The **(2)** __amniotic egg__ contains membranes that protect the embryo and provide it with nourishment while it develops in a terrestrial environment.

Reptiles also developed sense organs that allowed them to receive important information about their environment. The heads of some snakes have heat-sensitive organs that allow them to detect the presence of warm-blooded animals. Snakes and lizards also have a keen sense of smell. These reptiles flick their tongues to sense chemicals in the air. When the tongue is drawn back into the mouth, it is inserted into a structure called **(3)** __Jacobson's organ__ , where the chemical molecules are analyzed.

Unlike reptiles, which are ectotherms, birds are **(4)** __endotherms__ .
(5) __Endotherms__ maintain a constant body temperature that is not dependent on the environmental temperature. Birds **(6)** __incubate__ , or sit on their eggs to keep them warm, turning the eggs periodically so that they develop properly.

Other adaptations of birds aid in flight. The **(7)** __sternum__ of a bird, which looks like the keel of a sailing boat, is a large breastbone to which powerful flight muscles are attached. **(8)** __Feathers__ are lightweight, modified scales that provide insulation and enable flight. A bird uses its beak to rub oil from a gland near its tail onto the **(9)** __feathers__ to waterproof them.

Right page

Chapter Assessment

Chapter 31 Reptiles and Birds, *continued*

Understanding Main Ideas (Part A)

Match each letter that appears on the diagram of the amniotic egg with the appropriate term below.

__D__ **1.** albumen

__E__ **2.** allantois

__C__ **3.** amnion

__B__ **4.** chorion

__F__ **5.** shell

__A__ **6.** yolk

Match each of the terms above with its function in the amniotic egg.

7. The main food supply for the embryo is the __yolk__

8. The __amnion__ is a membrane filled with fluid that cushions the embryo.

9. The __chorion__ is the outer membrane surrounding the yolk, allantois, and amnion that allows for gas exchange.

10. The embryo excretes nitrogenous wastes into the __allantois__ .

11. The clear part of the egg is the __albumen__

In the space at the left, write the letter of the word or phrase that best completes the statement or answers the question.

__b__ **12.** A rattlesnake detects your presence by means of its
  a. rattle. **b.** heat-sensitive organs.
  c. sharp eyesight. **d.** keen hearing.

__d__ **13.** A snake flicks its tongue as a
  a. sign of aggression. **b.** way of breathing.
  c. warning. **d.** way to test chemicals in the air.

__c__ **14.** Which structures do birds share with no other animals?
  a. shelled eggs **b.** clawed toes
  c. feathers **d.** scales on their feet

Chapter Assessment

Chapter 31 Reptiles and Birds, continued

Understanding Main Ideas (Part B)

Answer the following questions.

1. How does a reptile's scaly skin make it suited to life on land?
The scaly skin prevents the loss of body moisture and provides additional protection from predators.

2. In what way did the skeletal changes in which the legs became positioned beneath the body allow reptiles to exploit resources and niches on land?
Having their legs beneath the body provided greater body support and made walking and running on land easier. As a result, reptiles had a better chance of catching prey or avoiding predators.

3. How did the amniotic egg liberate reptiles from a dependence on water for reproduction?
The amniotic egg provides nourishment to the embryo and contains membranes that protect the embryo and provide it with moisture.

4. How do birds resemble reptiles?
Both birds and reptiles have clawed toes and scales on their feet. Both have internal fertilization and shelled amniotic eggs.

5. How is a bird's body adapted for flight?
Answers may include: Birds have powerful flight muscles attached to the sternum and to the upper bone of each wing. They have a four-chambered heart that beats rapidly, moving oxygenated blood throughout the body. Their bones are thin and hollow, making it easy for birds to lift off the ground. Birds also have air sacs so that their lungs receive oxygenated air when they breathe in and out. Birds have a variety of wing shapes and sizes adapted for different types of flight.

6. How is being endothermic both an advantage and a disadvantage for birds?
Because they are endothermic, birds do not depend on the environmental temperature and can inhabit all climate regions. However, being endothermic requires high levels of energy, so birds must consume large amounts of food.

Chapter Assessment

Chapter 31 Reptiles and Birds, continued

Thinking Critically

Answer the following questions.

1. At times, the only fossil remains of a dinosaur biped are its footprints. Scientists use footprints to estimate the dinosaur's size. In bipeds, the footprint length is about one-quarter to one-fifth the length of the dinosaur's leg. If the track of a dinosaur measures 30 cm in length, estimate the range of the length of the dinosaur's leg.
If 30 cm = 0.25 l, then l = 30 ÷ 0.25 = 120 cm, or 1.2 m. If 30 cm = 0.20 l, then l = 30 ÷ 0.20 = 150 cm, or 1.5 m. The leg measured between 1.2 m and 1.5 m.

2. The feet of Canada geese and other birds that walk on ice have been found to have a much lower temperature than their bodies. Hypothesize why this is a useful adaptation for these birds.
Answers may vary. Lower temperatures in extremities that are in contact with the ice help these birds to minimize heat loss from their bodies. Also, if the feet were as warm as the body, the bird's feet would melt the ice; the water might then refreeze around the feet and trap the bird until the spring thaw.

3. Why did the discovery of the fossil *Archaeopteryx* support the view that birds evolved from reptiles?
Although *Archaeopteryx* had feathers and wings like a bird, it also had teeth, a long tail, and clawed front toes, much like a reptile.

4. A large, sluggish turkey has a heart that is about 0.12 percent of its body weight. A tiny, active hummingbird has a heart that is 2.4 percent of its body weight. What generalization might you make from this information?
One generalization might be that the smaller a bird is, the larger its heart will be in proportion to its body. It would be more accurate to say that the more active a bird is, the larger its heart is in proportion to its body.

5. An old saying states, "Birds of a feather flock together." What are at least three advantages of birds flocking together?
Some advantages of flocking are mutual protection from enemies, ease in finding a mate, huddling together when it is cold, and avoiding getting lost during migration.

Applying Scientific Methods

Each species of reptile has a high and a low body temperature beyond which the animal will die. Between these high and low temperatures, there is a critical maximum and a critical minimum temperature, above which and below which, respectively, the reptile loses its powers of locomotion. Temperature also influences a reptile's ability to digest food, as the table below shows.

Temperature	Rate of Digestion
38°C	normal or slightly below normal
25°C	normal
15°C	far below normal
5°C	zero

1. Interpret the table. What is the optimal temperature at which the reptile would feed? Explain.
   The optimal temperature for feeding is 25°C because at all other temperatures,
   digestion is slower than normal.

2. Propose a hypothesis explaining why digestion depends on body temperature.
   Answers will vary. Students may hypothesize that digestive enzymes require a cer-
   tain range of temperatures to be effective. Students may suggest that circulation
   and other body processes are so slow at extreme temperatures that digestion can-
   not proceed.

Plan an experiment in which you will determine the critical minimum and critical maximum temperatures of a species of lizard. For example, to find the critical minimum temperature, you might slowly cool the area where the lizards are detained, continuously recording their temperatures and that of the environment.

3. How will you know when the critical minimum temperature for this species has been reached?
   When the lizards cease to move about, even when attempts are made to arouse
   them, they have reached their critical minimum temperature.

Applying Scientific Methods   continued

4. How will you find the lizards' critical maximum temperature?
   Students will probably suggest that they will slowly raise the temperature of the
   environment of the lizards until the lizards stop moving about.

5. Why would it be a bad idea to leave the lizards at the critical minimum or the critical maximum temperature?
   The lizards cannot move about and their body functions are reduced at those tem-
   peratures. These conditions could be harmful.

6. What is the independent variable in this experiment?
   The independent variable is the temperature of the environment in which the
   lizards are kept.

7. What control would you plan?
   A group of lizards at room temperature would be the control.

8. In summer, certain lizards have a critical minimum temperature of 2.5°C. In winter, these same lizards have a critical minimum temperature of –1.2°C. The lizards do not freeze at the winter critical minimum temperature, even though it is below the freezing point for their blood. Propose a hypothesis explaining how the lizards can avoid freezing at temperatures below 0°C.
   Answers will vary but may include that the lizards produce an antifreeze chemical
   in their blood.

9. The critical minimum temperature can be used to distinguish between two species. Explain how this characteristic may be an adaptive factor in lizards.
   Students may suggest that lizards of the same species may have been separated
   by a geographical barrier in the past. Those lizards in a cooler area would have
   adapted by having a lower critical minimum temperature. Those in a warmer area
   would have adapted by having a higher critical minimum temperature. The two
   groups may have further differentiated to become two different species.

Name _____ Date _____ Class _____

Chapter 32 Mammals

Reviewing Vocabulary

Write the word or phrase that best completes the statement. Use these choices:

cud chewing	gland	monotreme	therapsids
diaphragm	mammary glands	placenta	uterus
gestation	marsupial	placental mammal	

1. A __diaphragm__ is the sheet of muscle located beneath the lungs that is used to expand and contract the chest cavity of mammals.

2. A __gland__ is a group of cells that secretes substances needed by an animal for temperature regulation, reproduction, or other life processes.

3. __Cud chewing__ is an adaptation that enables many hoofed mammals to break down the cellulose of plant cell walls into nutrients that they can use and absorb.

4. Female mammals have __mammary glands__, which secrete milk, enabling mammals to nourish their young until the young are mature enough to find food.

5. Scientists can trace the origins of the first mammals back to __therapsids__, a group of reptilian ancestors that had features of both reptiles and mammals.

6. The __uterus__ is a hollow muscular organ in female mammals in which the development of offspring takes place.

7. In most mammals, nourishment of the young inside the uterus occurs through an organ called the __placenta__, which develops during pregnancy. This organ is instrumental in passing oxygen to and removing wastes from the developing embryo.

8. The time during which young placental mammals develop inside their mother is called __gestation__.

9. A __marsupial__ is a mammal in which the young have a second period of development inside a pouch made of skin and hair found on the outside of the mother's body.

10. A __monotreme__ is a mammal that reproduces by laying eggs.

11. A mammal that carries its young inside the uterus until birth is a __placental mammal__.

Name _____ Date _____ Class _____

Understanding Main Ideas (Part A)

In the space at the left, write the letter of the word or phrase that best completes the statement or answers the question.

__c__ 1. The main advantage of hair is that it
 a. protects the skin.
 b. provides mucus.
 c. conserves body heat.
 d. can be shed.

__c__ 2. A jaw that has small incisors and canines but large premolars and molars may belong to a
 a. beaver.
 b. dolphin.
 c. horse.
 d. wolf.

__a__ 3. The folds in the mammalian brain
 a. increase the brain's surface area.
 b. secrete necessary fluids.
 c. form ridges for storing learned behavior.
 d. transfer heat from the body to the environment.

__c__ 4. Most marsupials are found in
 a. America.
 b. Antarctica.
 c. Australia.
 d. Africa.

__d__ 5. Which of these mammals is a monotreme?
 a. opossum
 b. kangaroo
 c. chimpanzee
 d. platypus

In the space at the left, write __true__ if the statement is true. If the statement is false, change the italicized word to make it true.

__placental mammals__ 6. Marsupials in continents other than Australia lost out in competition with *monotremes*.

__canines__ 7. Teeth called *incisors* are used to puncture and tear the flesh of prey.

__true__ 8. *Molars* are used for crushing and grinding food.

__primates__ 9. The most intelligent mammals are *carnivores*.

__Cenozoic__ 10. The golden age of mammals was the *Mesozoic* era.

__true__ 11. In most mammals, the nourishment of young inside the uterus occurs through the *placenta*.

__internal__ 12. Both mammals and reptiles share one aspect of their reproductive cycle: *external* fertilization.

Understanding Main Ideas (Part B)

Answer the following questions.

1. How do a mammal's sweat glands help regulate body temperature?
Sweat glands secrete water onto the surface of the skin. As the water evaporates, heat from the body is transferred to the surrounding air.

2. How does the diaphragm aid a mammal in taking in oxygen?
The diaphragm expands and contracts the chest cavity, moving air into and out of the lungs.

3. Why is cud chewing beneficial to some hoofed animals?
The cellulose of plant cell walls is difficult to digest. When grass is swallowed, bacteria in the stomach break down the cellulose. The food is brought back up to the mouth where it is chewed again before being returned to the stomach for further digestion. This allows the cud-chewer to extract the maximum amount of nutrition from the plant food.

4. What reproductive strategies help mammals to be successful?
Mammals guard their young and teach them how to survive. The females have mammary glands to nourish the young until they are mature enough to find their own food.

5. List three features that characterize mammals.
Answers may vary. Mammals have hair, mammary glands, a diaphragm, and a four-chambered heart.

6. What characteristics do mammals and birds have in common?
Both are endotherms, use insulation to retain body heat, have four-chambered hearts, and evolved from reptiles.

Thinking Critically

Use the table to answer the questions that follow.

Mammal	Body Mass (kg)	Average Heart Rate (beats/minute)
Sheep	50	70–80
Harbor porpoise	170	40–110
Horse	380–450	34–55
Elephant	2000–3000	25–50

1. Which animal has the highest body mass?
the elephant

2. Which animal has the lowest heart rate?
the elephant

3. Based on the table, what happens to heart rate as body mass decreases?
Heart rate increases as body mass decreases.

4. Would you expect a squirrel's heart rate to be higher or lower than a sheep's? Explain.
A squirrel's heart rate would be higher because a squirrel has a smaller body mass than a sheep.

Answer the following question.

5. The fat content of the milk produced in the mammary glands of humans differs from that of marine mammals. In human milk, fat makes up 3 to 5 percent of total nutrients. In the milk of marine mammals, fat makes up 30 to 40 percent of total nutrients. How would you account for this difference in fat content?
Answers may vary. Human infants are not exposed to very cold environments, such as those in which marine mammals are born. Because marine mammals must become active immediately after birth, they need the high energy of fatty milk. The fat also helps marine infants to build up a layer of blubber as insulation against the cold.

Name _____ Date _____ Class _____

Chapter 32 Mammals, *continued*

Applying Scientific Methods

Some mammals have a wide range of heart rates. For example, a resting brown bat has a heart rate of a little more than 450 beats per minute. The graph at the right shows what happens to a bat's heart rate during flight and at the end of flight.

Heart Rate of Brown Bat During Flight

1. What initial change occurs in the bat's heart rate during flight?
   The heart rate increases to 1200 beats per minute.

2. How long does it take for the heart rate to reach its maximum?
   It takes about 1 second to reach its maximum.

3. How long does the bat fly?
   about 2.5 seconds

4. After the flight, how long does it take the bat's heart rate to stabilize at its resting value?
   about 4 seconds

5. Hypothesize why there is such a wide range between the resting heart rate and the flight heart rate.
   During rest, the bat's heart rate is very low because there is a low oxygen demand. When the bat flies, the oxygen demand is very high, and the heart must beat very rapidly to meet this demand.

6. Plan an experiment in which you could determine a bat's heart rate at rest and during flight. Be sure to include the instruments you would use and how you would record your data.
   Plans may vary but might involve placing a device on a bat that would detect and transmit its heartbeats. The data might be recorded and analyzed by a computer.

CHAPTER ASSESSMENT

CHAPTER 32   BIOLOGY: The Dynamics of Life   **191**

Name _____ Date _____ Class _____

Chapter 32 Mammals, *continued*

Applying Scientific Methods   continued

7. What would be the dependent variable in this experiment?
   The dependent variable would be the bat's heart rate.

8. What would be the control?
   The control would be a recording of the heart rate of a bat that does not fly.

9. What other experiments dealing with heart rate might you carry out on bats?
   Answers will vary. Students might wish to study the effect of light on heart rate. They might also compare insect-eating bats with fruit-eating bats.

192   CHAPTER 32   BIOLOGY: The Dynamics of Life

CHAPTER ASSESSMENT

Chapter Assessment

Chapter 33   Animal Behavior

Reviewing Vocabulary

Match the definition in Column A with the term in Column B.

Column A

Column B

h	**1.** Complex pattern of innate behavior	**a.** aggressive behavior
k	**2.** Physical space that contains the breeding area, feeding area, or potential mates of an animal	**b.** behavior
g	**3.** Learning in which an animal uses previous experience to respond to a new situation	**c.** communication
a	**4.** Behavior that is used to intimidate another animal of the same species	**d.** courtship behavior
n	**5.** Learning by association	**e.** fight-or-flight response
b	**6.** Anything an animal does in response to a stimulus	**f.** imprinting
i	**7.** Use of symbols to represent ideas	**g.** insight
o	**8.** State of reduced metabolism that occurs in mammals living under intense heat	**h.** instinct
c	**9.** Exchange of information that results in a change of behavior	**i.** language
e	**10.** Behavior that mobilizes the body for greater activity	**j.** motivation
l	**11.** Inherited behavior	**k.** territory
f	**12.** Form of behavior in which an animal, soon after hatching or birth, forms a social attachment to another object	**l.** innate behavior
m	**13.** A form of social ranking within a group in which some individuals are more subordinate than others	**m.** dominance hierarchy
d	**14.** Behavior that males and females of a species carry out before mating	**n.** conditioning
j	**15.** An internal need that causes an animal to act	**o.** estivation

---

Chapter Assessment

Chapter 33   Animal Behavior, *continued*

Understanding Main Ideas (Part A)

In the space at the left, write the letter of the word or phrase that best completes the statement or answers the question.

c   **1.** When a male sea lion patrols the area of beach where his female sea lions rest, he is displaying
   a. habituation.
   b. pecking order.
   c. territorial behavior.
   d. circadian rhythm.

d   **2.** When a bird sings to signal others of the same species to keep away, it is showing signs of
   a. cheerfulness.
   b. insight.
   c. conditioning.
   d. aggressive behavior.

c   **3.** Which biologist first demonstrated conditioning in dogs?
   a. Dimitri Mendeleev
   b. Bruno Huber
   c. Ivan Pavlov
   d. Gregor Mendel

c   **4.** Which of the following is *not* an example of the use of a pheromone?
   a. Wolves mark their territories by urinating at the boundaries.
   b. Hyenas give off an odor that keeps different clans of hyenas apart.
   c. Poisonous snakes release a rotten odor when they are threatened.
   d. Skunks release a rotten odor when they are threatened.

c   **5.** Owls sleep during the day and are awake at night because of their kind of
   a. estivation.
   b. habituation.
   c. circadian rhythm.
   d. conditioning.

b   **6.** For trial-and-error learning to take place, an animal must receive
   a. a dose of imprinting.
   b. a reward for a particular response.
   c. conditioning.
   d. habituation.

a   **7.** Which of these is an example of imprinting?
   a. Young ducklings follow their mother.
   b. A bird makes a nest of grasses and twigs.
   c. Your cat rubs against your ankles when you open a can of cat food.
   d. A chimpanzee searches for a longer pole to reach for a distant fruit.

d   **8.** Animal communication can occur through
   a. sounds.
   b. touches.
   c. smells.
   d. all of these.

a   **9.** Solving math problems is an example of
   a. insight.
   b. conditioning.
   c. innate behavior.
   d. rhythmic response.

Copyright © Glencoe/McGraw-Hill, a division of The McGraw-Hill Companies, Inc.

Name _____ Date _____ Class _____

Chapter Assessment

Chapter 33 Animal Behavior, *continued*

Understanding Main Ideas (Part B)

Answer the following questions.

1. How does courtship behavior aid survival?
This behavior helps members of a species to recognize other members of the same species. In some species, it may also prevent females from killing males before they mate and may help females in choosing a mate.

2. Explain the role genes play in animal behavior.
An animal's hormonal balance and its nervous system, especially the sense organs, affect the animal's sensitivity to stimuli. Since genes control an animal's hormonal production and nervous system development, genes indirectly control behavior.

3. In what way does an instinct differ from a reflex?
A reflex is a simple reaction that takes place quickly. An instinct is a complex pattern of behavior that may have several parts and may take weeks to complete.

4. In a fight between two males of a species, how does the defeated male avoid serious injury?
Usually, the defeated animal shows signs of submission, which inhibit further aggressive actions by the victor.

5. What are three effects of setting up territories?
Setting up territories reduces conflicts, controls population growth, and reduces competition for resources.

6. Which external and internal cues stimulate an animal to migrate?
Lower temperatures and shorter days may be the external cues that stimulate an animal to migrate. The secretion of hormones may be the internal cue for the same purpose.

7. Birds are frightened away by a scarecrow at first, but after a few days, they ignore it and come back to feed. Explain this behavior.
The birds' behavior is the result of habituation, which causes them to stop responding to a repeated stimulus that is not associated with any punishment or reward.

CHAPTER ASSESSMENT

CHAPTER 33   BIOLOGY: The Dynamics of Life   **195**

Name _____ Date _____ Class _____

Chapter Assessment

Chapter 33 Animal Behavior, *continued*

Thinking Critically

Answer the following questions.

Black-headed gulls carry away eggshells of their already-hatched chicks. The animal behaviorist, Niko Tinbergen, hypothesized that this behavior makes it less likely that crow predators will discover nests and attack eggs that still contain live chicks. Tinbergen carried out an experiment to test his hypothesis. Refer to the table below to answer the questions.

Distance from eggshell to egg (cm)	Crow predation		Risk of predation (%)
	Eggs taken	Eggs not taken	
15	63	87	42
100	48	102	32
200	32	118	21

1. How do the data support Tinbergen's hypothesis?
When eggshells were closer to the eggs, more eggs were taken by crows.

2. Some eggs were still taken by crows even when the eggshells were 200 cm from the eggs. Hypothesize what this shows.
Answers may vary. When crows see eggshells, they may search the vicinity for eggs. However, if eggshells are scattered over a large area, crows have less chance of actually finding the eggs.

3. Do you think the gulls' behavior is instinctive or learned? Give reasons for your choice.
Answers will vary. Students may suggest the behavior is an instinct that evolved as an adaptation to an environment with predators. Other students may see the behavior as learned; gulls may watch predators investigating the shells and learn to remove shells from the nest.

196   CHAPTER 33   BIOLOGY: The Dynamics of Life

CHAPTER ASSESSMENT

CHAPTER ASSESSMENT

ANSWER KEY   BIOLOGY: The Dynamics of Life   **T333**

Chapter Assessment

Chapter 33 Animal Behavior, *continued*

Applying Scientific Methods

An animal behaviorist confronted with a particular behavior will try to determine its usefulness to the animal. One such behavior is exhibited by the Thomson's gazelle. In the presence of a predator, the gazelle jumps about a half meter off the ground with all four legs held straight and stiff and with the white rump patch clearly visible. This behavior is called stotting.

One behaviorist, Timothy M. Caro, devised eleven hypotheses that might explain stotting in gazelles. Here are a few of them.

A. Stotting warns other gazelles, particularly offspring, that a predator is near.

B. Stotting signals other gazelles to flee as a group, lessening the predator's chances of isolating a victim from the herd.

C. Stotting confuses the predator, keeping it from focusing on one animal.

D. Stotting communicates to the predator that it has been seen by the gazelle.

1. Which of these four hypotheses do you think is most plausible? Give reasons for your choice.
Answers will vary. Accept any reasonable explanation for the choice, since all of the hypotheses are plausible.

Caro then set about eliminating some of the hypotheses. First, he made predictions about how the gazelles would behave if a certain hypothesis were correct. In the table below, write Yes or No in each empty box after you consider each of the hypotheses and how it would affect the gazelles' behavior.

Questions to Be Answered	Predictions Based on Hypotheses			
	A	B	C	D
Would solitary gazelles stott?	No	No	No	Yes
Would groups of gazelles stott?	Yes	Yes	Yes	No
Would gazelles display the white rump to predators?	No	No	Yes	Yes
Would they display the white rump to other gazelles?	Yes	Yes	No	No

2. Caro continued his investigation to try to eliminate some of the hypotheses. He discovered that a solitary gazelle sometimes stotts when a cheetah approaches. Which hypotheses does this eliminate? Why?
It eliminates hypotheses A and B because if a gazelle is solitary, its stotting will not warn other gazelles. It also eliminates hypothesis C because the stotting of a solitary gazelle will not confuse the predator.

Chapter Assessment

Chapter 33 Animal Behavior, *continued*

Applying Scientific Methods *continued*

3. Caro found that all stotting gazelles turn their rumps toward the predator. Which hypotheses does this eliminate?
This eliminates hypotheses A and B since the behavior is directed toward the predator, not toward the other gazelles.

4. Explain which hypothesis now appears to be the most plausible.
Hypothesis D appears to be the most plausible because the other three were eliminated.

5. How would letting the predator know that it has been seen benefit the gazelle?
Answers will vary. The predator may abandon the hunt if it knows it has been detected. If the predator does not chase the gazelle, the gazelle will not have to expend energy fleeing.

Chapter 34 Protection, Support, and Locomotion

Reviewing Vocabulary

Match the definition in Column A with the term in Column B.

	Column A	Column B
h	**1.** Where two or more bones meet	a. ligament
e	**2.** Fluid-filled sac between bones	b. marrow
d	**3.** Potential bone cell found in cartilage of embryo	c. melanin
b	**4.** Soft tissue that fills center cavities of bones	d. osteoblast
g	**5.** Protein in dead epidermal cells that protects underlying cells and gives skin its elasticity	e. bursa
c	**6.** Cell pigment that colors skin and protects it from solar radiation	f. sarcomere
a	**7.** Band of tissue connecting bone to bone	g. keratin
i	**8.** Smaller fiber in a muscle fiber	h. joint
f	**9.** The functional unit of a myofibril	i. myofibril

Compare and contrast each pair of related terms.

10. compact bone, spongy bone
Compact bone is the outer layer of hard bone. The inner spongy bone is less dense and is filled with holes like a sponge.

11. axial skeleton, appendicular skeleton
The axial skeleton includes the skull, the vertebral column, ribs, and sternum. The appendicular skeleton includes the bones of the arms, legs, shoulders, and pelvic girdle.

12. voluntary muscle, involuntary muscle
Voluntary muscle is under conscious control, whereas involuntary muscle is not under conscious control.

13. epidermis, dermis
The epidermis is the outer, thinner portion of the skin. The dermis is the inner, thicker portion of the skin.

Chapter 34 Protection, Support, and Locomotion, continued

Understanding Main Ideas (Part A)

Write the word or phrase that best completes the statement.

1. Beneath the scab of a wound, _____ **skin cells** _____ begin to multiply to fill in the gap.

2. _____ **Red marrow** _____ produces red blood cells, some white blood cells, and cell fragments involved in blood clotting.

3. The mineral _____ **calcium** _____, found in dairy products, is a critical part of the diet for healthy, strong bones.

4. Contraction of _____ **smooth** _____ muscle, the muscle of internal organs, is slow and prolonged.

5. Bones grow in length at the _____ **ends** _____ of the bone. They grow in diameter on the _____ **outer** _____ surface of the bone.

6. Muscle strength depends on the _____ **thickness** _____ of the fibers and the number of fibers that _____ **contract** _____ at one time.

7. When an inadequate supply of oxygen is available to meet a muscle cell's oxygen needs, _____ **anaerobic** _____ respiration becomes the primary source of ATP.

Answer the following questions.

8. Why is the skin considered an organ? Name two important functions of skin.
The skin is an organ because it consists of tissues joined together to perform specific activities. Functions of the skin include regulation of body temperature, protection from physical and chemical damage, and sensing information from the environment.

9. Explain what causes a sprain and what the effects are.
Caused by forcible twisting of a joint, a sprain can result in injury to the bursae, ligaments, or tendons of the joint.

Name _____ Date _____ Class _____

Chapter Assessment

Chapter 34 Protection, Support, and Locomotion, *continued*

Understanding Main Ideas (Part B)

In the space at the left, write the letter of the word, phrase, or sentence that best completes the statement or answers the question.

b 1. The skin regulates the temperature of the body on a hot day by
  a. closing the pores.
  b. dilating the capillaries.
  c. constricting the blood.
  d. reducing access to the exterior.

c 2. After suffering widespread third-degree burns, the burn victim
  a. is unlikely to incur bacterial infection.
  b. recovers in a short time.
  c. has a harder time regulating body temperature.
  d. has slight damage to cells of the dermis.

d 3. Which of the following examples illustrates a pivot joint in use?
  a. You wind up to pitch a baseball.
  b. You wave good-bye to a friend.
  c. You kick a football.
  d. You look behind you.

c 4. By age 20, a person's bones stop growing because
  a. bone-forming cells are no longer present.
  b. less calcium is present in the body.
  c. hormones cause the growth centers at the ends of bones to degenerate.
  d. bone cells receive less oxygen and nutrients at that time.

Answer the following questions.

5. How does the sliding filament theory explain muscle contraction?
The sliding filament theory states that actin filaments within a sarcomere slide toward one another during contraction. Myosin filaments do not move.

6. How does the buildup of lactic acid in muscle cells result in more oxygen being delivered to your cells?
Excess lactic acid in the bloodstream makes the blood more acidic. This stimulates rapid breathing, which supplies more oxygen to the muscle cells. The oxygen breaks down the lactic acid.

7. Explain one beneficial and one harmful effect of exposure to sunlight.
When exposed to the ultraviolet rays in sunlight, dermis cells produce vitamin D, a nutrient that aids calcium absorption. However, exposure to ultraviolet light can damage skin cells and accelerate the aging process.

CHAPTER ASSESSMENT   CHAPTER 34 BIOLOGY: The Dynamics of Life **201**

Name _____ Date _____ Class _____

Chapter Assessment

Chapter 34 Protection, Support, and Locomotion, *continued*

Thinking Critically

Because it usually goes unnoticed until back pain or a spontaneous fracture occurs, osteoporosis is often referred to as the silent disease. This skeletal disease is characterized by a decrease in bone mass resulting in bones so porous they break as a result of even everyday activities. Though most prevalent after the age of 50, intervention before the age of 30 can significantly decrease the risk of developing osteoporosis later in life. The table below shows some of the risk factors associated with developing osteoporosis later in life. Use the table to answer questions 1 and 2.

Risk Factors	Description
Age	After the middle or later forties, bone mass begins to decrease.
Alcohol Intake	Excessive alcohol intake increases the risk of osteoporosis, especially in men.
Body frame/weight	Small-framed women and men are at greater risk for developing osteoporosis.
Cigarette Smoking	Smokers generally have lower bone densities than nonsmokers.
Diet	Calcium intake below the RDA throughout life increases the risk of osteoporosis.
Genetics	Having a close relative with osteoporosis or an osteoporotic fracture increases the risk of developing the disease.
Gender	Though both men and women develop osteoporosis, women are about four to five times more likely to develop the disease.
Physical Activity	Regular physical activity, especially weight-bearing exercise, increases bone density.

1. Which of the factors listed in the table are controllable? Which are not controllable?
Controllable factors are diet, exercise, smoking, and alcohol intake. Noncontrollable factors are gender, genetics, age, and body frame/weight.

2. Why would weight-bearing exercises increase bone density? **Answers will vary but should reflect the reasoning that the increased workload imposed by exercising muscles stimulates bone cell information. Increased bone cell formation results in denser bone tissue.**

Answer the following questions.

3. Bone fractures in children are often different from fractures in adults. Explain why this may be so. **The composition of a child's bones is different from an adult's bones. A child's bones have more cartilage and fewer minerals than an adult's. This makes a child's bones less brittle and less likely to break in two.**

4. A paramedic at an accident is aware of pressure points, areas where a major blood vessel crosses a bone close to the body surface. How might the paramedic use these points to stop bleeding? **By pressing a blood vessel against a bone, the paramedic can control bleeding temporarily.**

202 CHAPTER 34 BIOLOGY: The Dynamics of Life   CHAPTER ASSESSMENT

Name _____ Date _____ Class _____

Chapter 34 Protection, Support, and Locomotion, *continued*

Chapter Assessment

Applying Scientific Methods

The different function of skeletal, smooth, and cardiac muscle is reflected in the way each of the muscles contracts. Study the graphs below to see how the contractions compare. The black line indicates the electrical impulse that stimulates the muscle. The dotted line represents the muscle contraction.

Skeletal

Cardiac

Smooth

Electrical junctions

Electrical junctions

1. Study the graphs. Which of the three muscle types contracts most quickly following electrical impulse? Slowest? Explain the basis for your answer.
   The graph shows that skeletal muscle contracts in less than five milliseconds after electrical impulse. Smooth muscle takes the longest to contract, about 200 milliseconds after electrical impulse. Answers are based on the amount of time between electrical impulse and mechanical activity.

2. Compare the electrical impulses in each of the muscle types. How does the electrical impulse for cardiac muscle reflect the function of the heart?
   The impulse duration for each muscle type is: about 3 ms for skeletal muscle; about 250 ms for cardiac muscle; about 50 ms for smooth muscle. The long duration in cardiac muscle insures that all muscle cells contract. In this way, the chambers of the heart reach maximum contraction as a result of each electrical impulse.

3. Using the graphs and the illustrations, compare the contraction in smooth muscle to skeletal muscle.
   Smooth muscle contracts and relaxes more slowly than skeletal muscle. Because the fibers of smooth muscle are more interconnected than those of skeletal muscle, contraction is more diverse and widespread in smooth muscle.

4. Explain how the structure of cardiac muscle helps to stimulate muscle cells more quickly than in other muscle types.
   Because electrical junctions are found between each cell juncture, stimulation can be spread quickly to other muscle cells in the heart. This would help maximize the number of cells that contract.

Name _____ Date _____ Class _____

Chapter 34 Protection, Support, and Locomotion, *continued*

Chapter Assessment

Applying Scientific Methods   *continued*

Two muscles in your leg, the gastrocnemius and soleus muscles, help you to extend your foot. The gastrocnemius is used in jumping and performing other rapid movements of the foot. The soleus is used principally for support against gravity. In the laboratory, you can study muscle contraction by causing "muscle twitch" in these two muscles. You can apply a single stimulus to the nerve of an excised frog muscle. The time of contraction for these two muscles may be recorded, as seen in the graph below.

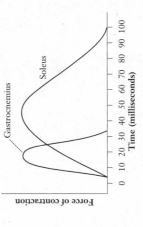

Gastrocnemius

Soleus

Force of contraction

Time (milliseconds)

0 10 20 30 40 50 60 70 80 90 100

5. Use the graph to decide whether the gastrocnemius or the soleus has the longer duration of contraction. About how many times longer is this contraction than the other?
   The soleus has the longer duration of contraction; it is about three times (100 milliseconds) longer than the gastrocnemius contraction (34 milliseconds).

6. Why do you suppose the one leg muscle contracts so much more quickly than the other one?
   The gastrocnemius muscle is responsible for fast movements, like running and jumping. So its contraction is fast. The soleus muscle is responsible for maintaining body position. Its contraction does not need to be as fast.

Chapter Assessment

Chapter 35 The Digestive and Endocrine Systems

Reviewing Vocabulary

Match the definition in Column A with the term in Column B.

Column A

d	**1.**	Digestive enzyme that breaks down starch into smaller molecules
g	**2.**	Muscular tube that connects the mouth to the stomach
m	**3.**	Series of involuntary muscle contractions along the walls of the digestive tract
a	**4.**	Flap of cartilage that covers the opening to the respiratory tract during swallowing
e	**5.**	Muscular, pouchlike enlargement of the digestive tract
b	**6.**	Digestive enzyme that begins the chemical digestion of proteins
l	**7.**	Chemical that breaks down fats into small droplets
c	**8.**	Last section of the digestive system from which feces are eliminated
k	**9.**	Regulates metabolism, growth, and development
f	**10.**	Specific cells in the body to which hormones convey information
n	**11.**	Unit of heat used to measure the energy content of food
i	**12.**	Narrow, muscular tube in which digestion is completed
h	**13.**	Organ that releases hormones directly into the bloodstream
j	**14.**	Organ that produces bile

Column B

a. epiglottis
b. pepsin
c. rectum
d. amylase
e. stomach
f. target tissue
g. esophagus
h. endocrine gland
i. small intestine
j. liver
k. thyroid gland
l. bile
m. peristalsis
n. Calorie

Chapter Assessment

Chapter 35 The Digestive and Endocrine Systems, *continued*

Understanding Main Ideas (Part A)

In the space at the left, write the letter of the word or phrase that best completes the statement or answers the question.

c	**1.**	Starches are large

    a. fats.   **b.** proteins.   **c.** polysaccharides.   **d.** monosaccharides.

d	**2.**	Which of the following is *not* mechanical digestion?

    a. chewing food   **b.** breakdown of fats by bile
    c. churning of the stomach   **d.** action of pepsin on proteins

a	**3.**	The surface area of the small intestine is greatly increased by

    a. a large number of villi.   **b.** chemical digestion.
    c. peristalsis.   **d.** mechanical digestion.

b	**4.**	Which of the following is part of the digestive tract?

    a. liver   **b.** small intestine   **c.** gallbladder   **d.** pancreas

b	**5.**	Which of the following occurs in the large intestine as the work of anaerobic bacteria?

    a. absorption of water
    b. synthesis of vitamin K and some B vitamins
    c. change of glucose to glycogen
    d. elimination of indigestible matter

b	**6.**	Vitamins are used by the body to

    a. provide energy.   **b.** maintain growth and metabolism.
    c. supply building materials.   **d.** digest proteins.

b	**7.**	Which is the most abundant substance in the body?

    a. fat   **b.** water   **c.** sugar   **d.** protein

a	**8.**	The body's preferred energy source is

    a. carbohydrates.   **b.** vitamins.   **c.** proteins.   **d.** minerals.

b	**9.**	As a result of digestion, proteins are broken down into

    a. monosaccharides.   **b.** amino acids.
    c. triglycerides.   **d.** glycerol.

d	**10.**	Cellulose is important in the diet as a source of

    a. energy.   **b.** protein.   **c.** fat.   **d.** fiber.

d	**11.**	Pepsin works best in the presence of

    a. amylase.   **b.** protein.
    c. saliva.   **d.** hydrochloric acid.

Name _____ Date _____ Class _____

Chapter Assessment

Chapter 35 The Digestive and Endocrine Systems, *continued*

Understanding Main Ideas (Part B)

Answer the following questions.

1. Name and describe the type of feedback mechanism that controls most endocrine glands.
The majority of endocrine glands operate under a negative feedback system. A gland makes and secretes a specific hormone. The hormone travels to its target tissue and an appropriate response occurs. Then information about the hormone's level or its effect on the body is fed back to regulate the gland's production of that hormone.

2. How do glucagon and insulin affect blood glucose levels?
Glucagon increases blood glucose levels by binding to muscle and liver cells and signaling them to release glucose. Insulin signals liver and muscle cells to take in glucose, lowering blood glucose levels.

3. Describe how a steroid hormone affects its target tissue.
Steroid hormones diffuse through the target tissue's plasma membrane and bind to receptor sites inside the cell. The hormone-receptor complex then travels to the nucleus and activates the synthesis of specific mRNA molecules. These mRNA molecules then activate the synthesis of certain proteins.

4. Describe how an amino acid hormone affects its target tissue.
Amino acid hormones bind to receptors embedded in the target tissue's plasma membrane. From outside the target cell, amino acid hormones activate enzyme pathways within the cell.

5. Describe the relationship among the hypothalamus, the pituitary gland, and the endocrine glands that are under the control of the pituitary gland.
The hypothalamus sends signals to the pituitary gland. The pituitary gland then releases hormones or stimulates other glands to release hormones.

6. Explain why the pituitary gland is considered the master gland of the endocrine system.
The pituitary gland controls most of the other endocrine glands, including the thyroid gland, the adrenal glands, and glands that control reproduction.

Name _____ Date _____ Class _____

Chapter Assessment

Chapter 35 The Digestive and Endocrine Systems, *continued*

Thinking Critically

Answer the following questions.

1. One cause of diabetes mellitus is the failure of the pancreas to secrete insulin. Describe the blood glucose levels of a person who has diabetes and goes untreated for the disease. How might a doctor test a person that he or she suspects might have diabetes?
Without insulin to signal the liver and muscle cells to take in glucose, blood glucose levels would become very high. Thus, a doctor may test the blood glucose level of a patient's blood.

2. Cholesterol, secreted by the liver, may cause the gallbladder to produce gallstones. At times, the gallstones block the common bile duct that leads to the duodenum. How might these gallstones affect the patient's digestion?
The gallstones would effectively prevent the bile from reaching the duodenum. Bile is needed to break down the fats in preparation for digestion in the small intestine. Without bile, the patient would have great difficulty digesting fats.

3. Many people have their gallbladder removed, but the absence of the gallbladder has little effect on their ability to digest fats. Explain why this is so.
The gallbladder serves as a storage area for bile. Even if it is removed, the liver can continue to produce and deliver bile to the small intestine. It just cannot store the bile.

4. Vitamin C is a water-soluble vitamin. Is eating a large amount of vitamin C once a week sufficient to keep the body healthy? What happens to excess amounts of vitamin C that may be consumed to prevent a cold?
No; because vitamin C is water-soluble, excess amounts of it are excreted and are not stored in the body. Therefore, vitamin C must be included regularly in the diet.

5. A person suffering from diarrhea may become dehydrated. How might this cause problems in the body?
Water plays an important role in regulating body temperature. Without enough water, the body might suffer large temperature shifts. Oxygen and nutrients would not be able to enter cells as easily without water as a solvent. Water is also necessary for the process of digestion.

Chapter 35 — The Digestive and Endocrine Systems, *continued*

Applying Scientific Methods

Although fats are an essential part of your diet, it is important to keep total fat intake at or below 30 percent of all the Calories you consume in a day. The fatty acids in fats vary in length and in the degree to which they are saturated by hydrogen atoms. Fats that are saturated are usually solid at room temperature. Most saturated fats, such as those in butter, dairy products, and meats, come from animal sources. However, coconut oil and palm oil are highly saturated fats from plants. A diet high in saturated fat can result in high blood cholesterol levels, which can lead to heart disease. You should limit your intake of saturated fats to no more than 10 percent of your total Calories. Most of your fat Calories should come from unsaturated fats. These fats do not have all the hydrogen atoms they can carry.

1. Calculate the percentage of fat Calories in each food in the table below. (Round answers to the nearest percent.) 1 g of fat provides 9 Calories.
   Notice that a hamburger contains 21 g of fat. To find the Calories from fat in the hamburger, multiply 21 g by 9 Calories = 189 Calories from fat. Divide the Calories from fat by the total Calories in a hamburger:
   189 Calories ÷ 289 Calories = 0.65 or 65 percent

Food Source (100 g)	Calories	Fat (g)	% of Calories from Fats	Saturated Fats (g)
Regular hamburger	289	21	65	8
Beef loin	184	7	34	3
Chicken breast with skin	197	8	37	2
Chicken breast, skinless	165	4	22	1
Drumstick with skin	216	11	46	3
Drumstick, skinless	172	6	31	1
Bacon	576	49	77	17
Ham, canned, extra lean	136	5	33	2
Tuna, yellowfin	145	1	6	<1
Shrimp	99	1	9	<1
Sour cream	214	21	88	13
Whole milk	61	3	44	2
Low-fat milk	50	2	36	1
Cottage cheese	72	1	13	<1
Cheddar cheese	403	33	74	21

Chapter 35 — The Digestive and Endocrine Systems, *continued*

Applying Scientific Methods   continued

2. Which food has the highest percentage of fat Calories?
Sour cream, at 88 percent of the total Calories, has the highest percentage.

3. Which food has the lowest percentage of fat Calories?
Yellowfin tuna has the lowest, at 6 percent.

4. It is recommended that a female student who regularly consumes 2100 Calories per day eat only 70 g of fat per day. How many of the Calories eaten by the female student should be fat Calories?
630 fat Calories

5. A male student who consumes 2800 Calories per day should eat only 93 g of fat per day. How many fat Calories is this?
837 fat Calories

6. If a student ate a hamburger with a slice of Cheddar cheese and a glass of whole milk, how many grams of fat could the student still safely eat at the rest of his or her meals?
Hamburger 21 g; cheese 33 g; whole milk 3 g = 57 g of fat consumed; female students would have 13 g left, and male students would have 36 g left.

7. Which foods have less than one-third of their fat grams as saturated fats?
chicken breast with and without skin, drumstick with and without skin

Copyright © Glencoe/McGraw-Hill, a division of The McGraw-Hill Companies, Inc.

Chapter Assessment

Chapter 36 The Nervous System

Reviewing Vocabulary

Match the definition in Column A with the term in Column B.

Column A

h **1.** Medicine that acts on the central nervous system to relieve pain

g **2.** Any drug that slows down the activities of the central nervous system (CNS)

d **3.** Psychological and physical dependence on a drug

m **4.** Automatic response to a stimulus

n **5.** Single extension of a neuron that carries impulses away from the cell body

l **6.** Occurs when a person needs larger and/or more frequent doses of a drug to achieve the same effect

i **7.** Layer of nerve tissue made up of sensory neurons that respond to light

f **8.** Light receptors adapted for vision in dim light

b **9.** Structure in the inner ear that helps maintain balance

k **10.** Controls involuntary activities such as breathing and heart rate

j **11.** Tiny space between the axon of one neuron and the dendrites of another neuron over which nerve impulses must travel

c **12.** Fluid-filled, snail-shaped structure in the inner ear

e **13.** Drug that affects the CNS, altering moods, thoughts, and sensory perceptions

a **14.** Chemicals that diffuse across the synapse and stimulate changes in a neuron

Column B

a. neutrotransmitters
b. semicircular canals
c. cochlea
d. addiction
e. hallucinogen
f. rods
g. depressant
h. narcotic
i. retina
j. synaptic space
k. medulla oblongata
l. tolerance
m. reflex
n. axon

Chapter Assessment

Chapter 36 The Nervous System, *continued*

Understanding Main Ideas (Part A)

In the space at the left, write the letter of the word or phrase that best completes the statement or answers the question.

b **1.** Sensory neurons
   a. process incoming impulses and pass them on to motor neurons.
   b. carry impulses from around the body to the brain and spinal cord.
   c. carry response impulses away from the brain and spinal cord.
   d. carry impulses across synapses.

c **2.** A nerve impulse travels from one cell to another by passing from
   a. one axon to another axon.
   b. one dendrite to an axon.
   c. one axon to a dendrite.
   d. one dendrite to another dendrite.

c **3.** Which controls involuntary activities of the body such as breathing and heart rate?
   a. cerebrum   b. cerebellum   c. medulla oblongata   d. none of these

c **4.** You can see the colors in a picture because you are aided by the
   a. rods of the retina.   b. right visual field.
   c. cones of the retina.   d. left visual field.

b **5.** A person who is addicted to a drug is experiencing withdrawal when he or she
   a. needs more of the drug to achieve the same effect.
   b. becomes ill after stopping its use.
   c. needs to take the drug more often.
   d. feels better when stopping its use.

d **6.** Cocaine is a stimulant because it
   a. causes blood pressure to drop.
   b. causes heart rate to slow down.
   c. relieves anxiety.
   d. causes levels of neurotransmitters in the brain to increase.

a **7.** Alcohol may act on the brain by
   a. dissolving through the membranes of neurons.
   b. speeding up the movement of sodium and calcium ions.
   c. increasing anxiety.
   d. increasing oxygen content.

Understanding Main Ideas (Part B)

Answer the following questions.

1. How is a nerve impulse transmitted through a neuron?
   When a stimulus excites a neuron, sodium channels in the membrane open up, allowing sodium ions to rush inside. The inside of the neuron becomes more positively charged than the outside, a condition that sets up a wave of changing charges down the length of the axon as the nerve impulse moves along it.

2. How does a nerve impulse pass from neuron to neuron?
   As an impulse reaches the end of an axon, the changing charges open calcium channels, allowing calcium to enter the end of the axon. The calcium causes neurotransmitters to be released. They then diffuse across the synaptic space to the dendrite of the next neuron.

3. How is the eye adapted for vision in a dimly lit place?
   The eye has special light receptors called rods, which are adapted for vision in dim light. The rods help the viewer to detect the shape and movement of objects in near darkness.

4. How do the semicircular canals help you to keep your balance?
   The semicircular canals are filled with thick fluid and lined with hair cells. The mechanical movements of the hairs stimulate the neurons to carry an impulse to the brain. Motor neurons in the brain then stimulate muscles in the head and neck to readjust the position of your head so you maintain your balance.

5. What is the role of the somatic nervous system in your body?
   Sensory nerves of the somatic nervous system relay information mainly from your skin to the CNS, which relays a response through motor neurons of the somatic system to the skeletal muscles. Reflexes, which are automatic, also occur through the somatic system.

Thinking Critically

If you enter a darkened room from a lighted area, you cannot see well at first. The retina of the eye lacks the light-sensitive pigment, called rhodopsin, in the rods. However, as the graph at the right shows, the concentration of rhodopsin builds up quickly, and the eyes adapt to the change in the amount of light.

Use the graph to answer questions 1–4.

1. How long does it take for the sensitivity of the retina to improve from 1 to 10 000 arbitrary units?
   about 12 minutes

2. After how many minutes does the retina have a sensitivity of 100 000 units?
   after about 40–50 minutes

3. How is the response of the retina to changes in light an adaptation?
   Most animals live part of their lives in the dark and part in the light. Therefore, they must be able to see well in both. A retina that is able to vary its receptivity between light and dark environments in a matter of seconds would presumably help the animal find food and avoid predators.

4. Upon entering a bright room after being in the dark, what happens to the levels of rhodopsin in the rods?
   Levels fall to almost zero.

The utricle and saccule are organs of the inner ear. Each of these organs contains a patch of epithelium called the *macula*. The macula is covered with tiny hairs, each of which is weighted by a small mineral grain. As the grains pull on the hairs, impulses are sent from the hair cells to the brain, alerting it to the head's position. The strength with which a mineral grain pulls a hair depends on the force of gravity.

5. In terms of the utricle and saccule, why might an astronaut in zero gravity experience space sickness?
   Without gravity acting on the mineral grains, the astronaut's brain would not know how his or her head was positioned. Until the brain was able to adjust, he or she would experience the headaches and dizziness characteristic of space sickness.

Chapter 36 The Nervous System, continued

Chapter Assessment

Applying Scientific Methods

Scientists in western countries have been searching for a chemical that will help curb an alcoholic's appetite for alcohol. Recently, some scientists have been looking at a treatment used in China for over 2000 years. Chinese healers have given alcoholics an extract made from the root of the kudzu vine, which they claim is about 80 percent effective in reducing alcohol craving in patients who have been treated for two to four weeks. Dr. Wing-Ming Keung of Harvard Medical School in Boston visited China to find out what modern researchers thought of the herbal remedy. He spoke to physicians who claimed to have treated 300 human alcohol abusers with the extract. They were convinced that the chemicals in the extract effectively suppressed the patient's appetite for alcohol.

After returning to Harvard, Dr. Keung and Dr. Bert L. Vallee decided to try the drug on a group of Syrian golden hamsters in their laboratory. These hamsters were specifically selected because they are known to drink large amounts of alcohol when it is available to them. Suppose you are a member of the Harvard Medical School research team. Your job is to design an experiment that will demonstrate the effectiveness of the kudzu root extract to suppress the hamsters' craving for alcohol.

1. Describe the experimental procedure you will follow.
Answers will vary but may include that you would divide the hamsters into groups. Each group would be injected with a different specified dosage of the extract for a definite period of time, such as two or three weeks. You would provide continuous supplies of water and alcohol to the hamsters and measure their intake of each liquid daily.

2. What will you use as your control?
One of the groups of hamsters will be given access to both water and alcohol but will receive none of the kudzu extract.

3. What will be the variable in your experiment?
The amount of kudzu root extract given to the hamsters will be the variable.

4. Predict the results of your experiment.
The treated hamsters will avoid the alcohol and drink water instead. Those that receive more of the extract may have their alcohol craving restrained sooner.

5. How might you follow up on your experiment?
You would want to observe previously treated hamsters to see if there is a relapse into alcoholism or if continuously treated hamsters develop a tolerance to the extract and require higher and higher doses to achieve results. You might also observe if any side effects occur.

Chapter 36 The Nervous System, continued

Chapter Assessment

Applying Scientific Methods   continued

6. Dr. Keung and Dr. Vallee discovered two active ingredients in the root extract, each of which had the effect of lessening alcohol use in the hamsters by 50 percent. The two compounds appeared to interfere with the metabolism, or breakdown, of alcohol in the body. Hypothesize what this discovery may tell us about the nature of alcoholism.
Answers will vary but may include that if the extract interferes with the breakdown of alcohol in the body, then it might be that alcohol is addictive only after it is metabolized.

7. How might Dr. Keung and Dr. Vallee's discovery help alcoholics overcome their addition?
If in fact alcohol only becomes addictive after it is metabolized, doctors may be able to give patients doses of root extract (or some other enzyme-inhibitor) in order to prevent them from metabolizing alcohol, thereby reducing their alcohol cravings.

Chapter Assessment

Chapter 37 Respiration, Circulation, and Excretion

Reviewing Vocabulary

Match the definition in Column A with the term in Column B.

Column A

- n   1. Passageway leading from the larynx to the lungs
- a   2. Sacs of the lungs where exchange of oxygen and carbon dioxide takes place
- k   3. Fluid portion of blood in which blood cells move
- i   4. Iron-containing protein that picks up oxygen after it enters the blood vessels in the lungs
- l   5. Cell fragments that help blood to clot after an injury
- c   6. A substance that stimulates an immune response in the body
- h   7. Microscopic blood vessel
- b   8. Protein that reacts with an antigen
- e   9. A kind of large, muscular, thick-walled elastic vessel that carries blood away from the heart
- o   10. A kind of large blood vessel that carries blood from the tissues to the heart
- f   11. An upper chamber of the heart
- p   12. A lower chamber of the heart
- d   13. Largest blood vessel in the body
- m   14. Regular surge of blood through an artery
- g   15. Solution of body wastes consisting of excess water, waste molecules, and excess ions
- j   16. A filtering unit in the kidney

Column B

- a. alveoli
- b. antibody
- c. antigen
- d. aorta
- e. artery
- f. atrium
- g. urine
- h. capillary
- i. hemoglobin
- j. nephron
- k. plasma
- l. platelets
- m. pulse
- n. trachea
- o. vein
- p. ventricle

Chapter Assessment

Chapter 37 Respiration, Circulation, and Excretion, *continued*

Understanding Main Ideas (Part A)

In the space at the left, write *true* if the statement is true. If the statement is false, change the italicized word or phrase to make it true.

- **red bone marrow**   1. Red blood cells are produced in the *spleen*.
- **valves**   2. The blood in the veins is prevented from flowing backward because of *pressure* in these blood vessels.
- **pulmonary veins**   3. The only veins that carry oxygen-rich blood are the *venae cavae*.
- **atria**   4. When blood first enters the heart, it passes into the *ventricles*.
- **true**   5. As the liquid passes through the *U-shaped tubule* in the nephron, most of the ions and water and all of the glucose and amino acids are reabsorbed into the bloodstream.
- **proteins**   6. The major waste products of the cells are ammonia and the wastes from the breakdown of *carbohydrates*.
- **glucose**   7. The urine of a person who has diabetes may contain excess *salts*.
- **water**   8. Carbon dioxide and *oxygen* are the waste products of cellular respiration.
- **true**   9. When your diaphragm *contracts*, the space in the chest cavity becomes larger.
- **true**   10. Breathing is controlled by changes in the chemistry of the blood, which cause the *medulla oblongata* to react.
- **artery**   11. Your pulse represents the pressure that blood exerts as it pushes the walls of a(n) *vein*.
- **anti-B**   12. If you have type A blood and *anti-A* is added during a transfusion, no clumps will form.
- **Cellular respiration**   13. *External respiration* uses oxygen in the breakdown of glucose in cells in order to provide energy in the form of ATP.

Copyright © Glencoe/McGraw-Hill, a division of The McGraw-Hill Companies, Inc.

Chapter Assessment

Chapter 37　Respiration, Circulation, and Excretion, *continued*

Understanding Main Ideas (Part B)

Answer the following questions.

1. How does the respiratory system prevent most of the foreign matter in urban air from reaching your lungs?

The nasal cavity, trachea, and bronchi are lined with cilia that constantly beat upward toward your throat so that foreign particles can be expelled or swallowed. Also, cells in the trachea and the bronchi secrete mucus that can trap the particles.

2. Distinguish between systolic pressure and diastolic pressure.

When the ventricles contract, blood pressure rises sharply. This high pressure is called systolic pressure. As the ventricles relax, blood pressure drops; the lowest pressure occurs just before the ventricles contract again and is called diastolic pressure.

3. What problem may arise when a woman with Rh⁻ blood is pregnant with an Rh⁺ fetus?

Toward the end of pregnancy or at delivery, the fetal blood may leak through the placenta and mix with the mother's blood. If the mother is Rh⁻, she will produce antibodies against the Rh antigen. If she becomes pregnant again, the antibodies will cross the placenta and attack the red blood cells of an Rh⁺ fetus. If the fetus is Rh⁻, there is no problem.

4. How does a pacemaker set the heart rate?

The pacemaker generates an electrical impulse that spreads over both atria, signaling the two atria to contract at almost the same time. It also triggers cells at the base of the right atrium to send an electrical impulse over the ventricles, causing them to contract.

5. How does the urinary system maintain homeostasis?

The urinary system removes nitrogenous wastes, controls the level of sodium in blood, and regulates blood pH by filtering hydrogen ions out of the blood and allowing bicarbonate to be reabsorbed.

Chapter Assessment

Chapter 37　Respiration, Circulation, and Excretion, *continued*

Thinking Critically

A marathon runner is able to increase the amount of blood pumped by the heart (cardiac output) from 5 L/min while resting to 30 L/min while competing. The runner's stroke volume (pumping capacity per heartbeat) measured in mL/beat, and heart rate, measured in beats/min, are also increased.

Use the graph to answer questions 1–3.

1. When the runner's cardiac output is 20 L/min, what is the heart rate?

120 beats/min

2. What is the stroke volume when the cardiac output is 20 mL/min?

160 mL/beat

3. Which has the greater effect on cardiac output, stroke volume or heart rate?

The heart rate has the greater effect because as the graph shows, cardiac output is at its maximum only when the heart rate reaches its maximum. Cardiac output is well below its maximum when stroke volume reaches its maximum.

Answer the following questions.

4. When a person has pneumonia, the alveoli become inflamed and the air spaces become clogged. What effect will these symptoms have on a pneumonia patient?

Gas exchange between air and blood cannot take place. Unless this is remedied, the patient will die.

5. Arteriosclerosis slowly reduces blood flow through the arteries to the brain. Explain how this may affect a patient who has this condition.

If the patient's blood flow is cut down, the amount of oxygen and nutrients that reach the brain is reduced. The patient may become confused and unable to perform normally.

6. The antidiuretic hormone (ADH) stimulates the reabsorption of water in the kidneys. Alcohol inhibits ADH secretion. Predict the effect of drinking alcoholic beverages on urine production.

Less water would be reabsorbed by the nephrons, so more water would be excreted from the body in urine.

Chapter 37 — Respiration, Circulation, and Excretion, *continued*

Chapter Assessment

Applying Scientific Methods

The vertebrate heart can beat spontaneously. If the heart of a vertebrate is removed and placed in a balanced salt solution with nutrients, it will continue to beat for hours. In fact, the muscle from each part of the heart beats at its own rate if it is not under the control of the pacemaker.

In a physiology laboratory experiment, a frog is anaesthetized and the heart is exposed. Recall that the frog has a three-chambered heart, with right and left atria and a single ventricle. It also has a sinus venosus, which receives oxygen-depleted blood from all parts of the body except the lungs. The sinus venosus is where contraction begins. (This role is assumed by the pacemaker in the mammalian heart.) For this experiment, the nerve connections to the heart are blocked. The sinus venosus, the right atrium, and the ventricle are each attached to a stylus for marking on a kymograph (an instrument that records changes in pressure). In the graphs, rises represent contractions.

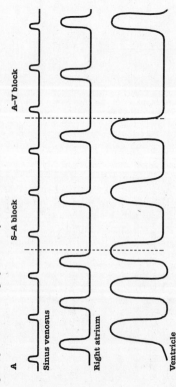

A   S–A block   A–V block

Sinus venosus

Right atrium

Ventricle

1. Interpret the data in A.
The sinus of the frog heart contracts slightly before the atrium. The atrium contracts slightly before the ventricle. The atrium and the ventricle contract at the same rate as the sinus.

2. To understand how the heart beats when the impulse from the sinus is blocked, a string is tied tightly around the heart between the sinus and the atrium. This is called an "S–A block." How does the S–A block affect the rate of the beat of the sinus?
It doesn't change the rate.

3. How does blocking the sinus affect the rate at which the atrium and ventricle beat?
The atrium and the ventricle beat more slowly after the block.

Chapter 37 — Respiration, Circulation, and Excretion, *continued*

Chapter Assessment

Applying Scientific Methods   *continued*

4. What could you do to find out the effect of blocking the atrium?
You could tie another string around the heart, between the atrium and the ventricle.

5. How does blocking the action between the atrium and the ventricle, which is called an "A–V block," affect the beat of the sinus, the atrium, and the ventricle?
The sinus and atrium continue to beat, but each at its own rate. The ventricle slows down considerably.

6. What can you conclude about the rate of beat of the different parts of the heart from this experiment?
Answers will vary but may include that each area of the heart beats at its own rate unless influenced by the sinus or by the lower part of the atrium. Also, students may conclude that although the sinus controls the rhythm of the heart, other heart tissue can initiate contraction if the sinus is blocked.

Chapter Assessment

Chapter 38 Reproduction and Development

Reviewing Vocabulary

Match the definition in Column A with the term in Column B.

Column A

h	**1.** Group of epithelial cells that surround a developing egg
e	**2.** Information provided by trained professionals about the probabilities of hereditary disorders in a developing fetus
b	**3.** Period of development in pregnancy during which all the organ systems of the embryo begin to form
a	**4.** Combination of sperm and fluids in which they are transported
c	**5.** Refers to the time when secondary sex characteristics begin to develop
f	**6.** Attachment of the blastocyst to the lining of the uterus
g	**7.** Ropelike structure that attaches the embryo to the wall of the uterus
d	**8.** Gland that secretes hormones that influence many physiological processes of the body

Column B

a. semen
b. first trimester
c. puberty
d. pituitary
e. genetic counseling
f. implantation
g. umbilical cord
h. follicle

Compare and contrast each pair of related terms.

9. bulbourethral gland, prostate gland
Both are glands that secret alkaline fluids in which sperm are transported. The bulbourethral gland produces a sticky fluid that neutralizes the acidic environment of the urethra. The prostate gland secretes a thinner fluid that helps the sperm move and survive.

10. epididymis, vas deferens
The epididymis is a coiled tube within the scrotum in which the sperm complete their maturation. The vas deferens is the duct that transports sperm from the epididymis toward the ejaculatory ducts and the urethra.

Chapter Assessment

Chapter 38 Reproduction and Development, *continued*

Understanding Main Ideas (Part A)

Label the diagram. Use these choices: ovary, implantation, blastocyst, ovulation, fertilization, uterus, zygote, vagina, oviduct.

1. ___vagina___

2. ___uterus___

3. ___ovary___

4. ___ovulation___

5. ___oviduct___

6. ___fertilization___

7. ___zygote___

8. ___blastocyst___

9. ___implantation___

In the space at the left, write the letter of the word or phrase that best completes the statement.

___b___ **10.** The fluid that provides energy for the sperm cells comes from the
   a. bulbourethral glands.   **b.** seminal vesicles.
   c. prostate gland.   **d.** urethra.

___c___ **11.** When FSH reaches the testes, it causes the production of
   a. testosterone.   **b.** LH.
   c. sperm cells.   **d.** secondary sex characteristics.

___d___ **12.** In the female, FSH stimulates the
   a. production of eggs.   **b.** production of progesterone.
   c. blastocyst.   **d.** development of a follicle in the ovary.

___c___ **13.** All the body systems of the fetus are present by the
   a. third week.   **b.** sixth week.   **c.** eighth week.   **d.** first month.

Thinking Critically

Answer the following questions.

1. Although the incidence is less than 1 percent, an ectopic pregnancy may occur, in which the implantation takes place in an oviduct or in the pelvic cavity. When would implantation in the oviduct be fatal for the developing fetus?
As the fetus begins to grow, the oviduct would probably not be able to accommodate its size. The fetus would probably die from lack of oxygen, because blood circulation would not be adequate.

2. How could it happen that implantation could take place in the pelvic cavity? What must happen for the fetus to be nourished there?
Since the oviducts open into the pelvic cavity, a fertilized egg may fall into the cavity, or an egg may be fertilized there. After implantation, the embryonic membranes and the placenta would have to develop there to transport oxygen and nutrients to the fetus.

3. Why would an ectopic fetus have to be removed by surgery, not by delivery through the birth canal? **The fetus is not in the uterus, which opens into the birth canal, so it would have to be removed surgically.**

4. Two groups of married women, about the same age and weight, participated in a test. The women in Group A were given a placebo, a sugar pill, each morning of their menstrual cycle. The women in Group B were given a pill containing estrogen and progesterone each morning of their menstrual cycle. The LH levels before, during, and after ovulation of both groups were recorded.

Group	Four Days Before	Day of Ovulation	Four Days After
A	17 mg/100mL	299 mg/100 mL	16 mg/100mL
B	20 mg/100mL	156 mg/100 mL	14 mg/100mL

The number of pregnancies during the year of the test in Group A was 25 times the number of pregnancies in Group B. What would you conclude, based on these data?
Taking estrogen and progesterone in addition to that supplied by the body upsets the luteal phase by inhibiting the amount of LH secreted during ovulation. The decrease in LH prevents the normal preparation of the uterus for implantation.

Understanding Main Ideas (Part B)

Use the diagram of the negative feedback system in the male to complete the following statements.

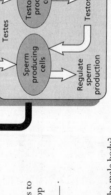

1. The release of LH by the pituitary is stimulated by a hormone secreted by the **hypothalamus**.

2. LH stimulates the production of **testosterone**.

3. **FSH** and testosterone affect sperm production.

4. An increase of testosterone inhibits **LH** production.

5. Cells that produce sperm send signals to the pituitary and hypothalamus to stop releasing **FSH**.

Answer the following questions.

6. Why is the scrotum located outside the male body? **Sperm can develop only at a temperature that is about 3°C lower than normal body temperature.**

7. What happens to the lining of the uterus if fertilization does not occur? **The lining is shed.**

8. What is the function of the corpus luteum? **It produces both progesterone and estrogen. The progesterone causes the uterine lining to thicken, to increase its blood supply, and to accumulate fat and tissue fluid in preparation for the arrival of a fertilized egg.**

Name _____ Date _____ Class _____

Chapter Assessment

Chapter 38 Reproduction and Development, *continued*

Applying Scientific Methods

The Smiths would like to have a baby. Mrs. Smith has begun to keep a record of her temperature readings during her menstrual cycle. She knows that she is fertile, or capable of beginning pregnancy, only for a period of about 24 hours from the time of ovulation. She also knows that her temperature rises about 0.3°C when she ovulates. She keeps a record of her temperature every day at the same time. The dates that are shaded on the calendars are the dates when Mr. Smith is away for National Guard duty. Use the temperature charts and the calendars to find out when Mrs. Smith has the best opportunity of becoming pregnant. (Note that sperm are able to survive inside the oviducts and uterus for several days.)

March

S	M	T	W	T	F	S
		1	2	3	4	5
6	7	8	9	10	11	12
13	14	15	16	17	18	19
20	21	22	23	24	25	26
27	28	29	30	31		

March Temp.	(°C)
19	36.7
20	37.0
21	37.0

April

S	M	T	W	T	F	S
					1	2
3	4	5	6	7	8	9
10	11	12	13	14	15	16
17	18	19	20	21	22	23
24	25	26	27	28	29	30

April Temp.	(°C)
16	36.7
17	37.0
18	37.0

May

S	M	T	W	T	F	S
1	2	3	4	5	6	7
8	9	10	11	12	13	14
15	16	17	18	19	20	21
22	23	24	25	26	27	28
29	30	31				

May Temp.	(°C)
14	36.6
15	36.9
16	37.0

June

S	M	T	W	T	F	S
			1	2	3	4
5	6	7	8	9	10	11
12	13	14	15	16	17	18
19	20	21	22	23	24	25
26	27	28	29	30		

June Temp.	(°C)
11	36.7
12	37.0
13	37.0

1. During which month or months do the Smiths have the best chance of producing a baby? Explain your answer.

When Mrs. Smith ovulates in May and June, Mr. Smith is at home. During these months, Mrs. Smith may have the best chances of becoming pregnant. In March and April, there is less of a chance because Mr. Smith is away on the day of ovulation; however, because sperm can survive for several days, fertilization may still take place.

Name _____ Date _____ Class _____

Chapter Assessment

Chapter 38 Reproduction and Development, *continued*

Applying Scientific Methods *continued*

2. Would changing Mr. Smith's National Guard weekend to the second Saturday of every month have helped the Smiths in their efforts to have a baby?

The change would have helped in March and April. In May and June, it is less likely the change would help.

3. Some researchers have noted slight physical variations in X and Y sperm. They postulate that because Y sperm are lighter than X sperm, the Y sperm travel more quickly. Hypothesize how this may affect the sex of the Smiths' baby, providing reasons on which your hypothesis is based.

If the egg is fertilized on the day of ovulation, there is a greater probability that the sperm will be a Y sperm, since they swim more rapidly than X sperm. An egg fertilized by a Y sperm will be a boy.

4. What if the Smiths tried for their baby the day before ovulation. How might this affect the sex of their baby?

There would be an equal chance that they would have either a boy or girl because sperm can survive for a few days. Both X and Y sperm would have had enough time to reach the oviduct by the time the egg was released during ovulation.

Chapter 39 Immunity from Disease

Reviewing Vocabulary

Match the definition in Column A with the term in Column B.

Column A

g **1.** Disease caused by the presence of pathogens in the body

i **2.** Substance produced by a microorganism, which kills or inhibits the growth and reproduction of other microorganisms

d **3.** Type of white blood cell that defends the body against foreign substances

e **4.** Disease-producing agents such as bacteria, protozoa, fungi, viruses

a **5.** Proteins that protect cells from viruses

b **6.** Defense against a specific pathogen by gradually building up resistance to it

c **7.** Small mass of tissue that filters pathogens from lymph

h **8.** Procedure used to determine which pathogen causes a specific disease

f **9.** Weakened, dead, or parts of pathogens or antigens that, when injected into the body, causes immunity

Column B

a. interferons

b. acquired immunity

c. lymph node

d. lymphocyte

e. pathogens

f. vaccine

g. infectious disease

h. Koch's postulates

i. antibiotic

Contrast and compare each pair of related terms.

10. T cell, B cell

A T cell is a lymphocyte that is produced in bone marrow and processed in the thymus gland. Different T cells perform different roles in immunity. A B cell is also a lymphocyte produced in bone marrow. It produces antibodies when activated by a T cell.

11. phagocyte, macrophage

A phagocyte is a type of white blood cell that ingests and destroys pathogens by surrounding and engulfing them. A macrophage is one type of phagocyte—a very large phagocyte.

Chapter 39 Immunity from Disease, *continued*

Understanding Main Ideas (Part A)

In the space at the left, write the letter of the word or phrase that best completes the statement.

c **1.** A bacterial disease becomes difficult to cure when the bacteria
 a. die off.
 b. make interferons.
 c. develop resistance to antibiotics.
 d. produce antibodies.

b **2.** Toxins produced by invading bacteria
 a. are always harmless unless released in vary large amounts.
 b. can, in some cases, cause fever and cardiovascular disturbances.
 c. rarely attack the nervous or circulatory systems.
 d. are the same as those produced by HIV.

c **3.** Interferons are a body cell's defense against
 a. all pathogens.
 b. bacteria.
 c. viruses.
 d. lymphocytes.

a **4.** Immunity occurs when the system recognizes a foreign substance and responds by producing
 a. lymphocytes that make antibodies.
 b. antigens.
 c. toxins.
 d. all of these.

a **5.** HIV can be transmitted by
 a. intimate sexual contact.
 b. contaminated food.
 c. air.
 d. shaking hands.

b **6.** A person with AIDS is susceptible to all kinds of infectious diseases because HIV
 a. destroys pathogens.
 b. weakens the immune system.
 c. causes an increase of antigens.
 d. causes antibody production.

b **7.** The symptoms of an infectious disease are caused by
 a. macrophages.
 b. toxins produced by pathogens.
 c. interferons.
 d. phagocytes.

a **8.** Active immunity is obtained when a person is exposed to
 a. antigens.
 b. injected antibodies.
 c. macrophages.
 d. antibiotics.

c **9.** Koch's postulates cannot be carried out on viral diseases because the viruses
 a. do not have hosts.
 b. are not pathogens.
 c. cannot be grown outside of cells.
 d. are too deadly.

Chapter 39 Immunity from Disease, *continued*

Chapter Assessment

Understanding Main Ideas (Part B)

Answer the following questions.

1. How do researchers identify the specific cause of an infectious disease?
   (1) They try to find a pathogen in the host in every case of the disease. (2) They isolate the pathogen from the host and grow it in a pure culture. (3) When they place a pathogen from the pure culture into a healthy host, it causes the disease. (4) The pathogen must then be isolated from the new host to prove it is the original pathogen.

2. How do interferons provide a defense against viruses?
   Interferons are host-cell specific proteins produced by an infected body cell. The interferon diffuses into uninfected neighboring cells, which then produce antiviral proteins that can prevent the virus from multiplying.

3. How does a nonspecific defense mechanism differ from a specific defense mechanism?
   A nonspecific defense mechanism is effective against a wide variety of pathogens. A specific defense mechanism achieves its goal by building up resistance against a specific pathogen or antigen.

4. What role do B cells play in immunity?
   A B cell is activated by a T cell to produce antibodies, which are released into the bloodstream. The antibodies bind to antigens to which they can fit. This binding results in an antigen-antibody complex.

5. How does cellular immunity protect the body?
   Cytotoxic, or killer, T-cells produce clones that then travel to the infected site and release enzymes directly into the pathogens, causing them to lyse and die.

6. Why is AIDS considered a disease of the immune system?
   HIV, which causes AIDS, kills helper T cells that are important in developing the immune response.

Chapter 39 Immunity from Disease, *continued*

Chapter Assessment

Thinking Critically

Answer the following questions.

1. You get a splinter in your finger, which becomes sore and swollen. In a few days, pus forms around the splinter. Explain.
   Inflammation occurs as a reaction to the injury and to the pathogens introduced by the splinter. Macrophages migrate to the infected area and engulf large numbers of pathogens. After a few days, the infected area contains pus, which is made up of dead phagocytes and body fluids.

2. Antibodies produced by the body to combat the pathogen that causes rheumatic fever may begin to attack the patient's own cardiac muscle cells. How might such a mixup occur?
   Antibodies recognize and initiate an immune response to proteins that are foreign to the body. If antibodies bind to the patient's own cardiac muscle cells, it may be because the proteins in muscle tissue must have something in common with the proteins in the rheumatic fever pathogen. This could lead to a mistake by which the body begins producing antibodies that attack its own tissues.

3. Organ-transplant patients are given a drug called cyclosporine to suppress the body's defenses against the transplanted organ. Why is this necessary?
   Without the cyclosporine, there would be an immune response to the organ transplant. The body would reject the new organ.

4. Unlike earlier drugs that suppressed the entire immune system, cyclosporine does not significantly suppress the bone marrow where lymphocytes are formed. What was the danger of taking the earlier drugs?
   The danger of taking drugs that suppressed the entire immune system was that the patient became highly susceptible to infectious diseases.

5. Suppose parents hear that a neighbor's child has chicken pox, and they take their young child over to their neighbor's house. Why would they do this?
   They might think their child should be exposed to the disease so that he or she will produce antibodies and build up an active immunity to it.

Chapter 39 Immunity from Disease, *continued*

Chapter Assessment

Applying Scientific Methods

Vincent Fischetti is a professor of bacterial pathogenesis and immunology at New York's Rockefeller University. His team of researchers has been studying why some Group A streptococcal bacteria manage to slip by the defenses of the human body. Group A streptococci cause strep throat, which often leads to acute rheumatic fever, a disease that damages heart valves.

First, Fischetti's team looked at Group A streptococci under an electron microscope. They noticed that some of these bacteria have long, hairlike filaments on their surfaces. The filaments were found to consist of a protein called M protein. They decided to find out if the M protein has anything to do with Group A's ability to resist ingestion by human phagocytes. They placed streptococci in a drop of human blood on a microscope slide. The phagocytes attacked any streptococci that lacked M-protein filaments.

Fischetti next wanted to know how the M protein resists the body's defenses. Figure 1 shows what they found. Four different repeated amino acid sequences (A, B, C, and D) make up 80 percent of the protein.

Almost immediately a discovery slowed the study. Fischetti found that there are 80 different varieties of M protein! He realized that M-proteins must be affected by rapid mutations. Further study of different varieties of M protein showed that most of the mutations occur in the numbers of repeated A and B amino acid sequences, as shown in Figure 2. Mutated streptococci show deleted copies of the amino acid repeat blocks normally found in the parent.

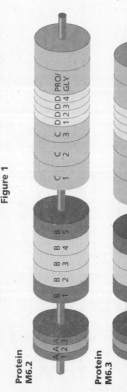

Protein M6.1

Figure 1

Protein M6.2

Protein M6.3

Figure 2

Chapter 39 Immunity from Disease, *continued*

Chapter Assessment

Applying Scientific Methods   continued

Suppose that you are a new member of Fischetti's team. After observing the experiments just described, you are asked the following questions about the work being done.

1. Which experiment provided evidence that the M protein protects streptococci?
   When streptococci are placed in a drop of blood, human phagocytes stay away from those with M protein but not from those without it.

2. Having mutations in the numbers of repeated amino acid sequences in the M protein is extremely helpful to the bacteria. How might this adaptation help them to survive?
   Every time the M protein changes, there is less chance that the human immune system will be able to identify and destroy the bacterium.

3. Figure 2 shows two mutations of the M protein. What differences do you observe between M6.1 and M6.2? Between M6.1 and M6.3?
   M6.1 has five A repeat blocks, whereas M6.2 has only three A repeat blocks. M6.1 has five B repeat blocks; M6.3 has only four B repeat blocks.

4. How might rapid mutation thwart the human immune system?
   As soon as the body builds up an immune response to one form of the M protein, several other mutant forms appear, to which there is not an immune response.

5. The M protein has an excess of negatively charged amino acids. This results in a net negative charge on the bacterial surface. Mammalian cells also have a negative charge on their surfaces. How might this affect the ability of mammalian phagocytes to ingest the bacteria?
   Since both surfaces are negatively charged and like charges repel, you would expect that the phagocytes would not be able to make contact with the surface of the bacteria and would not be able to ingest them.